SUSAN McBANE

EFFECTIVE HORSE AND PONY MANAGEMENT

· *A Failsafe System* ·

DAVID & CHARLES
Newton Abbot · London

By the same Author
Keeping a Horse Outdoors (David & Charles)
Your First Horse: a guide to buying and owning
Keeping Horses: how to save time and money
Behaviour Problems in Horses (David & Charles)
Ponywise
The Horse in Winter: his management and work
The Horse and the Bit (editor)
The Competition Horse: its breeding, production and management

In preparation
Practical Horsemastership (editor) (David & Charles)
A Natural Approach to Horse Management

Line illustrations by Joy Claxton

British Library Cataloguing in Publication Data
McBane, Susan
  Effective horse and pony management
  1. Livestock: Horses. Care. Manuals
  I. Title
  636.1'083

  ISBN 0-7153-9121-6

Typeset by Typesetters (Birmingham) Ltd
Smethwick, Warley, West Midlands
and printed in Great Britain
by Redwood Burn Limited, Trowbridge, Wilts
for David & Charles Publishers plc
Brunel House   Newton Abbot   Devon

PREFACE

Effective management is essential to the successful performance of any horse or pony, and there are many good books on the subject. What is the point of having another one, you may think? Many owners, indeed, feel they haven't time to read all the books which are already available as it is.

I hope this book will be seen as somewhat different. It is aimed neither at beginners nor experts, but has been written for those with at least a basic knowledge of stable management and horsemastership and who have probably read most of the existing books because they are concerned to look after their horses and ponies as best they can. It purposely omits many facts and aspects which are readily found in almost every good management book, but it does, I hope, present some different angles on management and offers food for thought on these and other aspects not usually seen in print.

So that the book can be 'easily digested', each chapter has been divided into main sections and, within them, sub-sections. In Part Two, there are concise summaries of the most important topics covered in each main section of a chapter and at the end of each chapter is a self-test checklist of important points to remember on that topic. It is hoped that this lay-out will make the book easy to use for reference after an initial reading. The main hope is that by complying with the checklists and putting those points into action, it will be very difficult for even the less experienced to make a serious mistake when looking after their horse or pony.

Part One is an introduction comprising two chapters on topics related to management. **Part Two** is the major section of the book and is concerned with management itself and the **Appendices** offer useful information, names and addresses, correct at the time of going to press, for interest's sake and to help owners and managers contact others who may be able to help them in their task and responsibility of looking after their animals. No one is an expert in every aspect of horsemastership; we all need help at some time. We cannot know everything, but our problems can often be solved if we know how to find out and whom to consult.

This book is for dear little SIMBA,
whose devotion and intelligence
can never be exceeded.

CONTENTS

Part One

1
BREEDS AND TYPES OF HORSES AND PONIES

The horse world is a vast one and there are many hundreds of different breeds and types of horses and ponies, in just about every country and climate of the world. In more recent evolutionary times, equines have evolved according to widely differing climatic and terrestrial conditions, so we have thin-skinned, long-legged, hot-blooded types as well as thicker-skinned, stocky, woolly sorts, with just about every blend and cross in between.

Although some breed enthusiasts have almost a fetish about so-called breed purity, the fact is that every single breed is a blend of different types, a process which began long before official breeds as such were recognised. Even the Arab and Caspian, two of the 'purest' breeds in the world, are made up of different types of equine, whether brought about by nature or man, to produce the familiar breed characteristics they exhibit today. Where a breed has evolved naturally, it will have become adapted to a particular environment to give it the best chance of survival. Where man did the mixing, it may be quite *un*suited to its environment (eg the British Thoroughbred) but man helps it survive with artificial clothing, stabling and feeding.

Whatever the case, genetically speaking they are all 'equine mongrels'. What is a breed anyway, and why and how to breeds come about? A breed can be described simply as a group of horses closely approximating to a particular physical type and complying with various conditions such as colours allowed, height and so on. Often man builds on the physical and the temperamental qualities already provided by nature in his local horse or pony type, moulding it more exactly to his needs – to ride or drive, look smart, work on the land, carry loads, win competitions (in itself demanding different types) or whatever. In this way, regional breeds remain basically suited to their environment and, if management policies embrace fairly natural methods, few problems arise.

It is when man introduces breeds with little resemblance to the regional type and which are not at all suited to the environment in which he places them that the most problems arise. For example, you could not imagine two more different animals than a Shetland and a Thoroughbred, yet they both exist side by side and thrive in the British Isles. The Shetland is ideally suited to a cold environment – 'the northerly regions' – with his dense, thick coat, his rounded body shape ideal for retaining body heat and his short legs in relation to his size. The Thoroughbred, descended largely from thin-skinned oriental stock, with his long legs, more oval body and fine hair, is patently not suited to our climate, at least not in winter, and has to have good feeding, shelter and often clothing if he is to thrive enough to be productive for us. However, if you turn out a Shetland on the lush plains of the south you will be lucky if you do not end up with laminitis, and a grossly obese animal prone to all sorts of other problems.

Breed type, when left to nature, is very specific. Man can manipulate it very successfully, particularly if he is prepared to inconvenience himself regarding the subsequent management of what he produces. Generally, the closer to nature we keep our horses and ponies the fewer problems we shall have with them, but this must always be tempered with regard to breed type and the environment. 'Nature' to a Thoroughbred or an Arab is *not* being left out for the winter on Dartmoor.

HOT- AND WARM-BLOODED HORSES AND PONIES

Generally, these terms apply to Thoroughbreds, Arabs, Caspians, and indeed all oriental breeds originating in hot climates, their crosses and breed derivatives – this group encompasses most of the horses bred for speed and competition. If we wish to be pedantic, we could say that the only 'hot'-blooded types are Arabs and Caspians, with maybe Barbs also included. (The Przewalski horse is a different type and has a different number of chromosomes from our domestic horses and ponies. Although originating in 'the orient', ie the bitterly cold tundras of eastern Europe and Asia, it certainly does not have the hot-weather characteristics of the breeds mentioned, but rather the cold weather ones typical of northern climes.)

The Thoroughbred still causes argument as to its true forebears in 18th century England. There is undoubtedly a great deal of oriental blood, mainly Arab with a good deal of Barb, in the breed but the 'ominous' blank spaces in the earliest generations simply cannot be identified now. It seems logical that they were native-type horses and/or ponies of cold-blood characteristics, but by that time (only two or three hundred years ago) man had already interfered considerably with the native stock – there are those who assert that many Arab horses existed in Britain before the well-documented importation of the early Arab and Barb stallions and which, unknowingly to all concerned at the time, were already engaged in the founding of the greatest artificial racing 'machine' of all time. The Romans are thought to have brought many Arab-type horses over, for a start, and medieval merchants and traders are known to have done so, perhaps in smaller numbers. These will certainly have bred with existing stock.

Furthermore the Vikings and Danes may well have introduced their native Scandinavian (cold-blooded type) ponies, as too the Normans and Angles with their mid-European (again cold-blooded type) horses and ponies. These will all have been put in the breeding melting pot and have affected the native stock, with which the hot-blooded stallions were later mated in order to produce what eventually became the Thoroughbred.

The Thoroughbred, then, is really more warm-blooded than hot-blooded. And what of such breeds as the Irish Draught and Cleveland Bay? No one could call them hot- or even warm-blooded, yet they are both fairly clean-legged and many examples of both breeds show considerable quality, a word generally taken to imply Thoroughbred characterisitics such as extravagant action, scopey stride, alert, quick temperament, proud outlook and so on.

Ireland did not have the dubious benefit of Roman invasion, but it is said of the Connemara pony that its more recent ancestors possess Iberian blood from stock shipwrecked from Spanish galleons – and if the Connemara, why not the Irish Draught? It might sound fanciful, but fact is often stranger than fiction. Iberian horses are believed to possess a good deal of oriental blood which came over to the peninsula from North Africa, again with the Moors and Romans, so the Irish types have their own melting pot.

The current vogue, apart from the constantly thriving Thoroughbred racing industry, is for producing warm-blooded performance horses. These are regional variations developed by European countries and embodying what they want in a dressage/show jumping/driving/event horse, and excellent many of them are, too. They are currently enjoying a positive tidal wave of popularity – the Dutch, Swedish, Danish and German breeds in particular, and we are trying to create our own in the UK. But when you get down to the roots of their pedigrees what do you see? Again, native types with mainly cold-blooded characteristics (the early forms of such as the Holstein and Hannoverian) bred 'up' with Arabs and Thoroughbreds – yet another melting pot.

The European warm-bloods and the British Thoroughbred have also invaded North America in no uncertain terms and a recognisable American type of Thoroughbred is emerging, at least in the American racing world; it is bred even more for short-distance speed than the British originator, with a higher croup, chunkier muscling and longer hind legs and with a quite idiosyncratic action behind, quite unlike the British type of Thoroughbred which really aims to be more of a middle-distance horse. This American type is filtering out elsewhere and influencing the breeding of competition horses.

America experiences a much wider climatic range than Britain and, having no indigenous breeds of her own, has imported those of other countries to mix with the Iberian stock brought over with the Conquistadores. Once again, we are back to that familiar mix of oriental and 'other' blood present in so many breeds.

America has created the fastest sprinting horse in the world, the American Quarter horse which is said to be able to fly for as long as it can hold its breath! The Appaloosa, originally bred by the Nez Percé Indians, is probably the next most famous American breed and then there is the ubiquitous (in America) Morgan horse, founded on the genes of a single pre-potent stallion, Justin Morgan, whose ancestry is unknown. I have always thought how much Morgans are like Welsh Cobs, particularly the youngstock, and Welsh blood could well have figured significantly in the make-up of Justin Morgan, from the imported British native breeds which went over with early settlers and later.

The Arab is also very widespread in America, therefore adding more oriental genes to those already present in that country, and often, to non-Americans, manifesting what could be termed an American-type Arab – in the same way there are recognisable English-type, Polish-type and Egyptian-type Arabs, all unmistakably Arab but carrying the equally unmistakable stamp of type favoured by one particular country or even one particular stud. The Arab is noted for its famous 'five strains' which are really types and have little relation to the actual genetic content of the strain members.

And, in fact, as far as formal breeds are concerned, genes are what it all boils down to. Some breeds have closed stud books, in other words the only new admissions to their stud book are animals bred entirely from those already registered. Other breeds (including the British Thoroughbred) have open stud books, which means that if a family or individual can prove by ability and appearance, as well as by reasonable documentary evidence, that it is entitled to be classed as a Thoroughbred (or whatever breed is concerned), it can be 'admitted to the stud book' and certain of its progeny are also then acceptable as members of the breed.

Problems can arise in breeds with small gene pools, such as the Caspian and Przewalski. It is difficult to avoid too much in-breeding with such breeds, and a very careful policy of breeding management, stud book maintenance and permitted matings often has to be employed.

TYPES RATHER THAN BREEDS

Many horses are classified by type, or even by colour, rather than by breed. The Palomino is a case in point, and the catch-all British hunter and riding horse are others, along with hacks and cobs (other than registered cobs such as the Welsh Section D). Such animals are sometimes more easily recognisable than specific breeds.

These 'types' all have the same blood (genes) as formal breeds, but in differing amounts and variations. Some British hunters are Thoroughbreds, others look more like a Thoroughbred than a Thoroughbred, yet aren't. And a horse's abilities often bear no relation to its classification – for example, if you entered a formal hunter class with a pure-bred Arab, you would certainly not win however good a hunter your horse might be, and may even be asked to leave the ring!

Probably the least practical way of classifying horses, as regards their management needs, is by colour, yet we have societies committed to promoting horse of a specific colouring – palominos, coloured horses (skewbalds, piebalds, pintos or paints), spotted horses and ponies which do not qualify as Appaloosas (and not all Appaloosas are spotted) and in the past cremellos and others. Other horses are registered according to what they can do (whether or not they are a recognised, registered breed or type) such as the British Sport Horse or various reining horse organisations.

TEMPERAMENT AND MANAGEMENT

Horses' mental characteristics and temperaments dictate to a large extent how we manage them. Hot-blooded breeds are generally felt to be more difficult, 'lively', or nervous, though more courageous, than cold-blooded types which are regarded as more phlegmatic, stolid, even stupid. Yet this by no means always applies. There are many 'dozy' Thoroughbreds and Arabs around, and seemingly stupid ones, too, and then many highly-strung cobs and children's ponies; but as a *general* rule it is probably reliable to class hot-blooded breeds as quick and nervy, cold-blooded ones as calm and laid-back (to put it politely) and warm-bloods as somewhere in between! There have been many warm-blood competition horses which have been noted for their personality and character, for instance the show jumper Gladstone, yet these horses seem to be regarded as bland, characterless and almost robotic in their submissiveness – partly, some say, because they have been bred, largely by Germans, to be easily dominated! Which is a whole other topic . . .

I hope this introductory chapter may cause some readers to think of breeds and types of horses and ponies in a slightly different light. They all come from the same root stock, a common ancestral type which seems to have died out (not the Przewalski because of the differing chromosomes). When we talk of a formal breed we simply mean a group of horses with a specific mix of the original genes, which produces the specific morphology aimed for in that particular breed.

As far as management is concerned, the characteristics of your living original are far more important than the traditional qualities of the breed as there are so many exceptions to the rule in our domesticated equine mongrel *equus caballus*. The first and probably most important rule of good horse management is that 'each horse is an individual and should be treated as such'.

2

Make and Shape

During the examination of a horse before purchase, the prospective buyer should make as thorough an inspection and judgement of the horse's conformation as his or her knowledge allows – this is not the veterinary surgeon's job unless there is something so obviously wrong that it will cause physical problems at some time in the future if not now.

Horses are often described in a perhaps rather affected way as machines (I've done it myself elsewhere in this book!) and although there is a degree of truth in this because they are governed by the same basic rules of physics and mechanics as a machine proper, they are actually far more effective at what they do than any machine. No non-living machine has yet been invented that can even walk just like a horse, let alone jump and gallop, lie down, buck, roll and do all the many other things our horses do. And like any other animal or machine, everything they do puts stress and strain on their bodies and wear and tear on the individual parts.

The horse's locomotory system, like his digestion, mentality and other systems, evolved over millions of years to suit his way of life and environment as a mobile grazing animal whose main defence against predators is galloping away. Experts in animal physiology – vets, zoologists, evolutionists – all agree that the horse is one of the most efficient, specialised running animals in the world. Although other species of prey animal can run faster, such as some of the antelopes, and predators themselves often match their prey in speed (the exception being the cheetah which, at about 70mph (112.6kph), is the fastest land animal on earth), the horse is generally regarded as having endurance as his forté in addition to reasonable speed (about half the speed of a cheetah).

He has evolved from a small, three- and four-toed creature the size of a fox to one of the largest land mammals with a single 'toe' on each foot, the ultimate in speed specialisation. The horse's hoof is the equivalent to the tip of our middle finger.

All this talk about specialised speed may confuse us when we think about heavy horses who are certainly not built for that! In the animal kingdom, animals built for speed are usually fairly light for their size and long and lean in shape (such as the predatory cats and dogs, extreme examples of which are the cheetah and the greyhound), or are compact

Heavy horses are not normally noted for their speed!

and chunky for strength (such as the elephant and bull terrier). But the fact remains that even the Shire's conformation is based on the speed skeleton of his family.

Actually, heavy horses really can move when they want to and have the opportunity. We tend to think of them plodding slowly along in traces and not many of us get the chance to see them at liberty kicking their heels and racing each other on a crisp spring afternoon. I was lucky enough to see just this a few years ago on a visit to a Shire stud. The stallion had been kept in during the morning (unusually) pending my visit so I could see him in action.

I was truly amazed to see the speed he achieved in his 20-acre field, the athleticism with which he turned and cavorted, his sudden stops and surging, racing starts. My Anglo-Arab gelding could have beaten him, certainly, but he wouldn't have left him standing. And the earth did not tremble either.

So, all sorts of equine have this essentially identical skeleton which, with its muscular attachments, are the means of the horse's locomotion.

Because we make even more specialised demands on our horses, from hacking to flat racing, jumping to drawing vehicles sometimes at speed over difficult country, there are, within the basic 'blueprint', different requirements in type and conformation. For instance, for driving a more upright shoulder is usually wanted because the collar can 'sit' more easily and the horse can lean horizontally into it and push against it, so 'pulling' the vehicle. For riding of any kind, a sloping shoulder (about 45° to the ground) is sought as this makes for a more comfortable ride. For speed, often a flattish croup – which almost inevitably accompanies a fairly high-set tail – is usually most effective, whilst for work involving more agility such as dressage and jumping (although not at speed) a more sloping croup is thought advantageous to enable the horse to 'get his hind legs underneath him' and manoeuvre more easily.

The purpose of this chapter is to give a basic understanding of the principles of conformation required in any horse but particularly in those used for performance, in other words for general competition work involving a bit of everything: athletic/obedience work (dressage), whereby a horse has sufficient training to become a comfortable, obedient ride; jumping, for eventing, show jumping or hunting; and speed and endurance, again for eventing or hunting, or to take you on active hacks or long distance rides, many of which involve jumps and other hazards to be negotiated. This basic conformation plan is the same for any horse but can be adapted by breeders wishing to produce minor differences for specialised pursuits.

THE ALL-PURPOSE HORSE

Because a fault in one part of a horse can produce not only injury to that part but undue compensatory stress and strain elsewhere, the first thing to look for in any horse is symmetry. The horse or pony must look as though he is in proportion – without this, his natural balance will be adversely affected and he will have to work harder to balance himself under a rider. This in turn produces too much stress on his physical structure and can lead to sprains and other injuries. Horses' bodies do 'learn' to compensate for this stress and strain, either by the part concerned becoming stronger or some other part taking extra stress due to the failing of the faulty part. And another vital point to remember is that no horse is perfect. They all have something wrong with them. It is often only when that something is pronounced that it becomes significant under working conditions.

Whatever his individual type and physical appeal, the symmetrical, well-proportioned horse should fit the following measurements as closely as possible.

The length from the poll to the point of the withers should be about equal that from the withers to the croup, and that from the croup to the root of the tail should be about half the latter. The distance from withers

A good type of modern competition carriage horse, substantial without being coarse and with a slightly more upright shoulder than normally looked for in a riding horse

A good type of modern competition saddle horse, with a lighter build than the carriage horse and a more sloping shoulder

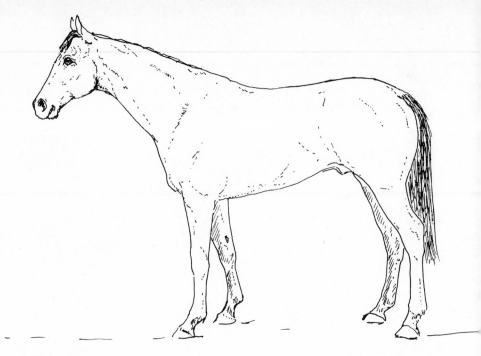

A Thoroughbred racehorse of the lean, stayer type, with the flattish croup which denotes speed

A modern dressage type with good natural head carriage and neck shape for this sport, slightly sloping croup to facilitate hind leg engagement and of the rather leggy type now favoured for loose, elastic and easily extended paces

Hindquarters conformation known as 'jumper's bump'

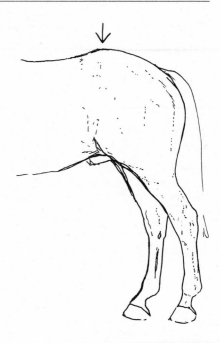

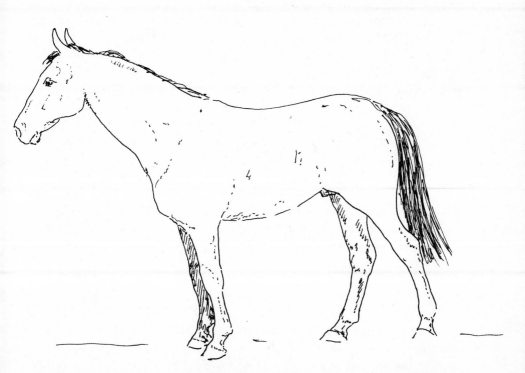

A longish neck and rather large, heavy head naturally puts a horse on the forehand

to girth should be at least half that from withers to ground. This may sound too standardised to be true, but it is surprising how many good horses comply with it.

The breastbone should run parallel to the ground for its length, then the belly should slope gently up towards the stifles. This ensures a secure position for the girth which would otherwise be constantly slipping back and taking the saddle with it unless you fitted a breastplate. The latter is sometimes necessary in any case with a very fit horse on a high concentrate diet and carrying no significant belly. You should be able to fit the width of your hand, roughly, between the horse's last rib and his hip (actually the pelvic bone, not the actual hip joint). If there is too much space here the horse is probably too long in the back which could indicate inherent weaknesses, quite apart from a ride which moves you uncomfortably back and forth with each stride. Conversely, an over-short back can cause a rather jolting, choppy ride and often causes the horse to over-reach and forge.

The head and neck are the horse's balancing equipment, equivalent to our arms. If the neck is too long and the head appears big and heavy, and particularly when they are carried naturally low and forward, too much weight will be thrown on the forehand and the horse will 'go into the ground', be heavy in hand and difficult to balance and collect, which may put extra stresses on the forelegs. If they are carried higher, these effects will be minimised, but generally it is felt that if a horse has 'a good length of rein' (ie the rider feels there is plenty of horse in front of the saddle) this length should come from a good front and not a long neck.

A short neck carried too high does not, frustratingly, cause the horse to carry his weight on his hocks and make him easy to balance and collect; rather it seems to cause a hollow back, resulting in hind legs trailing and a horse difficult to 'bridle' or persuade to accept the bit, as by nature he will be above the bit.

If the quarters are too short, it can result in lack of power so the horse would not be a wise buy for pursuits involving speed or jumping.

Sway (hollow) backs are comfortable and weak, roach (arched) backs are uncomfortable and strong. A living horse's back seems to go down in a very slight dip, but in fact, if you look at a correctly mounted skeleton, you will see that the actual spine ('chain' of vertebrae) is arched slightly upwards, a very strong mechanical structure from which weight (in this case the horse's voluminous, heavy intestines) can be slung with much more security than from a straight-rod structure, which is more prone to sagging in the middle, especially if too long. The dip effect is caused by the varying lengths of the bony projections (called processes) protuding from the top of each verteba and which act as muscle attachments.

A short neck and high head carriage causes a hollow back with the hind legs inclined to trail. It is difficult to 'engage' this type of horse

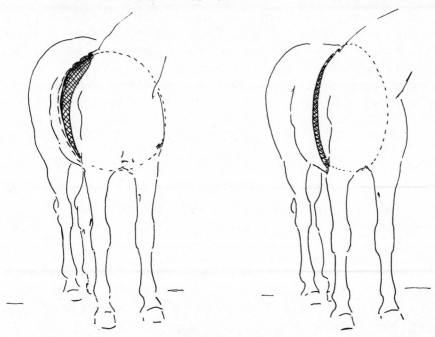

(left) A horse with an over-rounded ribcage is difficult to sit, and if shallow in build can also be too leggy and with not enough lung room. (right) A more oval conformation in the girth area is more comfortable to sit to and, provided there is depth there, is a more desirable feature than that shown in the previous illustration

Withers which are not too high and are moderately wide give ample room for muscle attachment without making saddle fitting difficult. Sharp, high withers often need a special cut-back pommel whereas low, broad withers fail to keep the saddle in place but allow it to roll from side to side and slip forward. Much can be done to help matters with saddle design, stuffing and a competent saddler, but extremes of both these conformational faults are best avoided.

Looked at from the front, the ribcage or barrel should appear well rounded and not flat, and from behind, the thigh muscles behind the stifles should be the width of the hips above, although horses in poor condition may not achieve this. A 'well-sprung' barrel, particularly when coupled with a deep girth (in accordance with the measurement given earlier) means there is plenty of lung room for efficient breathing – very important in an athletic animal. Obviously, if the ribcage is too flat and lacking in depth as well, the reverse is true, but it should be remembered that, particularly in Thoroughbreds, the ribcage is often more oval-looking than rounded, but usually with good depth. As long as the total amount of lung room is there, this oval shape is fine and certainly makes for easier 'sitting', particularly in riders with rather short legs, than if the ribcage is really shaped like a barrel.

Good muscling in the hind legs and quarters is essential because this is the horse's power-house or engine. The horse's propulsive power comes from the back end, which thrusts the horse forward with each stride. The front end simply catches the thrust and prevents the body falling down! Well, it's not quite that simple, especially as the horse carries about two thirds of his weight on his forehand, not to mention that of the rider who should sit just behind the withers as nearly over the horse's centre of gravity as possible.

· THE LIMBS ·

The front legs in particular come in for a good deal of stress and strain as they have to bear the weight and force put upon them by the driving force of the hindquarters.

Looked at from the front, you should be able to draw an imaginary straight line down from the point of the shoulder, through the middle of the knee and fetlock, and finish it in the centre of the toe so that the weight falls evenly down the leg. From the side, the front legs should fall straight down from elbow to fetlock and the pasterns should slope at roughly 45° (to match the shoulder angle), this angle being carried on down the front of the hoof.

As for the hind legs, viewed from the side with the horse standing squarely, you should be able to imagine a plumb line from the point

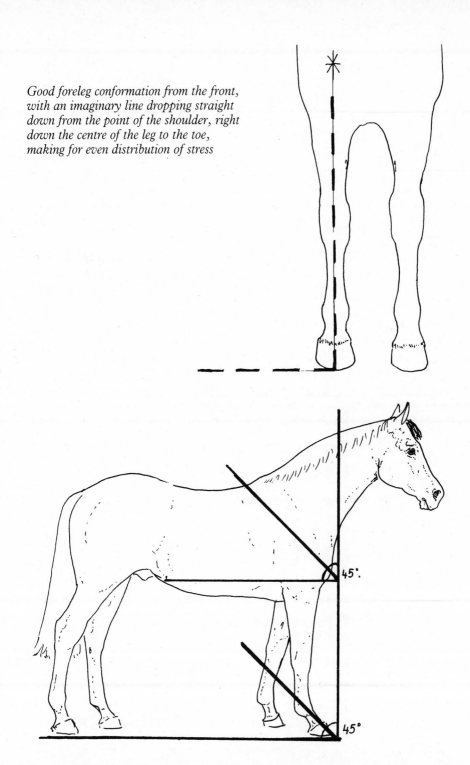

Good foreleg conformation from the front, with an imaginary line dropping straight down from the point of the shoulder, right down the centre of the leg to the toe, making for even distribution of stress

Diagram showing the desirable 45° angles of shoulder and hoof/pastern axis. This horse has slightly more upright shoulder/hoof/pastern angles than normally required but the difference is so slight as to make little difference. No horse is perfect!

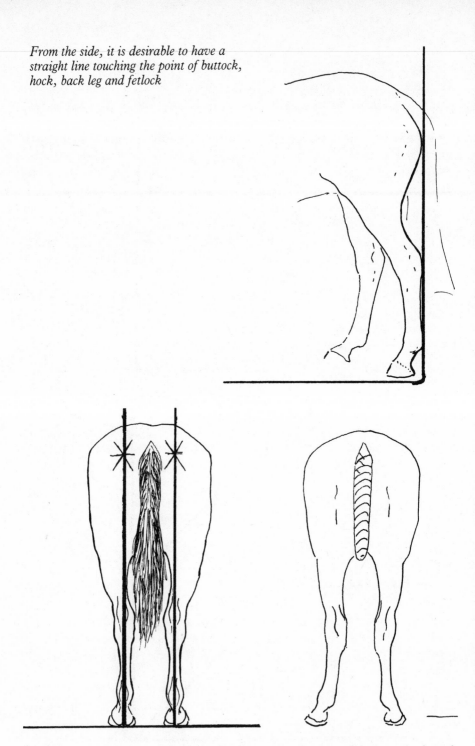

From the side, it is desirable to have a straight line touching the point of buttock, hock, back leg and fetlock

(left) *From the rear, there is a straight line down from the point of the buttock, through the centre of the hock, cannon, fetlock and heel. This conformation has been selected for by breeders and is, in fact, not entirely natural to the horse family, in which* slight cow hocks are normal . . .*although not as much as this!* (right)

of the buttock, touching the hock and passing straight down the back of the cannon to the fetlock. The hind pastern/hoof angle to be aimed for is slightly more upright than the fore, about 50° to the ground.

From the back, your line should drop from the point of the buttock, through the hock and straight down to the fetlock, cutting the heel in two between the bulbs before reaching the ground. In fact, this is not a *natural* conformation either for the horse or its relatives the asses and zebras, which are all, horror of horrors, very slightly cow-hocked! – unless they have been selectively bred by man to be otherwise.

Horses which have been bred for performance rather than for the showring often exhibit this tendency to cow-hocks and hind feet, there-fore, turning very slightly outwards, and you will soon spot this trait in future, particularly in clear photographs of high-class equine athletes, and especially in posed conformation shots. This, and the diagonal rather than vertical wear marks it produces on the tops of the hind cannon bones, is one feature which helps palaeontologists and zoologists identify fossils and bones of equidae.

· THE FEET ·

The principle of symmetry applies just as much to feet, and the same basic guidelines apply to both forefeet and hind. The only real difference is that, looked at from the ground surface, the forefeet are more nearly circular than the hind, which are more oval in shape and often very slightly smaller.

When viewed from the side, imagine a straight line running up the front of the hoof and on up the long pastern bone in the same angle; if the coronet 'breaks' downwards the toes are probably too long and the heels too low, an apparently common trimming error in farriery today which encourages laminitis and navicular as well as placing undue stress on tendons and other structures within the feet. If the coronet protrudes upwards, so that the hoof wall is at a steeper angle than the pastern, the toes are too short and the heels too high, a conformation often said to indicate navicular disease. The causes and results of such foot formations are multiple and complex so there is not space here to discuss this matter fully.

From the front of the foot, the ends of the coronet should be the same height from the ground on each side, with the sides of the hoof (quar-ters) having the same degree of slope and not being 'flared' out evenly. However, although these guidelines are ideal, some horses, by nature or due to neglect when foals, do deviate from them. Sometimes more recent neglect can cause deviations, too. It should be remembered that very little can be done to correct faulty foot or leg conformation that is natural to

A slightly more upright hoof/pastern axis as normally found in the hind leg. The angle of the heel wall matches that of the toe, as it should, and shows a good height of heel. Many animals today have, or are trimmed to produce, heels that are too low

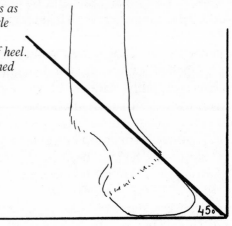

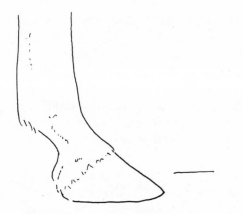

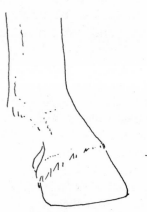

(left) *Long toe and low heel with the coronet starting to 'break' downwards.* (right) *Short toe, upright pastern and high heel – 'boxy' feet with the coronet starting to 'break' upwards*

From the front, the ends of the coronets should be the same height at each side. The outer walls of the hoof are normally slightly more sloping than the inner

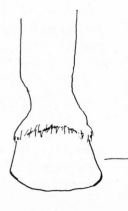

the horse after it has reached roughly weaning age (about six months or slightly older) as after this age the bones do not lend themselves to being 'remoulded'. Sometimes tiny, repeated corrections can at least improve a condition if not correct it altogether, especially if you have a competent, caring farrier.

However, when faulty conformation of the foot has been caused by more recent trimming and shoeing errors, gradual, or sometimes more drastic, correction is both possible and desirable. This whole subject is one to discuss with your vet and farrier.

THE HORSE IN ACTION

A brief look at the horse's way of going will help clarify why unusual limb and foot conformations can lead to lameness due to the uneven stresses and strains placed on the limb. After all, we breed horses to move and what happens in action is the 'eating' part of the pudding. There are of course, exceptions to disprove every rule and many apparently poorly made horses seem to work satisfactorily for years with no trouble, and give a better ride than you would expect from their appearance. I once owned a horse with a short front (although well sloped shoulder), a rather tied-in elbow and a very short back. All these faults would lead one to expect a rough ride and a feeling of nothing in front, yet he was a truly lovely ride and everyone who did ride him agreed. However, none of his faults were seriously marked. When faults *are* quite marked, however, if the work is demanding and if the horse's physical compensations are minimal, then wear, tear and strain usually arise which result in injury.

The horse starts a stride with a hind foot. As the hind leg comes forward it extends, the foot lands and the hock flexes slightly to absorb the impact, the horse's weight travels over the leg and the muscles then extend the leg again while the foot is still on the ground, which has the effect of pushing the horse forwards.

The force travels up the leg and is transferred to the spine via the hip joint and pelvis, then along the spine to the foreleg by means of the shoulder and so-called thoracic sling. The shoulder has no bony joint to the spine to compare with the hip, but has a contact of sorts to the ribcage by means of the chest or pectoral muscles and associated ligaments and tendons. This absorbs the force and weight of the forehand which now descends on this sling, and travels down the foreleg.

The foreleg acts as a spoke in that, unlike the hock, the knee is not bent but acts as a column over which the weight passes. *It has no muscular propulsive action.* Concussion and weight are absorbed by the fetlock, pastern and hoof. The fetlock joint flexes under the force coming down the leg (and up it from the ground) and is sometimes even pressed to the ground at the ergot as the tendons running from the forearm muscles and the supporting ligaments take the stress and stop the joint collapsing. The tremendous energy received is partly transferred to the ground and partly 'stored' in the tendons until the leg is past the vertical, when they 'spring' back – being very slightly elastic – thus giving the horse a little impetus in his forward motion.

This very over-simplified version of the distribution of weight, force and stress during a horse's stride may clarify why reasonable conformation is necessary if injury is to be avoided. If legs are out of alignment, twisted or too fine for the weight and type of animal and the nature of the work, injury due to uneven stress or unreasonable wear and tear is likely to occur.

· THE IMPLICATIONS OF SOME LIMB · CONFORMATION FAULTS

A foreleg which is back at the knee instead of straight can be thought of as a 'bent spoke'. If you push down on a single spoke with even a slight bend in it, the force stresses the bend and increases it, so your spoke is bent even further. In the horse, the force going down the leg is just as great as if the leg were straight, and either a bone injury can occur, the bones at the front of the knee being crushed as they are compressed, or the tendons and ligaments down the back of the leg and around the joints will be overstretched and their protective sheaths damaged. If, also, the pastern is too long and sloping, this effect is exacerbated.

If the pastern is too upright, it will not play the same part in absorbing jar and the force transmitted to the knee joint will be that much greater.

If the leg is over at the knee instead of back, the problems are not nearly so serious, but uneven stresses are still placed on the joint itself and on the ends of the forearm and cannon bones, because the force is not passing evenly down the leg. If one limb cannot cope with the stress and force it should, the amount in question is simply transferred to another body part, which may then be overstressed and injured since it ends up bearing more than its fair share.

In the hind legs, if the cannons are sloping slightly backwards when the horse is supposed to be standing four square, or if the point of the hock is not on a vertical line with the point of the buttock, the horse will find it difficult to get his legs under him for maximum propulsion. He will not be able to jump anything significant and will be difficult to balance and collect. If he is going constantly on his forehand, this puts extra work on that part of the body and the horse will probably feel heavy in hand.

Sickle hocks are when the cannons slope forwards putting extra stress

Although the leg looks straight, the 'straight line' test shows that it is inset and the stresses will fall mainly down the outside of the cannon, over-stressing and probably injuring this area

(right) *A severe case of 'pigeon toes'.* (left) *Admittedly exaggerated (although seen in real life), splay-footed conformation with the right leg seriously deformed*

on the hock joint, tendons and ligaments.

All these conformation faults put uneven stresses and strains on the limbs and can result in all sorts of hard and soft 'lumps and bumps' and lameness from self-inflicted injury. Despite this, the horse may nonetheless move straight, its legs 'following each other's path'– in other words, when seen from front or back the horse may look as if he only has one pair of legs, the front or back respectively. Other conformation faults can cause the legs to deviate from this straight path and may even cause the horse to hit himself. Any twisting or bending of a leg from top to bottom (such as knock knees and bandy legs) can result in this, as can the two faults known as 'base wide' and 'base narrow'. These can occur in fore or hind legs.

In base wide, the legs slope outwards from the top which means the feet are wider apart than if the legs were straight; this is common in narrow-chested horses and causes the horse's weight to be carried too much down the inside of the leg and hoof. Base narrow is where the feet are closer together than the tops of the legs; it can result in the horse hitting himself, and can cause excess weight stress on the outsides of the legs and feet. In base wide and base narrow, the insides and outsides of the shoes respectively will be more worn but this can be lessened by welding a hardener such as borium along the fullering on the appropriate side.

Toeing-in and toeing-out are two more action faults which cause trouble. Toeing-in or 'pigeon toes' is often associated with base-narrow conformation and such horses often brush on the insides of the fetlocks. They also dish, or throw the feet outwards in an arc, outside the normal flight path of the hoof.

In toe-out or splay-footed conformation the feet are thrown inwards and can cause severe brushing and speedicutting. This gait is called 'winging' and is often accompanied by base-narrow stance,which makes its consequences even worse.

(*top*) An Exmoor stallion, technically of the so-called cold-blooded type of equine equipped with the heat retaining features of ample hair, thickish skin, small ears and normally narrow nostrils to help it survive in cold climates. Although Exmoors are small, these basic characteristics occur in all equidae originating in cold climates, whatever their height (*Mike Roberts*)

(*below*) An Arab stallion. Compare his finer lines, longer ears, more open nostrils, longer legs and finer hair with that of the Exmoor. A so-called hot-blooded type, the Arab originated in hot, dry areas and has the physique to facilitate heat loss. From man's point of view, this conformation makes for speed whereas the conformation of the Exmoor stallion makes for strength and pulling power (*Peter R. Sweet*)

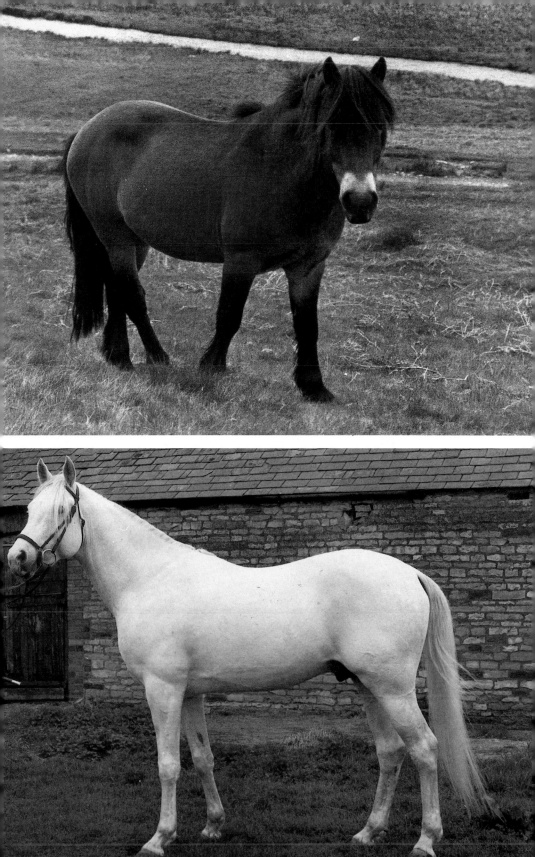

A horse of old Iberia. An Andalusian stallion who could be described as warm-blooded, not so chunky as the Exmoor or so fine as the Arab. Andalusians and similar types are neither fast nor ponderous, being used as parade horses under saddle or in harness, ideal for high school work with their showy action and possessing considerable presence. Some Andalusians are much coarser than the one shown here (*Peter R. Sweet*)

This Standardbred mare was taken in by the Horses and Ponies Protection Association after retiring from harness racing. Note the upright pasterns, brought on by arthritic fetlock joints, caused by the over-stress of continual racing. The deformity and arthritis soon became so bad the mare had to be humanely destroyed

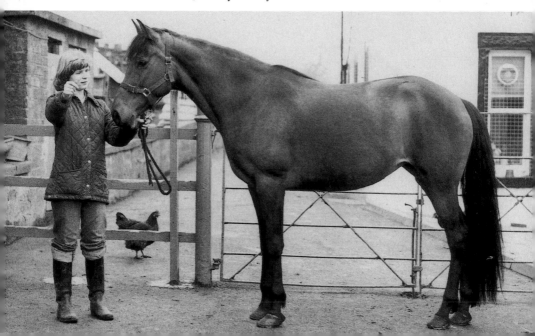

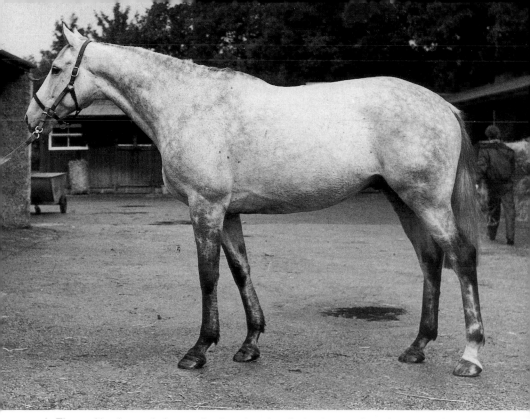

A Thoroughbred steeplechaser who has the virtually perfect conformation proportions described in Chapter 2

A professionally trimmed and laid hedge is a well worthwhile investment, providing an effective barrier and a windbreak, too. For horses, the hedge should be higher than this one, because of their propensity for jumping out (*MAFF, Crown Copyright*)

It can be good practice to graze horses and cattle together because of their complementary grazing habits and preferences and as an aid to parasite control. There should always be more cattle than horses. The cattle should be dehorned and free from ringworm and brucellosis. This sheltered, spacious field is especially suitable for animals because the trees virtually surround it and are particularly thick on the windward side, a factor quickly grasped and appreciated by the occupants

A herd of Exmoor ponies in their native surroundings, which are very different from a bare, fenced-in domesticated field or paddock. Here, the herd are free to wander and seek their own shelter and grazing over many square miles of country (*Mike Roberts*)

A catching pen at the entrance to a paddock is a very useful facility, particularly where the gate opens on to a roadway or where there are many horses in a field. The white gate on the left is normally closed, and, obviously, the two gates are never open at the same time (*Peter R. Sweet*)

A loose box can be improvised with a strong sliprail, like this. Some means is necessary of preventing the horse lifting the bar out of the end holders (in this case a length of plaited binder twine is knotted round it, although some horses would learn to undo this). The temperament of the occupant is also important. This arrangement would not be safe for those prone to jumping out or who are restless when stabled (*Clive Hiles*)

A row of stalls in use in a military yard. The partitions are sturdy, low enough to allow the horses the reassurance of seeing each other, and the stalls are wide enough, just, to allow them to sleep flat out. A simple swinging bail partition *can* be used between stalls, and is suitable for quiet, friendly horses, but not, obviously, for kickers, bullies or enemies (*Clive Hiles*)

Although loose boxes are the accepted way of stabling horses in many countries, by no means all horses are happy kept this way, even when well exercised. The teeth marks on the doors of these boxes indicate nervous habits brought on by frustration and confinement, yet both these horses receive more than the accepted two hours per day exercise

A large foaling box on a Thoroughbred stud, photographed from the doorway leading outside. At the back of the box is another entrance opening on to a covered corridor. The corners in both doorways are rounded off for safety, the paint is epoxy resin (easily cleaned, hard wearing and non-toxic), and there is tiling around the mangers (again for easy cleaning), one of which is for food and one for water. The mangers themselves are of galvanised metal, harder wearing than polythene which easily cracks. The box is lofty and airy and there are two infra-red heat lamps. The mangers are corner type, and filled in beneath, both safety features. A strong metal grille at the back allows safe ventilation and observation. Hay is fed from the floor in this establishment (as in many top studs) as it is felt safer and more natural (*Peter R. Sweet*)

A conventional pre-fabricated loose box which is rather too low for adequate air change, and there are no ridge-roof ventilators but the idea of leaving the bottom door open in warm weather is excellent. The hanging basket is attractive for humans and is kept well out of reach of the horse, many garden and house plants being poisonous

A Victorian brick barn partially used as a covered yard for horses on a Thoroughbred stud. It opens directly into a paddock, but in inclement weather the high doors can be closed to keep stock in without fear of their jumping out, yet still permitting air-flow. The photo was taken from another doorway, with similar doors, permitting a valuable cross-flow of air. However, even in an environment like this, animals susceptible to the effects of dust and spores from straw (used here) would probably start coughing! (*Peter R. Sweet*)

Horsewalkers, like this, can be an invaluable facility for extra exercise or cooling down hot, blowing horses, provided they are not used to excess. Half an hour a day is enough for most horses

The Ridry stable flooring system (see Chapters 5 and Part 3)

The result of little or no feeding, this emaciated pony was restored to good health by the Horses and Ponies Protection Association

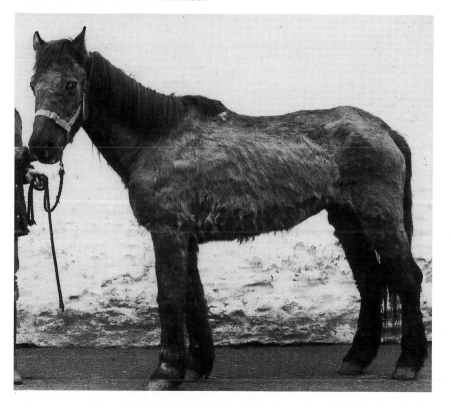

(*right*) Dust-extracted shavings bedding used in a racehorse's box. This generous banking-up round the sides is too often not seen in boxes bedded on shavings and woodchips, yet is just as necessary, particularly as shavings are not as warm a bedding as straw

(*below*) A hoof pad over a firm polyurethane sponge filling. Felt by some to provide protection for thin-soled horses, such fittings can encourage the development of horn infections such as thrush, as polyurethane absorbs and retains moisture

(*right*) The pinch test, where a fold of skin is lifted just in front of the shoulder, like this, is a test of dehydration. The skin should fall back flat almost immediately. Taking a fold of skin like this and twisting it slightly, with a firm hold, known sometimes as a neck twitch, is also a useful means of quietening a fractious horse for some worrying attention such as wound treatment, as it is believed to release into the bloodstream the body's own pain-killing and tranquilising substances – endorphins and encephalins. A nose twitch has a similar effect

(*below*) Despite the fact that most of our horse-management doctrine is said to have come to us from military sources, practice sometimes belies dogma. These army horses returned to barracks covered in mud. There was no suggestion that the mud be allowed to dry and then be brushed off. They were all hosed and sponged down, then immediately dried. 'We can't afford for them to get cracked heels and mud fever,' said the officer in charge (*Clive Hiles*)

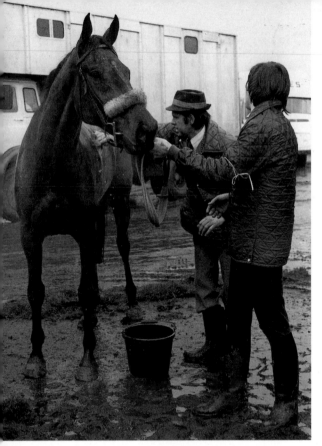

(*left*) Even in winter, washing down muddy horses is a safe, effective way to clean them up, provided they are dried thoroughly and kept warm with rugs and bandages. Washing down a sweaty horse on a hot day is refreshing and makes grooming easier. Clear, lukewarm water is all that is needed. Too-frequent use of soap dries the skin and coat of natural oils (*Peter R. Sweet*)

(*below*) A hot or wet horse can be cooled down and dried off by having an anti-sweat rug put on under a top rug, turned back and secured like this, and being walked, which not only prevents chilling on a cold day but keeps the circulation going and assists in the more thorough removal of toxins from the bloodstream, the result of strenuous exercise

(*above*) Horses, too, can learn from experience provided they are correctly treated. This four-in-hand team (international competitors) made a hash of a tight turn round a tree through not listening to their master's voice! He stopped them, let them stand and think about it for a minute. They then extricated the vehicle and negotiated the turn twice more, carefully and without mishap

(*right*) Even a small pony can pull a large man along in hand with no effort. Leading with the palm downwards, like this, gives a firmer grip, when necessary, by a simple clockwise turn of the wrist. There is less possibility of the arm being easily pulled forward and many animals will respond to the extra control by coming back to hand promptly

(*left*) Letting horses have a bite of grass after work acts as a reward, a relaxation and calms them down before being stabled again. Stabled horses also benefit considerably by being allowed to graze in hand daily when, for some reason, it is not possible to turn them out. Just being out but not working is a small treat (*Peter R. Sweet*)

(*below*) Exercise sheets should be firmly fixed under the girth like this if there is no girth loop on the bottom edge to secure them

(*right*) A good, modern New Zealand rug, from Hydrophane Limited. Made of lightweight, synthetic, waterproof and windproof fabric, it is also tear-resistant, is properly shaped and has crossed belly surcingles and leg straps. It fits well, coming in front of the withers (not pressing on top of them as is so often seen) and extending past the root of the tail for extra warmth. In depth, it comes below elbow and stifle, as it should, again to help protect the belly area from draughts

(*below right*) A quilted, synthetic stable rug from Hydrophane Limited, which, like the New Zealand rug in the previous photograph, fits correctly, is properly shaped and has belly surcingles and leg straps. This type of rug is much more comfortable for the horse than the type which has to be secured by means of a surcingle or roller round the girth, and is much lighter, too, and easier to launder

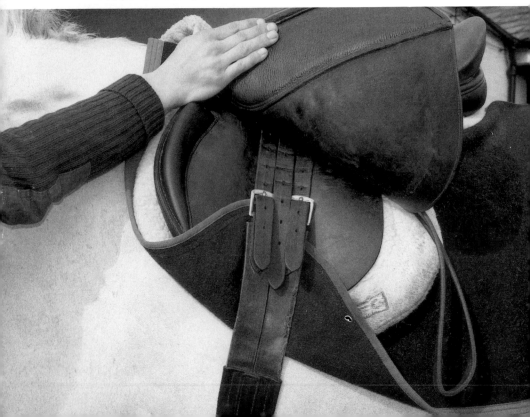

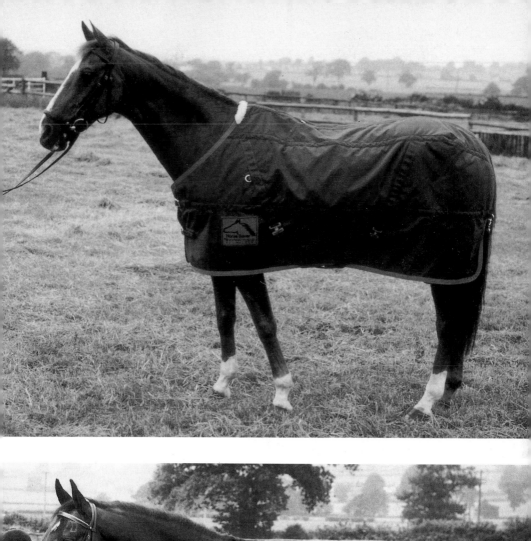

If a horse 'stands over in front' it means that the whole front leg slopes backwards so that the elbow appears to be in front of the fetlock; in 'standing under in front' the reverse is the case. These both result in incorrect stresses on the leg and, in the former, on the tendons and ligaments running down the back of the leg. A short, uncomfortable stride will probably also result.

There are many more conformation and action defects, but I hope this survey of the more common ones has helped emphasise that *any* abnormality results in extra stress, weight, and strain being placed on *some* part of the body or legs, and that although nature will strengthen that part a little in response to the stress, it will be unable to stand up to anything like hard work.

If action faults result in interfering, you can always put boots on your horse, but remember that such horses are more likely to bring themselves (and therefore you) down. If you only want a horse for light work, you can put up with all sorts of faults and should get the horse significantly cheaper. No horse is perfect, but if you buy a serious fault you are probably buying trouble in the form of injury, vets' bills and a horse you cannot ride or drive. A good horse costs just as much to keep as a bad one, and the purchase price of any horse will be forgotten years after you are working (or nursing) him.

(*top left*) Long-reining as a means of exercise and training is not as much used in Britain as it might be. Here, Sylvia Stanier, LVO, long-reins Mary Chipperfield's Andalusian stallion, Pedro, using the Danish method of long-reining which she favours, with the reins through the terrets of a driving pad and in more or less the position they would be held by a rider. Long-reining offers more variety and interest to both horse and trainer and work of a high standard can be achieved. Here Pedro performs *passage* (*Peter R. Sweet*)

(*centre*) Miss Sylvia Stanier's Arab stallion, Hussein, jumping on the lunge, a form of exercise for which he has great enthusiasm. The sloping pole on the outside wing for the rein to run up is an essential safety feature (*Peter R. Sweet*)

(*below*) The traditional English method of long-reining, with the reins passing through the stirrups, which are fastened together beneath the horse's belly to prevent them swinging about. Mr Syd Taylor and the Trakehner stallion, Cannabis, demonstrate (*Peter R. Sweet*)

Part Two

3

MANAGEMENT SYSTEMS

The horse has been a domesticated animal for about 5,000 years. The often patchy and incomplete fossil and historical records nonetheless indicate that it was already an established type when man's ancestors were still lolloping about on all fours. By some quirk of evolution, man evolved with lightning speed to supposedly overtake all other animals in intelligence and attain 'dominion over them'. He learned to hunt other animals for food first; then, rather than following wild herds, he started to build up his own, probably by initially capturing youngsters, and so exploited them for meat and milk.

Eventually, he presumably got the idea that the horse could carry his chattels. Because early man's predominantly hunter/gatherer lifestyle dictated that he follow the herds of his prey animals on their wanderings to fresh pasture, anything that could help him transport his worldly goods came in useful. This could hardly be described as the start of equitation, however, and all the earliest historical references indicate that man's first so-called *civilised* use of the horse was as a draught animal.

This early way of life must have suited the horse reasonably well. He was still doing what came naturally – wandering from place to place eating his natural food, grass. Before man learned to farm, the nomadic lifestyle was obligatory if he wanted to keep horses because he had no way of feeding them. Once he got the hang of growing crops, however, the horse's problems really started, from a management point of view. Farming meant a static lifestyle, quite foreign to the horse, and the practices of picketing, tethering and eventually stabling horses gradually came about.

Man also began to feed the horse more grain than he was used to, harness became more complicated, ploughing had to be done and chariots and heavier forms of transport were devised so that man could move about his claimed territory and trade or fight with his neighbours; ultimately it must have been realised that riding a horse is often faster and more convenient than driving one. So very gradually, the horse came to be used for very varied tasks.

But all this change has been too sudden for the horse – even now, 5,000 years later, the horse still has trouble in adapting to this kind of lifestyle. Individuals can adapt slightly to changes placed upon them by their environment (for example, the changing of the coat to suit the seasons, and the conditioning or fittening process) but major and significant changes within a species can only come about by evolution which is largely controlled by genes. A species living in a stable environment tends to remain stable. Any genetic mutations (alterations) which do occur will actually die out if they mean the affected individual is not so well suited to its environment – if it is not well suited it will not thrive, and its offspring which inherit the change (if it breeds at all) will similarly not thrive, and so it will not become established.

However, if the environment changes, as has the domestic horse's, the horse evolved by nature will not thrive so well under the new conditions, and it is a fact that many of the diseases and disorders horses and ponies suffer from in domesticity are man-induced, such as azoturia, frequent colic, laminitis and so on. For any species to thrive in an altered environment a genetic mutation – or several – is needed which causes the introduction into the species of features which will enable the horse to change with the environment, and so thrive and continue to survive.

An example of such change would be a modification to its digestive system, making it more like ours (geared to a few moderately-sized meals a day) – rather than the one it still has which is the result of millions of years of evolution, and which a few thousand years of domestication has not come near to changing. Most domestic horses, certainly those stabled or yarded, are not fed in accordance with the horse's natural requirement which is to have a little food passing almost constantly through the intestines. They are usually given hay only night and morning, with up to four feeds of concentrates – this system leaves horses for many hours with no food available and results in considerable hunger, both of which situations are largely unheard of in normal feral and wild conditions, and the horse does not cope well with them.

NATURE'S HORSE

The horse's lifestyle in natural conditions is well known. It is generally thought of as a creature of the wide open spaces, galloping about, mane and tail flying and grazing and browsing whenever it wants. This is largely correct, except that the natural conditions supporting these horses and ponies were, and are, very much more varied than open plains and include scrubland and wooded areas. Also, left to themselves, horses rarely move much faster than a walk – obviously they do trot and canter during social intercourse, but only normally gallop, apart from when playing, when being pursued.

Furthermore in the early stages of its evolution, the horse's ancestors were swamp and forest dwellers, grasslands not having at that time appeared. It is felt by many experts that this forest stage of its past life is the reason some horses seem to be naturally good jumpers (as are many forest animals), and why some do not automatically gallop flat out away from threats, but run and hide behind some convenient object such as a field shelter or a hedge, or into a spinney, if available. It could also be the reason why many horses, if correctly managed, seem quite happy to spend a good deal of time stabled; being in small, closed-in spaces is not that unnatural to them if you think about the dense forest environment of a primeval landscape.

Even in such an environment, however, the horse could still wander as it wished and its food was all around it in the form of vegetation. It did not live underground in a den or earth, or even, as far as we know, in caves except possibly when shelter was needed. Even then, it was essentially an open-air creature which sought shelter as and when required among dense undergrowth.

Later, as grassland developed, the horse adapted genetically to be more of a plains-dwelling, grass-eating creature, but he still found it appropriate to eat for many hours a day (about 16 or more), and, of necessity, to walk about while eating in order to move from one patch of grass to the next. How many stabled domesticated horses get 16 hours a day gentle walking exercise with the odd spurt of more energetic exercise in between?!

Sleep is always a luxury for any prey animal. Horses seem to sleep for a total of only about four hours out of the twenty-four, and then not all at once. They, like other mammals, need and experience two kinds of sleep, short wave sleep (SWS) and rapid eye-movement sleep (REM sleep). Different types of electrical brainwaves occur in each type of sleep: in SWS, the waves are slow, indicating that the brain is fairly inactive (although certain functions such as hormonal control go on round the clock). Horses can both doze and experience SWS when standing (due to 'locking devices' in the elbows and stifles) and when lying propped on their breast bone with their legs curled around them. To any prey animal to be able to sleep standing up is a big advantage because when danger threatens and the animal is alerted he is already on his feet ready to flee. Because of this, the horse is fairly easily aroused out of dozing or SWS.

REM sleep is different. Here, the brain waves are almost the same as when the horse is fully awake and alert, yet for this kind of sleep, he lies flat out on his side and is quite difficult to arouse. This is the most dangerous kind of sleep for a horse and is only snatched for minutes at a time, perhaps about 15 or so. One reason is because, due to the very heavy weight of the horse, the lung on the 'ground' side is severely hampered in its function due to being compressed by the body. Since it is not functioning normally because of this, it can fill with fluid, which is expelled during normal activities when the horse is not flat out.

It has been noticed that horses experience REM sleep on alternating sides of the body, so the lungs take it in turns, as it were, to be squashed.

Many people have reported seeing the rapid eye-movements characteristic of this kind of sleep because it is fairly easy to approach and observe a horse in this state – despite the brain appearing to be almost awake, the body seems to be almost paralysed. Apart from small muscle twitches, almost as if the horse were galloping, there is a complete lack of muscle tone; the body, as opposed to the brain, is completely relaxed and presumably recuperating from previous physical activity.

It is during REM sleep that animals and humans are thought to dream. Certainly humans awakened from it by research workers are able to recall events passing through their minds in the moments before being awakened, whereas those aroused during SWS could not remember anything.

Another reason for REM sleep being dangerous for the horse is obviously because he is much more vulnerable to predators in this state – he is not only deeply 'unconscious' in a purely natural way, he is down and flat out. It takes a horse several seconds to wake up, get to his feet and accelerate to a useful speed to escape a predator – and a predator can travel a significant distance in several seconds. It could certainly mean the difference between life and death.

REM sleep, however, *is* vital. Horses appear to need, according to various sleep studies, about two hours REM sleep in twenty-four. It also seems that it is deprivation of REM sleep rather than SWS which causes irritability and, in extreme cases, mental breakdown and illness. Horses prevented from lying flat on their sides, which is the only position in which they can experience REM sleep, are heading for trouble. Even one night travelling to some competitive event can significantly affect a horse's feeling of well-being and, therefore, his ability to perform next day.

So although horses obviously need sleep, they do not need much by our standards and they do not take it all at once but in short snatches, and all round the clock.

Because this style of sleeping evolved due to the horse's always having to be on guard for danger, this also gives us a clue as to his basic mentality. The horse is essentially a nervous creature, watchful even when apparently settled, and easily startled.

Most horses greatly prefer life in a herd to a solitary existence. If you are one of a crowd there is less chance of your being singled out for a meal by a predator, unless you are so old, sick or young that you cannot keep up with the herd, in which case you *are* likely to be caught. Although most predators have roughly the same top speed as their equine prey (except for the cheetah), they cannot keep it up for as long as the horse whose speciality is endurance. If the horse and its relatives can, by keeping a watchful eye out for predators, get a good start on them by means of distance and rapid acceleration, and keep running as fast and as long as possible, the predators will tire much sooner and the horse will get away. In fact, in wild and feral conditions where equidae are still hunted by natural predators, roughly one hunt in four is successful over the species, so equus usually wins.

We now have a fairly accurate picture of the horse that Nature has produced and which we have in our care: a large land mammal specialised for running, a herbivore which needs to eat for many hours a day and to take gentle exercise for just as many hours. This horse needs a fibrous diet based on grass, not grain, it has a nervous temperament and needs company to feel secure and content.

In domesticity, these needs are only met in horses kept mainly out in the open but with shelter facilities, where food is constantly available and other horses and ponies are present in a domestic version of a herd. Obviously, most working and performance horses are not kept in this way, and it is in such animals that most management-related disorders are found.

Different countries have differing traditional management methods, as do the different regions of those countries too. In Britain alone we go from the extreme of keeping horses completely stabled, even tied in narrow stalls – as in many military and police establishments, besides others – to letting them run almost wild in areas such as the southern moors and northern fells.

The same extremes occur in many countries. The traditional method in many eastern European countries is to breed and keep horses in large herds on grassy plains. In America, and particularly in the west where ranching predominates, horses often have a plains existence though in controlled areas and are accommodated in enclosures (corrals) when wanted regularly; they are stabled sometimes as well. Australia and New Zealand usually keep their horses out most of the year by tradition, but in countries where open land is even more at a premium than in Britain, such as Scandinavia and Norway in particular, the normal method of keeping horses is to stable them.

Because the horse has proved itself to be an extremely adaptable animal, any of these methods can suit it well provided its basic needs of food and water, exercise and shelter are catered for. Many completely stabled horses thrive well enough provided they are exercised adequately: many outdoor ones suffer greatly because they have no proper shelter facilities. The important principle is to remember the basic needs and comply with them and not automatically to think that any method is right or wrong because superficially it seems to be so.

FACILITIES NEEDED

We need ample supplies of food in order to keep any animal, and in the case of the horse this means having extensive storage and acquiring sufficient quantities of hay or a roughage-type substitute, with concentrates (grain/cereal-based foods) as a secondary food added as required – and probably in smaller amounts than most of us imagine provided the roughage is of good enough quality. We need some form of shelter. This can range from high, thick hedges round a field particularly on its windward side and overhead shelter such as can be found in woodland, to a man-made shelter such as a conventional field shelter, a large run-in shed able to accommodate many horses, or actual stabling, either loose boxes (box-stalls) or standing (tie) stalls. Horses out in more natural conditions than a fenced field can seek shelter according to the nature and lie of the land; our mountain and moorland ponies, for example, are adept at knowing where there is natural scrub to break the force of the wind, bluffs or cliffs, or rises and hollows in the ground, all of which affect the wind flow through their area.

Because of the horse's natural need for exercise, we must obviously arrange exercise facilities. Turn-out facilities are a boon because the horses stay more mentally settled because of the freedom they provide and, hopefully, the natural social contact they can have with the other horses turned out with them. This takes the burden off us somewhat because we need give less exercise ourselves.

If the horses can only be exercised during work because of lack of other facilities, we should be prepared to give rather more than the normally recommended two hours a day for a fit, healthy horse. This is minimal compared to the exercise a horse would take given the freedom to do as it wished, and we should try to create other facilities – maybe provide a mechanical horse-walker which can walk and trot horses for half-an-hour a day or look round our establishment for some small area to turn into a surfaced 'play-pen', for want of a better expression. This need *not* be large, just enough to allow the horse to stretch his legs, perhaps get up a little canter, buck, roll and feel less constrained than when he is stabled all the time.

Loose boxes with pens leading off them, perhaps not even much bigger than the boxes themselves (such as old-fashioned bull-pens), are nonetheless well recommended. The horses, wearing waterproof clothing when appropriate, choose to spend most of their time outside and can be kept just as fit and clean as an ordinary stabled horse. Existing yards may, with a little imagination and modification of facilities, be able to add such pens leading off either the front or the back of each box, and the pens themselves could be roofed, either fully, partially or not at all, as desired. There would need to be a suitable entrance for the horses, obviously – probably the present one at the front of the box, and the pen could lead off that. To avoid having to take feed and other supplies and equipment through the pens each time, a human-size door could be made in the back of the box, if there is space for a working area there.

Alternatively, the front of the box and the existing doors could be left as they are and a pen built on the back of each box, so the horses could

A 'play-pen' made for turning out horses for freedom where grazing is unavailable. Hay is provided by tying nets to the posts/top rails, and water simply given by the familiar plastic dustbin in a tyre to stabilise it, and tied to a post. It may be better to have two bins, sited in different corners of the pen and inside the rails, so it is not then necessary to omit a top rail for the horses to reach the water and facilitate their jumping out. The rails should always be flush with the tops of the posts (here angled to help rain run-off) as should a horse try to jump out over this type of fencing the sharp corners could cause serious injury

come in and out either way but the humans could work from the front, as at present. There are all sorts of arrangements which would depend on the exact layout of the existing yard.

Many yards have at least one area which is currently under-used, clogged up with weeds and rubbish, or tucked away due to lack of yard design. Such areas could be cleared and suitably surfaced, then fenced off and the horses put out there on a rota for, say, an hour at a time. The area really need only be about twice the size of a stable – quite small but big enough to give the horse room to potter about, stretch his legs, have a sense of freedom and a change of scene. Give him a haynet and, if the area is big enough, put a friend in with him.

Surfacing materials can either be natural earth, sand, sand and peat mixed, fine shale or used bedding (minus droppings, see chapter 5) but nothing like gravel or cinders which could hurt the horse should he roll. If the area is already surfaced with something like concrete or asphalt, this could either be removed or covered with some non-slip product such as a self-bonding rubber flooring, or mesh reinforced mat (not with metal links) of the type laid beneath the turf of sports' areas and some racecourses. Then the other materials could be laid on top.

If cash is at a premium and the area is fairly small, used bedding can simply be laid straight down onto concrete, tarmac or whatever is present – after all, this is the arrangement in many stables, bedding on concrete.

Larger areas should have something more secure in case the horses slip when cavorting about. If money is not a first priority, artificial turf could be considered or something similar such as sports arena coverings. If the area is earth, why not sell the top soil (the purchaser to excavate it out) and put down a rubble base, covered by gravel with an artificial surface on top, or simply wood chips, as for a normal outdoor manège?

There are all sorts of possibilities which could easily be put into operation in most yards, with a little imagination and modification of existing facilities and layout. The benefits of such play areas are tremendous, and those who install them always say that, like having an indoor school, they do not know how they managed without them. In fact, many larger establishments which do have indoor schools and outdoor manèges often under-use them. There is no reason why horses could not be turned into them at times when they are not in use; many establishments use their indoor schools for housing ponies at night in winter.

· ALTERNATIVES TO STABLING ·

Although conventional stabling is very convenient for humans the labour needed to care for horses so housed is becoming prohibitively expensive, and in Britain we could make much more use of the yarding system used in other countries to accommodate horses.

Here, one or more animals are kept in a covered area with a ground surface of one of the materials mentioned earlier. Droppings can be removed once or twice daily but there is no time-consuming mucking out and more horses can be accommodated in a smaller space than is taken up by the necessary number of individual stables. Obviously, care is needed not to put enemies together, but this would apply in any situation. The yard can open out onto a grassed area such as a normal paddock and the horses can come and go as they wish, or they can be kept indoors in the covered yard. Disused barns are often ideal for this type of accommodation. Some yards are unroofed but this is generally unsatisfactory as horses often need some kind of shelter from harsh weather in winter or heat and flies in summer. There should be at least a part-roof, and a solid wall on the windward side of the structure if not all round.

This type of facility can be used in *any* establishment from studs to riding centres, private yards to large commercial concerns. Some establishments in Britain and particularly Ireland do use the system, and also in Europe, but it could be exploited much more to the benefit of all concerned.

Feeding – at least of hay – is usually done communally; concentrates are often fed in long troughs, but a careful watch needs to be kept on greedy bullies, so that individual attention can be given to the shy, more picky feeder. The system is not a substitute for this vital personal care, it simply greatly facilitates and makes more economical the keeping of horses in general, and is a system we would do well to consider more.

·VENTILATION·

Ventilation needs special mention because most ordinary stabling, particularly indoor loose boxes such as those in the American barn system, is sadly lacking in this respect.

An ordinary loose box or box stall opening to the outside is usually considered well ventilated enough if there is an open top door and window on the same side, but this is not necessarily the case. The most practical and simple way to test the ventilation of your horse's box is to test it by means of your own nose after he has been indoors for some time, particularly first thing in the morning. Go in after you have been outdoors for a while, take a slow, deep breath and tell yourself honestly whether you can detect any noticeable difference in the smell and temperature of the air. If you can smell mustiness, closeness, too much 'horse', dust or, more sinister, the ammonia smell of decomposing urine, you have a problem.

Horses are athletic animals born to be outside. Their respiratory systems are extremely sensitive to lack of oxygen and to dust and mould spores in their airspace. Many show signs of breathing problems such as chronic obstructive pulmonary disease – COPD – which is an allergic reaction to fungi and is also popularly known as broken wind, heaves and emphysema, and sometimes as small airway disease (see chapter 11, p.227). Basically, as soon as horses are put on a combined regime of clean air, dust-free roughage and bedding, plus perhaps veterinary assistance with drugs, they improve dramatically and are usually able to return to work when previously they had been written off.

Conventional loose boxes have double-leaved doors and the top one is usually recommended to be left open. Unfortunately, there is still a significant number of the 'old school', particularly in racing, who believe that closed doors and a warm (in other words stuffy) atmosphere improves the look of a horse's coat, helping keep it short and shiny. This fact is unimportant when compared to the considerable damage this can do to the horse's wind. Most yards, in my experience, do leave top doors open day and night except when a strong wind is blowing directly into the box, and even then the window should normally be left open.

Windows are usually recommended to be on the same side as the door to prevent cross-draughts. In fact, a cross-draught is often a highly desirable thing, particularly in the warmer seasons. There should be windows open on both sides of the stable in normal weather, there should be gable-end louvres at each end of a line of boxes, or actual windows high up in the end walls, and much more use should be made of ridge-roof ventilators which allow the warm, rising (stuffy) air to escape.

Ridge-roof ventilators which run the whole length of the stable block are used in many of the yards at the Irish National Stud and I have seen them in other establishments. They are a really effective form of ventilation which should be incorporated in all new or converted build-ings. In existing boxes, at least an ordinary ridge-roof ventilator should be installed – this can be done without too much hassle, as can extra opening vents or windows or even just a removeable plank – almost anything which will help improve the air flow in what is to the horse an artificially small airspace.

Air flow when excessive can mean draughts, which should be avoided. Deciding the right airflow for your stable or stable block can be a problem. In American barns, stale air often pools in the boxes while the aisle down the centre or sides of the building is clear due to having the wide doors at each end open -- apply the simple ventilation test described earlier and you will prove it! Each stall should have its own ventilation devices and human attendants should be prepared to

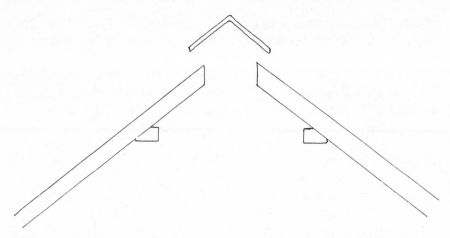

Side view of ridge-roof ventilator made to go the whole length of the line of boxes. There are periodical supports, obviously, to keep the ventilator up. The roof itself, of course, does not meet in the middle like a normal roof but is open all along to facilitate the exit of stale air

spend time, up to half-an-hour, in a stable to see how the air really feels and smells to them.

Many prefabricated loose boxes are sold in Britain every year and they are nearly all sadly lacking when it comes to ventilation facilities. Most of them do not have ridge-roof ventilators nor a window in the back of each box as well as the front. Most significantly, they are all too low in their standard formats. If you want a decent height you have to pay extra for it.

In an average box of roughly 12ft (4m) square with a ridge-roof, you should have an eaves height of the same, plus an open top door, windows and other ventilation devices if you want an adequate air flow and change. Most prefabricated boxes offer an eaves height of only about 7ft 6in (2.4m) which is not enough. For a single plane roof, the height of the lowest part of the roof (which should be at the back) should really be about 14ft (4.6m) for good ventilation, which sounds unrealistic but is not. The headroom in a stable can also affect a horse's feeling of security. Most do not like low roofs and those who are fairly active in their boxes are in danger of hitting their heads on them, particularly if something startles them. This can subsequently cause handling problems.

In still, hot weather, even with all the ventilation devices so far mentioned, it may still be difficult to maintain a comfortably cool atmosphere inside the stable buildings without some mechanical assistance to create a cooling draught. Two extractor fans fixed in the gable ends of a short row of loose boxes (say four to six boxes) is a relatively cheap way of creating an air-flow above the horses' heads to remove stale air and bring in fresh. They should be set to take air out, then the air movement will 'suck' in fresh air through doors, windows and louvres.

Larger complexes, particularly American barn systems, may need more complicated systems of ducting, inlets and outlets, and where conditions demand and money is available, a proper air conditioning system may be necessary, providing refrigerated air in summer.

Whatever system is decided upon, remember that it should be quiet, and all working parts, switches and so on must be out of reach of the horses – if you want the system to last more than five minutes!

· STABLE AND YARD EQUIPMENT ·

The equipment we use can make a big difference to the ease and effectiveness with which we care for horses. There are many stable fittings which may make life easier but are not essential if cash is tight. Horses who eat fairly quietly can certainly eat on a clean piece of sheet or sacking in a corner of the box floor, and hay, too, can be fed from the floor – this is policy in many high class studs where it is felt desirable to minimise the number of fittings in a stable for safety's sake. No matter how safe we may feel a stable is, a foal or some other inquisitive, active horse can still get into trouble on something as basic as a haynet, a hayrack or a water bucket.

A particularly dangerous fitting, in my experience, is a window guard which projects inwards to protect the horse from the inward-opening window; it presents something hard and immoveable for him to bang his head on, as these guards are usually about horse's head height. Unless your windows can be well above the height of your horse's head, *do not have inward-opening windows*. This is contrary to the advice given in every horse management book I know, but it is much safer to have windows that open down and out, as in ordinary house windows, than up and in. Again, the Irish National Stud uses such windows in many yards and, having experienced them, the expected draughts are no more than with the usual type, and they are much safer as you can simply fit a flat grille or mesh on the inside which is quite safe for the horses.

Any stable fittings should be the corner kind to minimise danger – corner mangers, corner hayracks and corner watering devices or bucket holders. Mangers should be filled in underneath; the space can possibly be used as a cupboard to store grooming kit, with a hole for your finger to open the latch which should be on the inside to prevent the horse fiddling with it. No sharp edges, particularly of hard materials such as metal or brick, should be allowed in a stable. Electric cables should be inside corner conduits so the horse can neither interfere with them nor injure himself on the protective conduit. Fitted electric lights should be high up in the roof and switches outside the box well out of reach of straining necks and investigating muzzles. Naturally, they should be of the waterproof type.

When fitting any new item, from a bucket holder to a tie-ring, always think carefully about what could possibly go wrong, then try to prevent it. Tie-rings, for instance, should be on the outside wall of a box securely fixed through the wall by means of a screw shank and nut. There should be a metal plate between the nut and the wall through which the shank fits to prevent wear and to spread the pressure should the horse pull on the ring from the other side. The nut and shank will inevitably protrude through the wall a little way, which is why the rings should be fitted to the outside walls to prevent injury to the horse in the next stable.

Haynets can be tied to such rings or at least to strong staples, again preferably in a corner, and should be at horse's head height. Hay racks if used should be very slightly above horse's head height. The old reason for not having them high was to prevent bits falling into the horse's eyes; however, if they are too low the horse can knock his head on them. This risk is minimised if only the corner type is used.

Yard equipment to make life easier normally relates to mucking out and sweeping. If your establishment is a large commercial one, you may be fortunate enough to have a vacuum machine for clearing up the yard, but most of us are stuck with the time-wasting and onerous task of sweeping by hand. Use one of the newer metre-wide brooms which sweep three times as much yard with one push and so get the job done just as well but much more quickly.

Muck barrows should be as large and well-balanced as possible so that trips to the muck heap are minimal, thus saving time and energy. The single-wheeled type are bad, as they are very difficult to balance when

Tie ring with screw shank, nut and metal plate, which goes on the far side of the wall to prevent injury by spreading the force on the nut, so preventing its being pulled through the wall

full unless they are small, in which case they simply don't hold enough to be really useful. With the larger ones, you need only hit a pebble or uneven patch on the yard, get caught in a gust of wind or simply not hold the handles evenly and the whole lot swings over and leaves you with a large pile of muck to be cleared off the yard.

Get barrows with two wheels centrally placed on an axle so all you need do is balance them from front to back; they tip easily forward onto the muck heap with a direct push and no awkward manoeuvring.

If you have many boxes to muck out, treat yourself to a really large barrow with four wheels and a spring- or hydraulically-assisted tip-up mechanism – you simply press a small handle and the body of the barrow tips up all by itself, which is a great help if you are not particularly burly. Failing a barrow, use an opened-out sack.

Summary

●The horse has evolved as a running prey animal, a herbivore which needs as its norm a constant supply of food running through its intestinal tract and many hours' gentle exercise per day. It needs a fibrous, grass-based diet (not cereals); it feels more content and secure in the company of other horses: and it has a basically nervous temperament, easily startled. To manage horses effectively, we must simulate these requirements in practise and not merely pay lip-service to them.

●The accommodation facilities for horses must provide close social contact with other horses, shelter, space and good ventilation; and we must provide a more or less constant supply of roughage-based food if we are to mimic the natural conditions in which the horse has evolved and in which he thrives best. Otherwise, management problems will probably develop.

●Labour and money-saving alternatives to stabling deserve more attention – yarding in particular is useful, economical and convenient. Ventilation should be very efficient to ensure adequate respiratory performance and maintenance of health.

●Keep stable fittings safe and to a minimum, and purchase equipment which will make your tasks easier.

SAFETY AND SECURITY

Horses are nervous, powerful, fast animals; even apparently quiet-natured, settled horses can be easily startled as part of their natural, in-built defence mechanism against predators. Many of them are also naturally inquisitive and easily bored. Their natural state keeps them occupied eating, wandering around and socialising with herd members. Domestic horses who are restricted and allowed to become bored often look for entertainment (which we might call mischief) which can result in their sustaining injuries.

Stabling should have no unnecessary projections, and certainly nothing sharp on which the horse could knock itself, or loose (such as kicking boards) which it could prise off for something to do, resulting in splintered wood and exposed nails and screws. There should be ample head room, and enough room to lie down and sleep flat out (for REM sleep), roll and get up without the horse being at risk of knocking itself or becoming cast.

Cast horses struggling to rise can injure themselves internally and externally, and become extremely frightened and exhausted. Some horses subsequently refuse to lie down again, thus depriving themselves of essential rest and sleep.

A useful device to prevent a horse becoming cast is to have grooves or ridges on the walls horizontal to the ground at heights of 3ft (1m) and 4ft 6in (1.4m) approximately to suit horses, ponies and foals. These enable the animal to get a purchase on the wall with its hooves when scrabbling around trying to get up (as evidenced by the scratch marks on the stable wall of a horse who habitually gets cast). Also, the kicking boards could be sloped inwards at the base so that although the stable floorspace is very slightly reduced, the horse is prevented from getting too near the wall; banking the bedding high and thick round the sides has a similar effect.

As well as doors having bolts top and bottom and being made to open outwards rather than in, I should like to see wider doors as standard – at least 5ft (1.6m) – to lessen the chance of horses hitting their hips, and have them higher, too, so there is less risk of a bang on the poll should a horse hesitate and throw up its head when coming in or out. A rearing horse's head can reach a height of twice its own height at the withers, in other words a 16hh horse would reach a height of about 10ft 6in (3.5m) when rearing – not many stable roofs, let alone entrances, allow for this.

Rollers are an effective way of preventing injury to hips as horses pass through doorways and can be set into the door jambs at an appropriate

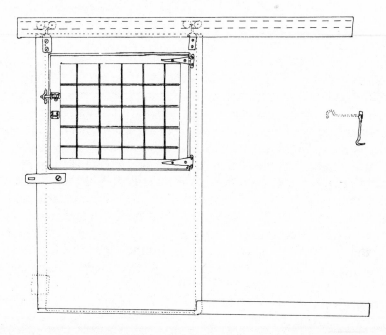

An excellent type of stable door – sliding on an overhead rail so that the normal groove in the doorway at the bottom (here absent) does not fill with debris. There is a half-inch metal ridge instead to stabilise the bottom of the door. The top door is grilled and can be opened so that the horses can put their heads out and not feel shut in, even though they can see out anyway

height. Failing this, if the jambs cannot be rounded or smoothed off, old sacking can be fixed to them to help cushion any impact – though some horses tear this off for entertainment.

As far as possible, the area surrounding the stables – yard, accessway to the highway or paddocks – should be free of dangerous items. This basically means looking out for anything at all on which a horse could tread and injure itself, collide with or entangle itself in: wheelbarrows left parked carelessly about, wire hanging off the fence or on the ground, slippery fertiliser bags blowing about, broken glass or rusty metal panels hanging off old barns. This is elementary, but it is surprising how familiarity with our surroundings can blind us to danger spots.

In the paddock, you should always be watching out for any litter thrown in by passers-by, for farm implements and equipment left lying around (harrows are especially dangerous) and particularly for weakened or broken fences and gates. If your land becomes badly poached in wet weather in such areas as gateways, much used tracks round the field, shelter entrances and around troughs, do *not* tip down rubble as so many farmers do for their poor cattle. If the land is too bad for you to excavate at present, put down thick layers, regularly, of used bedding, sand, sand and peat – in fact anything which will help soak up water, stabilise the mud and be safe for the horses. These areas are not going to grow any useful grazing even in summer, so improving the surface by spreading something suitable on them will do more good than harm.

Fencing is an expensive item but is obviously vital to good horse management. Avoid the obvious disasters such as barbed wire and sheep netting, both so common on farms but highly dangerous for horses, but perhaps more attention should be paid to modern fencing materials such as flexible pvc fencing which comes on a roll and can be nailed onto existing fence posts or specially erected (there are several brands regularly advertised in the horsey press). It is excellent for patching up broken fences as it can be cut to any length you want (and on a do-it-yourself basis), and for running as a single rail along the top to reinforce or raise existing fencing of any kind. If you have to rent your grazing when and where you can, you can use it to mend fencing which might otherwise be so dilapidated as to put the field concerned out of consideration. Then when you leave you can easily dismantle it.

Diamond-mesh fencing is slowly making its way onto the British market, having been widely used in America for years. Its small mesh makes it quite impossible for a horse ever to get a hoof through, something which often happens with the square-mesh fencing sold here for horses, especially on the upper rows if horses are playing about. It is secured with staples to posts, and to wooden rails top and bottom with occasionally an extra supporting rail across the middle of a section, and appears to be extremely safe and strong.

Electric fencing is often frowned on by horse-owners but can be useful in the same way as flexible rail fencing for keeping horses away from, say, broken fencing, poisonous trees, ponds and so on. The kits for agricultural use have powerful battery units or can be run from the mains in nearby paddocks. The safest is the shiny metal ribbon type which horses can see easily. If you use the usual wire type, at least make sure it is heavy gauge wire and attach coloured plastic strips (such as cut-up fertiliser bags) which flutter in the breeze and remind horses it is there.

The usual method of introducing horses to electric fencing should be followed: damp the horse's nose, lead it up to the wire and press its nose against it. Be ready for the jump, and if the horse is exceptionally nervous have someone else with you and the horse kitted out in a lungeing cavesson with two lead-ropes for more secure handling, in case it reacts unusually violently. Most horses simply throw up their heads and jump back a step. Repeat this two or three times (if the horse will let you) along the fence so the horse learns its extent.

Well maintained natural hedging is probably the best fence of all, but if you still prefer post and rail fencing, which is probably the safest choice of the readily available materials, you can economise, for adult horses, by having only two rails. The top rail should be the height (at the withers) of the tallest horse likely to occupy the field, and the second one just above the horse's knee height. If you have three or more rails, the bottom one should be no less than 1ft (.3m) from the ground with the others evenly spaced in between – the horses will be less likely to get a foot over the bottom rail, but it is low enough to ensure that foals do not lie down or roll near the fence and get up on the other side.

Wire fencing of any kind must be kept really well strained and taut, and a set of wire clippers must be kept handy where everyone knows where to find them, so if a horse does happen to get a strand caught between hoof and shoe or becomes tangled in a broken and sagging strand, rescue can easily be effected – provided the predicament is spotted in time – without the horse injuring itself further or pulling down the whole fence.

Since horses will always congregate at the gate when waiting to be fed or brought in, these are subject to hard wear and frequent use and should be strong and properly hung. The safest gates are the tubular steel ones with the bottom halves filled in with strong metal mesh and recessed handles which horses cannot open, and which can be easily padlocked. Hunting latches which protrude upwards should be avoided as they can cause injury, become caught in headcollars and so on. Heavy duty galvanised fittings (bolts and hinges) should be used and your aim should be to avoid completely any sharp metal. Rounded bolt heads and smooth nuts should be used, and fastenings which the horses cannot open or injure themselves on.

If a chain and spring clip is used, the clip must be kept on the outside of the post – horses will fiddle, and not uncommonly tear their lips on them while trying to discover how to undo them.

· LEGAL OBLIGATIONS ·

It is the legal obligation of the animal owner to ensure that it does not stray, except (usually) in the case of grazing let short-term (perhaps by the season) or where there is no formal long-term arrangement in writing. If an animal does stray and/or causes damage, the owner is liable in law. This is why it is essential, from a good sense point-of-view, to have third party insurance, and it means that it is normally your responsibility to maintain fencing so as to keep your horses where they belong.

A very real problem nowadays is that of theft. If thick high, natural hedging is the best for your horse for both keeping him enclosed and providing a windbreak, it is also the most effective for keeping thieves and vandals out. While wooden and wire fencing can be summarily dealt with by means of saws and wire clippers, it takes considerably more effort and time to hack through a thick, prickly hedge, particularly one that has been professionally laid where the main branches are laid diagonally and secured with a row of twisted thinner branches along the top. Such hedges form a tough barrier; they *can* be demolished with a good deal of work, but few horse thieves would tackle them. Combined with a metal gate padlocked at both ends, of the type that cannot be lifted off its hinges, and sturdy gateposts, this is the best and most secure *practical* fencing available to most horse-owners, chain-link security fencing being too costly for most people.

The cost of electrically operated alarm systems for large areas such as farms, equestrian establishments and the like is coming down as modern technology brings out new systems, many of which are advertised in equestrian journals. Even a simple make-and-break contact wired to a car battery which will sound off an alarm or bring on a strong light can be enough to confuse and put off thieves

A visit from your local Crime Prevention Officer from your police force is free and well worth requesting. He or she will give advice, recommend products, perhaps explain aspects of security which you had not thought of, or point out particularly vulnerable areas on your premises.

Freeze-marking will almost certainly be recommended as the most effective way of safeguarding your horse. There are now several reputable firms carrying out this service nationwide, and the chances of a freeze-marked horse being stolen are minimal – most horses are stolen to be sold for meat at an imminent auction, and the rewards offered by the freeze-marking companies for the recovery of stolen, marked horses far exceed the meat price of the carcass. And the recovery rate is excellent.

In addition to freeze-marking, take colour snapshots of your horse from both sides, back and front, and also close-ups of any identifying marks – the freeze-mark itself, any scars, and all four chestnuts which are as individual to the horse or pony as our fingerprints are to us. Check through your regional Yellow Pages telephone directories for the details of all sale yards, and ring them for the dates and times of their auctions; the police should also be able to give you some of this information, also HAPPA (The Horses and Ponies Protection Association) who run a 'Lost and Found' register (see Appendix B for their address).

If your horse or pony does go missing, immediately inform the nearest sale with an auction due, then the police, HAPPA and the

British Horse Society who work with many freeze-mark companies, and your freeze-mark company itself. Visit the sales as they occur to look out for your horse, as the only way you can get him back if stolen is to buy him once he has gone through the auction ring. Useful, detailed leaflets on security are available from HAPPA and the BHS.

Basically, the best policy is to deter thieves by freeze-marking your horse and marking your tack and other valuable equipment with your National Insurance number – this is yours for life and better than your post code, which is what is usually recommended. Keep gates, doors, cupboards, tack rooms and offices under secure lock and key when not being used, even during the daytime, and employ every device you can to delay, hinder and confuse thieves and vandals.

Summary

●So, we have determined that horses are powerful, fast animals, though nervous and easily startled and, due to their natural lifestyle, easily bored. If there is any trouble to be found in the way of damage or injury they will usually find it, particularly ponies!

●Stabling must present as smooth an interior and with as few fittings as is reasonably possible. The stable should be large enough for the horse or pony to move around, lie down, roll, sleep flat out, get up and shake without being encumbered, and it must be kept in good repair.

●Anti-cast ridges or grooves on the stable walls are an excellent way of helping a cast horse regain his feet.

●Doorways should be higher and wider than is normal to reduce the risk of injury.

●Well maintained fencing is essential, natural hedging being the best. It is the owner's liability in law to compensate for damage done by horses.

●Freeze-marking is the most effective way of preventing your horse or pony being stolen. Mark tack and other valuable items with your National Insurance number and make good use of strong padlocks, locks and keys when premises are not in use, even during the daytime. Request a visit from the Crime Prevention Officer of your local police force for extra, individual advice.

BASIC SYSTEMS AND WHAT IS INVOLVED

· KEEPING A HORSE STABLED ·

This is obviously the most time-consuming and restrictive system for both horse and attendants. Everything must be done for the horse who is virtually a prisoner, even if a much loved one, in a cell much smaller than he would probably choose for himself. If well cared for, adequately exercised and properly fed (ie not being allowed to become really hungry), many horses do, obviously, thrive on the system and come to feel secure and at home in their stables. It is when exercise is insufficient and feeding not truly in line with the natural pattern (see chapter 4) that problems occur. Many horses are claustrophobic and become very distressed when stabled, showing their mental state by undue restlessness, excessive nervousness, development of stable vices, misbehaviour during exercise, lack of performance and other behavioural aberrations.

Stabled horses need at the very least two visits a day from their attendants for feeding, watering, mucking out, grooming and exercising, and just generally checking. Working owners may find this inconvenient but it must be done for the sake of the horse; it may be possible to devise a rota to care for communally-kept horses on, say, do-it-yourself or part livery away form home. Matters are obviously eased with horses kept at home since family members should be available at different times to care for them.

In professional yards or those of 'full-time' competitors, attendants are constantly present so the problems are lessened.

The main disadvantages for the horse are erratic attendance and feeding, plus unreasonable confinement, and the fact that he may well be denied any real contact with his peers. Well cared for, however, horses do adapt reasonably well to this lifestyle.

· THE COMBINED SYSTEM ·

This system combines stabling and turning out to grass. The horse usually spends several hours a day at grass, and may be stabled only at night in winter or during the day in summer; the method can be worked out according to the owner's needs and the time available.

The horse can exercise himself and eat his natural food, grass. Hopefully, he will be turned out with at least one companion so can socialise with others of his kind. He has the shelter and privacy of his stable at other times and will probably spend much of his time there resting and eating.

Even very fit competition horses will benefit mentally and physically from just an hour or two, preferably more, turned out on most days as part of their routine.

From the owner's point of view the system is much less tying than stabling, yet the horse can still be kept very fit and his diet largely controlled. He can be kept clean by wearing either a New Zealand rug or a light waterproof sheet according to the season, and neck hoods are also available. The small amount of mud he might pick up is easily dealt with.

· YARDING ·

This system is excellent provided the flooring of the yard is dust-free. If the horses are constantly kicking up dust which will irritate their throats, lungs and eyes, health problems can obviously arise. Large strawed yards are best avoided because of the fungi involved. Special flooring materials such as wood chips intended for use on outside schools can be purchased and may be topped up with used bedding (minus droppings, see chapter 5). Sand alone can certainly be used as it is not dusty and will not cause respiratory problems, but in some areas it may be difficult to acquire, and expensive.

Yards can be wholly roofed and walled in, entirely open with ordinary fencing round them, or part and part; the latter arrangement gives the best of both worlds so the horses can shelter at any time of year, as they wish.

Feeding is usually done communally, with hay being fed in large racks all down one side of the yard. Concentrates are often fed in the same way, particularly when the horses are of the same age and type. However, individuals needing special feeding must be fed separately.

Mucking out is a time-consuming chore which with this system you are spared, but it is best to remove droppings as often as possible, at least once or twice a day depending on the number of horses and the space available.

Horses remain quite clean on this system, the materials normally used being easily brushed off. This method can also be used in conjunction with turning out to grass, horses being brought into yards under cover at night, or during the day in summer.

· OUT AT GRASS ·

Although this method may seem to be the most natural this is not always the case – very large tracts of land are needed for a genuinely natural existence and, in Britain and many parts of Europe, and in the more heavily populated areas of Australasia and America, this is just not possible as far as working animals are concerned. In the UK and Ireland, only native ponies have the chance, in a few isolated areas, to live a wild, natural life. Cross-bred ponies may be turned out on the moors and fells but can rarely stand the very harsh winters and suffer badly, as indeed can the true natives in a bad year.

Domestic horses and ponies confined to a small field or paddock are *not* living in natural conditions. Their area is too restricted to allow for natural progression from one feeding area to another, shelter is often severely and unnaturally limited, the land becomes horse-sick and battered from too many hooves and mouths and the animals' diet suffers.

Conditions can be good if areas are large enough, and if proper land management is practised combined, possibly, with the use of cattle on the land (preferably more cattle than horses); but shelter needs attention, as wooded areas to give overhead shelter are quite rare in most areas. A hedge, however high and thick, is rarely enough – shade, in particular, is essential in summer and few hedges provide enough of this.

Even with a carefully formulated grass-seed mix, it is hard to really control the diet, particularly in the case of ponies and cobs who are prone to laminitis and who easily become very fat. The animals are usually quite dirty and mud fever and other exposure ailments are not uncommon. Fitness is difficult to attain if the grass is too rich in spring and summer and laminitis and colic can also occur.

Provided the weather is reasonably equable and the grass supply adequate, horses are often very content out at grass, even if only because of the extra space, the company (usually) of other horses and ponies and the ability to spend much of the time walking about and grazing, as in nature.

Disadvantages for us include, in bad weather, unpleasant working conditions, filthy horses and less than ideal facilities for feeding, grooming (such as it can be with outdoor horses) and general care.

It is often believed that horses at grass can be left largely to their own devices because they are *au naturel* and wouldn't particularly welcome our visits, anyway. This may well be true provided the horse's every need is catered for in his field, but he really must be visited at least once and preferably twice or more each day, depending on circumstances. A horse can become very ill and die in 24 hours, 12 hours or even less. He can be stolen during the night or early morning and, if the owner only visits at night, he could already have been slaughtered between one evening and the next without the owner even knowing he had been taken, most thefts taking place just a few hours before an auction. The horse could be well out of your immediate area within an hour, thanks to our excellent road network, and by the time you sound the alert he could have been sold and shot.

In winter at least, depending on the weather, the horses' feed requirements may mean that enough feed, and particularly hay, just cannot be transported in one trip a day.

Generally speaking, unless facilities are unusually good, this method is the least convenient to us, and often the least pleasant to the horse. In summer, flies make horses' lives an absolute misery; a residual fly repellant (one whose effects last several days) should be used consistently, and renewed at the time intervals stated on the instructions or if the horse gets wet. This, combined with a proper field shelter to provide real shade, is the only way to help grass-kept animals (or those in open yards in summer) cope with flies. Their natural defences (mane, tail, forelock, muscle twitching) go some way towards dislodging flies, but they land again instantly and the animals are in constant torture from their attentions, even at night when night-flying insects come out. Some insects cause painful bites and skin reactions, warbles still occasionally occur, and bot flies create stomach parasites – so everything should be done to protect horses from insects.

Checklist

✓ 1 For truly effective management, we must imitate the horse's natural lifestyle – most domesticated horse suffer from over confinement, insufficient exercise (particularly of the slow category), lack of natural social contact and a feeding régime which is more suitable to the human digestive system.

2 Statistics show that respiratory problems are on the increase – this is largely due to inadequate ventilation, environmental dust and mould spores on feed and bedding materials. Do all you can to improve your horse's airspace (see p.60), and even if he is not noticeably affected by wind problems, seriously consider using dust-free bedding (chapter 5) and forage (chapter 4) to reduce the challenge to his system.

3 Horses are by nature inquisitive but panic easily. Anticipate every possible source of trouble and make sure that it cannot occur. Be always alert to potentially dangerous situations.

4 Make sure your horse is freeze-marked; this is the most effective way to prevent him being stolen.

5 The basic management policy which will cover your horse's everyday requirements includes six things: food, water, shelter, space, company and exercise (at least part of which should preferably be taken at liberty). Keeping horses on the combined system, possibly with yarding, will enable you to meet all these requirements most adequately.

4
FEEDING

Feeding is a subject most horse owners and managers find interesting and rewarding, and is a complex subject about which entire books are written. Research in the field, both by companies with a vested commercial interest in their own products and by organisations whose only desire is to find out what is best for the horse, is producing much new information, changing many old ideas and yet confirming some of them, too. Information which has been regarded as gospel until fairly recently may well have been relevant decades ago, but as farming practices have changed the very products we are talking about may themselves have changed. For instance, those who can remember the oats fed to horses in the 1950s and before, agree that today's oats are noticeably inferior.

But time has brought improvements, too, and in many ways some of the products available today make feeding easier, by providing ready-balanced rations with known vitamin and mineral contents. The horse's requirements are better understood, especially the relationship between feeding and work, as well as feeding for growth and correct, optimal development in youngstock.

The horse himself has not changed, however. His digestion evolved over millions of years into a unique one in the animal world, highly specialised to suit his particular lifestyle. He still puts his feed to the same use in the same way and is almost entirely dependent on us for his rations.

THE PURPOSES OF FOOD

The horse puts his food to four main uses:

1 The maintenance of body temperature. The body's systems perform best at an optimum temperature of roughly 38°C (100.4°F). The average varies slightly for each individual horse, and also according to the time of day and whether or not the horse has recently been exercised. Youngsters and ponies will have a higher average temperature than mature horses, that of older or athletically fit horses will be lower. (Obviously, this applies to the healthy horse; a sick or overstressed horse could have a significantly higher or lower temperature.)
2 Growth and repair of the body's tissues – skin, muscle, the various organs, hair, tendons, horn etc. This has particular significance in

pregnant broodmares and growing youngstock.

3 Work. This can be hard and strenuous – racing, hunting, eventing etc; or less hard – pleasure hacking, showing or simply ambling about the field or scratching an itch.

4 Weight gain. Surplus energy (derived from food) is stored around the body in the form of fat reserves, and in the liver. When the horse is receiving more food than he needs, he obviously puts on weight. When his energy requirements exceed his food (fuel) supply he calls on his fat reserves which are gradually depleted – so he loses weight.

If body temperature is not maintained, everything else counts for naught, as it were, because the horse will die. Food is allocated by the body in order of priority, more or less, and body temperature is the most important. It is especially so in cold weather or when the horse is subject to the chilling effects of wind and wet, particularly when combined.

Growth and repair come next in importance. The very substance of the physical structure has to be produced, from conception to death – the foetus, growth in youngstock and the repair of any body tissues which are damaged during everyday life.

These two requirements are the most important of the four. If a horse's ration is just enough to satisfy these two needs he will remain in reasonable condition but will not put on weight and will not have much energy for anything but light work. We can, of course, force him to work harder but his body, sensing the need for extra energy which is not forthcoming in his diet, will call on whatever fat reserves he has, and he will lose weight. If the forced work continues, the body will start using up its own tissues as fuel and weight loss will be quick and marked. Ultimately, the 'skin and bone' stage will be reached, the body temperature will drop and the horse will die.

On the other hand, if the horse receives more than enough food for maintenance of temperature and for growth and repair, he will store much of the excess as fat, to be converted to energy when needed. He may well be bouncing with health, but if he is allowed to become obese he will find physical movement an effort and a strain, and over-fed horses are subject to various familiar and distressing conditions such as laminitis, azoturia and lymphangitis plus general overstressing of heart, tendons and bones etc.

THE DIGESTIVE SYSTEM

The horse's digestive system is, in many ways, very like our own and that of other animals such as the dog and cat in that it has many of the same 'departments', but these vary in type, size and importance. For instance, the horse has a comparatively small stomach in relation to its size, ours is larger and the dog's is the largest, because of the differing methods of feeding.

Unlike other grass-eating animals which are ruminants (cows, sheep, etc) the horse does not take its food into a rumen – in cattle and other cloven-hooved animals, the rumen is like a large fermentation vat and comes *before* the true stomach; in the horse, fermentation takes place
lower down the intestinal tract, after the food has passed through the stomach. The horse's fermentation vat is its large intestine – the caecum and large colon – where a large population of bacteria (gut micro-flora or gut micro-organisms) breaks down the cellulose in the diet. (We, too, have a caecum, no bigger than your finger and called the appendix!) Cellulose is a form of starch or carbohydrate and makes up part of the bulky, fibrous material in hay, hayage and grass. Grass is the horse's natural food, of course, so the importance of this digestive process is paramount.

Another form of fibrous bulk is woody fibre or lignin which has no nutritional value but helps fill out the digestive tract to provide that full, contented feeling which should accompany eating. The lignin can be seen in the droppings as tiny stiff fibres. It also helps physically break up food to assist exposure to the digestive juices, enzymes and bacteria which all 'process' the food into a form in which it can be absorbed into the blood and carried round the body for use or storage, as needed.

Horses, the, are herbivores who, in natural conditions, eat large amounts of bulky greenstuff made up significantly of cellulose-walled plant cells. Humans are omnivores; we eat both plant material and meat. Dogs and cats in natural conditions are basically carnivores, eating meat and bones.

Grass and leaves *can*, obviously, provide enough nutrients for the horse, but because these are not sufficiently concentrated, large amounts have to be consumed fairly continuously. Horses left to themselves with an adequate supply of foodstuffs will graze and browse for about 16 to 18 out of the 24. They are 'trickle feeders'; in other words, a steady stream of food 'trickles' through their digestive system most of the time.

Humans eat plant material but mostly in the form of fruit and vegetables, nuts and grain, which are more concentrated than leaves and stalks, and also meat which is a highly concentrated food. Therefore, we do not need to eat most of the time like our horses, but usually have about three distinct meals a day.

Dogs and cats as predatory animals eat a very concentrated food, and one meal a day will provide their requirements. In fact, in wild conditions they often manage well on one large feast every few days, and their stomachs are correspondingly large to receive a large amount of food all at once.

One of the main management mistakes which occurs with horses is that we try to convert their digestive systems into something more like our own. Many stabled horses are given three distinct feeds a day and hay only night and morning, with too many concentrates and not enough essential bulky roughage. We are constantly told that we must copy the horse's natural method of feeding by giving food little and often, yet in practice we do not do this.

Three feeds a day with hay only night and morning results in horses having many hours with virtually no food passing through their digestive systems. This inevitably creates a feeling of hunger *even though* the nutrient content of their diet may be accurate for their needs. Again, we are exhorted to give the largest feed and most of the hay ration at night, yet a quick check in almost any yard at midnight will reveal that all the hay and certainly all the concentrates have gone, yet the horse will not be fed again till 7 or 8 o'clock next morning. This means his digestive system will be seven or eight hours with no food passing through it – a highly unnatural and unsatisfactory, even dangerous, situation.

The digestive bacteria need a constant supply of food if they are to thrive – some bacteria can even start dying off after as little as four hours without food. Obviously, without a healthy population of these micro-organisms, digestion must be seriously impaired. Not only will the horse not be making the most of the food he does get, when he gets it, but he is likely to suffer from indigestion (colic) as well. I feel many ostensibly unexplained cases of colic must be due to our erratic, yet largely standard, methods of feeding horses.

In yards where horses are given several small feeds a day (four, five or more) and a more or less *ad lib* supply of hay (except for just before work, when feed should be withheld for one or two hours, depending on how fast or strenuous the work is going to be) digestive disorders are rare and the horses are physically more content and so mentally more settled and relaxed. There is little wood chewing, nervous tension or other behavioural trouble, and the horse makes better use of the food he does receive (which must also be more economical).

Horses who are not fed according to this fairly natural pattern also eat their bedding, when it is edible – their attendants' answer to this 'naughtiness' is to remove this last resort of hunger appeasement by bedding them on inedible material. This may well stop the bedding consumption but it certainly does nothing to improve the digestion.

Although food consumption should undoubtedly be fairly constant, horses obviously cannot consume concentrates indefinitely! It is generally believed that horses need some concentrates in order to be able to work other than lightly. Like any biological system, energy has to go in in the form of food before it can come out in the form of physical effort. A horse on a maintenance ration, receiving maybe just grass or hay if good quality, *can* certainly perform light work – say an hour's gentle hacking daily – without losing condition, but most people would give concentrates for more strenuous work than this.

Normally, horses cannot consume enough nutrients for hard work if eating hay alone – the limits of their appetite would be reached before the required energy, protein etc had been taken in. In any case, it is considered not generally desirable to have an athletic horse weighed down with vast amounts of bulky roughage.

In practice, it does not necessarily work like this. If the roughage food (usually hay or a hay replacement such as one of the branded hayage products) is of top quality (best determined by laboratory analysis) horses certainly can work very hard with nothing but that, or maybe with comparatively small amounts of concentrates. I have personally known event horses and point-to pointers trained and managed on such a régime, and successfully, too.

In his natural state, the horse eats far more grass and probably leaves, too, than he does grain, and his digestive system, even after a few thousand years of domestication, still works better on food as closely approximating to grass as possible. Obviously, horses wandering freely at all times of year over varying terrain will encounter different forages in different stages of development. In the autumn, they would certainly have come across grain 'on the stalk' and, having ripened, on the ground, too. In winter, only the dried-up stems and leaves from the previous summer's growth would be available, the nearest thing to man-made hay a feral horse would get.

Obviously horses can cope with grain (concentrates), but feeding a lot of it does present problems, and some horses can take only a little, too, because of the amounts of natural waste products resulting from the digestion and metabolism of this more concentrated food. The problems in question can be excess nervousness and 'spookiness', behavioural problems ranging from restlessness to the formation of actual stable vices (resulting from nervous tension), azoturia, filled legs and lymphangitis, laminitis and digestive disturbances resulting in colic.

At the time of writing there is a product being marketed by Natural Animal Feeds Ltd under the name of Thrive, which is a clay product containing many minerals and trace elements – in particular sodium montmorillonite and calcium carbonate – which appears to neutralise toxic waste products and helps the horse cope with grain more successfully.

Those who do wish to keep their horse's diet 'natural' by feeding top quality forage (hay/hayage) alone may feel that the sheer bulk will create a 'hay belly' on their horses. This does not necessarily happen – if the forage is of poorer quality it will have correspondingly more fibrous matter in it which is digested, as explained, lower down the digestive tract; in this case horses may develop large bellies to cope with the extra proportion of cellulose.

The population of gut bacteria (along with the various digestive enzymes) is obviously crucial to efficient digestion. They are living creatures themselves and need a regular supply of the food they are adapted to 'process' if they are to remain alive and healthy. Anything which disturbs the flow of food through the digestive system can cause them to die or malfunction in some way – this can include erratic timing of feeds; sudden changes of either routine or ingredients; mental or physical stress; sickness; colic (which may also be a *result* of these things); even a course of anti-biotics may kill off 'goodie' bugs along with the 'baddie' ones.

To counteract such effects, and also to provide a healthy bacterial population in the gut, probiotics ('goodie' bacteria) can be given in the feed: two which are currently available are Transvite (from Equine Products (UK) Ltd), and Probiotic Equine Standard and Probiotic Equine Stress (from Glentona Equestrian). The beneficial bacteria in such products are more efficient and proliferate faster than the potentially harmful bacteria – which, in fact, are only harmful when their numbers reach excessive amounts (they are present in the gut in any case but normally cause no real problems); if this happens, the 'goodies' will block them out and re-establish a healthy environment in the gut.

It is well worth discussing such products with a veterinary surgeon or equine nutritionist if you have horses who seem prone to inexplicable digestive disorders, or for those subjected to high levels of stress as when working hard or travelling a good deal.

However, it should be remembered that the equine digestive system *is* very sensitive and that the normal Golden Rules of good feeding should always be observed. Any of the conditions mentioned above can cause upset and therefore disturbance. Probably the most common cause of trouble is not truly adhering to the 'little and often' rule, and missing out feeds due to the horse being out working for the day. Hunters, for example, nearly always miss their mid-day feed; performance horses, also, frequently go down with 'unexplained colic' a day or two after a competition or a long journey including a stay away from home. Even if home supplies of feed and forage are taken, strange water can inhibit some horses from drinking freely enough which does not help the digestion. If supplies of forage are available at the venue, owners often take only their own concentrates, not realising that the change of hay, or even bedding straw which the horse will probably nibble at, also constitutes a change in feeding.

If the digestive bacteria do not receive a constant, reliable supply of the type of food to which they, individually, are adapted, they *will* suffer. For instance, the type of bacteria able to digest oats cannot cope with barley and vice versa. Even different batches of the same grain can be slightly different in content and require an adaptation in the bacterial population of the gut.

When a new batch of feed is delivered, do not use up your old batch and then start on the new. Instead, reduce the amount of the old batch by a few grammes/ounces daily and make up that amount from the new batch – *in each feed* – so that the bacteria 'get the message' that a change is afoot and adaptation is necessary. Make the changeover gradually so that the bacteria have time to build up and/or die down, as appropriate. This goes for *any* feed, including hay and if you use straw for bedding, that too – and it is obviously particularly important when a different *type* of food is being introduced.

The practice of 'mashing' horses (feeding bran mashes) certainly constitutes a very sudden change in feeding. The old idea of a bran mash being easily digestible, tempting and suitable for sick, convalescing horses has been superseded. Bran is almost entirely an indigestible form of fibre (being the outside husk of wheat grains), it is tasteless, not tempting, and therefore not at all suitable for a sick or tired horse. The reason it has a laxative effect is that the digestive system tries to get rid of it as soon as possible. Also, a bran mash with no concentrates at all means the bacteria are missing a feed and could die as a result, resulting in subsequent poor digestion or even colic.

If you still feel the need to feed a mash, a suitable mixture would be dried grass with soaked sugar beet pulp added – but make sure your horse is used to these items first or they, too, will constitute an undesirable change in feeding.

For efficient digestion, every feed should contain some of every ingredient you wish your horse to receive in his diet – only the amounts should alter according to the horse's workload. In your mash of dried grass and sugar beet pulp, then, you should add just a few ounces of his normal concentrate to keep the bugs happy. Even supplements and additives should be put in each feed, split into a portion of their recommended daily amount. The practice carried out in some yards, therefore, of giving, say, nuts for breakfast, oats for lunch, coarse mix for tea and so on, is a thoroughly bad and harmful one and could actually be the cause of digestive disturbances. Apart from the very real possibility of colic, the horse cannot possibly be making the best of his feed, so money is being wasted as well.

The different digestive enzymes, as well as the bacteria, need time to build up and adapt to changes in diet, and the importance of adhering to this method of feeding cannot be overestimated.

· STRUCTURE AND FUNCTION ·

The digestive system obviously starts with the mouth and sense of smell. The horse selects what he wants with his lips and nose and gets hold of it – grass, hay or concentrates – with his front or incisor teeth. The tongue manipulates it into the mouth and, with the help of the cheek muscles, moves it around between the back or cheek teeth (molars) for grinding up and mixing with saliva. The teeth break up the hard cellulose cell walls of the plant material and generally break up the food into small particles so the saliva can reach the digestible material in it. The saliva prepares the food for further digestion by mixing it with weak chemicals, all of which makes it rather like a soggy pulp.

The teeth obviously play a major role. If they are sharp or jagged the food could be imperfectly masticated and the sensitive parts of the horse's mouth (tongue and cheeks) could be cut, causing pain and reluctance to chew.

The horse's lower jaw is narrower than its upper jaw, so the chewing motion causes the insides of the lower cheek teeth and the outsides of the upper cheek teeth to become sharp. Hooks can also form on the front and back cheek teeth if the arcades of teeth do not meet fully at the ends during chewing. A veterinary surgeon once told me he was called to an old farm horse many years ago because it apparently could not close its mouth. The horse was absolutely emaciated and very old and could not, indeed, close its mouth. On investigation, the vet found hooks several inches long on the upper back teeth! After removal, and having checked the other teeth which were quite badly worn, the horse did pick up in condition and put on weight.

So the horse's teeth play a vital role in digestion, unlike the domestically fed dog which bolts its food down without chewing (wild and feral dogs, of course, use their teeth to tear off flesh and hold on to prey).

Once in the stomach, the food, which has swollen to about twice its original volume because of the saliva, is mixed by means of the churning and pummelling action of the stomach muscles with strong digestive juices, which get to work on proteins and fats in food. It becomes even more liquid as the strongly acid digestive juices are secreted into it.

The stomach works best when about two thirds full, and this stage is usually reached when about 4lbs (1.8kg) of food plus digestive juices are present. Concentrates stay longer in the stomach than roughage foods, which are mainly digested further down the tract. Therefore, if the horse keeps on eating concentrates because too large a feed has been given, the stomach will release some food which may be only partially digested out into the next part of the tract, the duodenum, which leads off the stomach. Digestion is therefore incomplete and could cause colic.

If the horse is given a large feed and eats quickly, or if it gorges itself on food to which it should not have access – if the feed room door is left open and it has found its way inside – the stomach can become much too full and swollen. The pressure interferes with blood circulation in the stomach wall, and with the normal nervous activity which releases food into the duodenum when the stomach becomes too full. Also, the usual movements of the stomach cannot take place. The contents of the stomach begin to ferment and gases therefore form, distending the stomach even further. Discomfort, pain and maybe even rupture of the stomach and subsequent death can then occur. If the horse survives, laminitis may result.

With roughage food (hay/hayage), the horse can eat for hours at a time quite safely. Horses normally chew hay well and it takes longer to eat than concentrates. Also, it does not stay long in the stomach because it will be released through into the duodenum in the normal way, and problems do not occur.

When food continues on its way down the tract into the small intestine absorption of nutrients begins. Carbohydrates in the form of starches and sugars are digested and become mainly glucose here, which is absorbed into the bloodstream through the permeable walls of the tiny blood capillaries (thread-like vessels) in the intestinal wall. The food is pushed along by means of wave-like muscular contractions of the wall called peristalsis. Proteins continue to be digested and broken down into their 'building blocks', called amino acids, which are also absorbed to be carried in the blood wherever needed. Protein which is excess to requirements can be stored as fat in the body, but it then loses its essential creative properties by means of which it enables tissue growth and repair to take place, and is reconverted into energy. Therefore protein must be provided every day, although its importance is not so critical as was formerly believed, and roughly 10–11 per cent protein in the diet is adequate for mature horses, even when in hard work. Youngstock, broodmares and emaciated animals need more, about 14 per cent in the total diet, depending on circumstances.

Bile is secreted by the liver into the small intestine to enable fats and oils to be broken down into tiny globules of glycerol and various fatty acids, which are transported in the lymphatic system and bloodstream, again for use or storage. The vitamins and minerals in the diet also begin to be absorbed during this stage of digestion.

From the small intestine, food passes into the caecum and the large colon (which, together with the small colon and finally the rectum, form the large intestine) where digestion of roughage and its cellulose content takes place. The large colon forms two U-shaped loops joined together at a narrow point called the pelvic flexure, and it is often at this point that impaction colic occurs due to imperfectly digested material blocking the narrow juncture. This may be because of some disturbance to the bacterial population already discussed, or if the horse is on a low quality, too-fibrous diet (poor hay or dried-up grass) impaction can occur because of the very nature of the food. The liquid nature of the food during digestion has already been mentioned; one of the functions of the large colon is to reabsorb some of this liquid back into the body to avoid too much water loss. However, if the food is travelling too slowly through the colon, too much water may be reabsorbed, so making the contents too dry and impaction even more likely.

Blockages can occur elsewhere, but this pelvic flexure is more susceptible because it is so narrow compared with the rest of the large colon.

From this stage onwards the food is drier, and by the time it reaches the end of the small colon and the rectum all that remains is undigested material (largely fibre) and the waste products of metabolism which have been carried there in the bloodstream from various parts of the body for passing out with the droppings. Other waste products are passed out in the urine, in sweat, and from the lungs when the horse breathes out.

Although this is only a simplified description of the major stages of digestion, I hope it has clarified them and given increased understanding of what happens and what can go wrong.

TYPES OF FEEDS AND THEIR CONSTITUENTS

All horse owners and managers are familiar with the types of feed given to horses today – oats, barley, flaked maize, and compound feeds such as coarse mixes, cubes or nuts; also hay, hayage products, sometimes silage and a thoroughly bewildering range of supplements and additives.

Basically, the purpose of any feed is to provide fuel for the body to live and work on. The main feed constituents are carbohydrates (starches and sugars), proteins, fats or oils, vitamins and minerals. Water is a vital element of any horse's diet, and is dealt with in this chapter, beginning on p98.

Most foods contain some or all of the above constituents, but in differing proportions.

Carbohydrates are used for the production of heat and energy. The body stores excess amounts as fat around the body and as glycogen in the liver and muscle cells. Glycogen is the major store of energy.

Proteins are the only foods which can make body tissue. Excess protein can be stored as fat but it then loses its tissue-making quality and simply provides extra energy when needed.

Fat is a heat and energy producer. It is good for helping put weight on a thin horse and is 'energy dense', providing one and a half times more energy than carbohydrate. It is useful, therefore, for hard-working horses, particularly endurance horses and those doing sustained work (hunters, eventers and competitive carriage horses) at the limits of their appetites. It also helps condition skin, hair and horn.

Fibre is the tough, 'woody' part of plant material comprising the cell walls and the outer husk of grain. It is needed to break up concentrated food which might otherwise impact into a stiff, doughy mass in the stomach and intestines which the digestive juices could not penetrate. Fermentation could then result, and/or impaction, with possibly fatal results. Some fibre (cellulose) can be digested as carbohydrate, but some (lignin) cannot and this serves a purely mechanical, filling-out role. It also stimulates the peristaltic movement of the gut.

Vitamins, minerals and trace elements are all needed as vital nutrients, but often in only very small quantities. All commonly given foods possess different amounts of different ones, all having an individual purpose. Serious physical and mental disturbances can occur due to deficiencies or overdoses of these substances, so expert advice on formulating a balanced ration, with or without a supplement, is essential. Even knowledgeable owners are sometimes reluctant to seek advice and rely solely on the product label when deciding whether or not to feed a supplement.

The horses most likely to need supplements are those on a low plane of nutrition (on poor pasture with no regular feed – a large feed block would help these); hard-working performance horses; broodmares in the last three months of pregnancy or first three months of lactation; and older horses whose digestion and metabolism may have deteriorated with age. The owners of such horses should discuss the matter of supplementation with a veterinary surgeon or nutritionist.

The basic difference between a supplement and an additive is that a supplement forms part of the feed in that it helps to balance it, whereas an additive is something which is 'added' to a hopefully already balanced diet – it may not even be a nutrient, and may even *un*balance the diet. Vitamins, minerals and trace elements are part of the feed, and are therefore supplements. They can be bought as a specific, maybe even single-item product such as a single vitamin, or as a broad-spectrum, comprehensive one containing many different vitamins. Additives are not necessarily nutritious – even worming pellets can be described as an additive.

The only way to find out accurately whether your horse does need a supplement is to obtain an analysis of his entire diet (including concentrates and roughage), discuss it with a specialist, and then decide if anything need be added or taken away; finally you should arrive at the optimum diet for the horse's circumstances. Buying blindly because the product sounds good in the advertising literature will not do your horse any good. He may become ill due to an overdose of a certain product or nutrient, and you could also waste money – many supplements are quite expensive.

Where supplements are concerned, *more* is not necessarily *good*. Stick to the recommended dose and do not mix supplements, or feed more than one, unless your specialist recommends it. It is all too easy for the non-scientifically minded to think that because something sounds good it must do *their* horse good, and that this can apply to several products. A little bit of this and a little bit of that given indiscriminately can do a great deal of harm and the horse may well be better off with no supplement at all.

Horses on a conventional diet of grass hay, cereal (oats/barley/maize) and some bran are most likely to need calcium (probably in the form of ground limestone) and salt (roughly 1oz/28mg a day, depending on the weather and work – horses working hard in hot, humid weather will sweat more and lose more salt). In winter, fat soluble vitamins A, D, E and probably K will have been depleted from the body stores by about Christmas and will probably need supplementing. In fact, supplementation could be needed for fully stabled horses at any time.

A mainly cereal-based diet could well be deficient in two important amino acids, lysine and methionine, so look for these in the analysis table of any supplement you consider when feeding such a diet.

The whole subject of supplements is so complex and wide-ranging that owners are strongly advised to sit down with their vet or nutritionist, go. through the horse's basic diet and find out whether any supplement is needed, and if so what type and brand. As with any feed, a supplement should be fed a little in each feed. If giving a supplement in a cooked feed, allow the feed to cool to eating temperature before adding the supplement as the heat could otherwise kill off valuable nutrients, making the whole operation pointless and a waste of money.

· FEEDSTUFFS ·

Feeds can be broadly divided into roughage/bulk feeds, concentrates and succulents. Roughage/bulk feeds are hay, hayage and silage, and also bran; concentrates include oats, barley, maize, cubes and coarse mixes; and succulents are obviously carrots, apples, soaked sugar beet pulp and turnips, and also hydroponically produced grass. These are the most commonly used feedstuffs. Grass is a major feedstuff for horses allowed it, and is a greatly underrated feed in many establishments; so many people regard it as a 'treat' instead of the staple food it could be if properly formulated for the type of stock grazing it, whether breeding stock, family pets or athletically working horses.

Hay is the basis of any diet, and despite efforts on the part of cube manufacturers to devise 'hay-less' diets these are largely unsuccessful because they usually result in the horse suffering considerable hunger and boredom. I have known many horses on such diets and without exception found them unsettled, uncomfortable, unhappy and generally sorrowful sights. The reason for devising so-called 'complete' cubes was initially – a couple of decades ago – to prevent a sudden change of forage in an Olympic team. It was then decided to market 'complete' cubes of various brands for horses who showed an allergic reaction to the mould spores and fungi found on even good samples of hay. During years when it was difficult to procure hay supplies, complete cubes were again aggressively marketed and although some managers and owners claim their problems have been solved by them, this has never been my experience. I do not see how we can possibly change the specialised, bulk/roughage-orientated digestive system of the horse by depriving it of its essential type of feed just to suit our convenience. Although the cube makers state that the fibre content of their product is adequate to meet the requirements of the digestive system, in practice I have never found this to be so.

Owners who do feed hay and similar products are often reluctant to feed adequate amounts (see p.00). As already mentioned, three feeds a day with hay night and morning is *not* little and often, and is insufficient if the horse is to be physically and mentally comfortable and functioning properly.

The basic types of hay are seed or racehorse hay, mixture hay, meadow hay, (which these days is specially sown) and, when available, clover hay; there is also, though more rarely these days, lucerne (alfalfa) hay.

Traditionally hay has always been assessed by appearance and 'nose' ('eyeballing' as the Americans so graphically put it), but work has recently shown that these methods fall far short in practice. Experienced yard managers, during one study, were asked to evaluate different samples of hay in the traditional way, judging colour, smell, feel and general appearance. Almost without exception, the hay these expert horsemasters chose was far below the nutritional value of rejected samples. The hay had all been properly analysed in a laboratory before the study, so the research workers knew the nutrient content of each sample before the practical tests were carried out.

So, however galling for those with years of practical experience, the only true way to know what is in a feedstuff is to get it analysed. Many owners and managers are now having all feedstuffs, including hay, analysed for their top class competition animals and racehorses, and appear to be happy with the results.

Any hay that has visible mould (white, green or black patches), dust when shaken out, or areas of damp should be rejected, but given an apparently good sample, and if your priority is to provide a balanced diet for your horse, then have it analysed. Some of the best merchants have an analysis all ready for purchasers, but this state of affairs is not common.

Hay substitutes sold under various brand names like Hygrass, Propack and Horsehage have the analysis and energy content readily available, and come in differing grades so that the purchaser can choose the right grade for the work his or her horses are doing. These products are particularly useful for horses with respiratory allergies to the moulds and fungi found in most hay and straw, but many non-afflicted horses are now eating them because of their known content and consistent quality – early problems concerning variable quality have been largely overcome now.

One complaint about these usually excellent products is that one cannot feed them *ad lib* because the recommended amount is too small, or the horse simply gets through them at a faster rate than ordinary hay. This can be overcome by feeding more of a lower energy grade product (in a special net with a small mesh), and also by adding other bulky items to the feed such as roots, sugar beet pulp, and a particularly useful feedstuff for virtually any horse, molassed chop (commonly but incorrectly called chaff, the latter being the outside husk of grain).

Chop is hay and straw, sometimes mixed, chopped up small (1in [2.5cm] long) and added to a normal feed at about one double handful per feed and thoroughly mixed in. For allergic horses it is no use at all as ordinary chop will make them cough just as quickly as would hay to eat, or straw to sleep on. Prepared, branded molassed chop however, is a controlled product. Moulds and dust have been eliminated, and to add palatability and moistness, plus a little extra energy value, molasses has been added. Horses readily eat the product, and it is very useful to have some on hand not only to add to feeds without unbalancing them (there is an analysis available) but to have loose in a container of its own (say a long manger) in the stable for the horse to eat as he wishes.

With hayage, extra roots in the feed (particularly sugar beet pulp which is quite fibrous) and molassed chaff, the diet side of an allergic horse's régime can be satisfactorily handled.

Thoroughly soaking hay is also an effective way of making it safe to feed; this must be for at least four hours, pushed well under the water and maybe weighted down with (clean) bricks. This causes the spores to swell up to such a size that they cannot reach the tiny air passages and sacs in the lungs where they would otherwise set up their allergic reaction, causing swelling and narrowing of the airways and excess mucous formation. Simply dipping the net in a tub of water and letting it drip, or merely throwing a bucket of water over it, is pointless. This will probably not even damp down any other dust, which will act as an irritant to the sensitive lungs even if an actual allergic response is not stimulated.

Soaking should not be used as a way of feeding rotten hay; hay should always be the best quality available, and if it is not of acceptable quality, feed straw instead. Oat straw, particularly, is a fair substitute for hay and the same rules about general quality and freedom from obvious moulds apply. Barley straw is also acceptable; the old complaint about the prickly awns irritating the digestive tract no longer applies as these are removed with today's harvesting methods. Straw will contain less protein than hay so a protein supplement or higher protein concentrate ration will be needed.

Horses who will not eat soaked hay or hayage can usually be 'converted' by introducing it into their normal rations a little at a time until the changeover is complete.

Silage This gradual changeover is also important when feeding silage; this 'gradual' policy applies to any feed and should be second nature to the conscientious horsemaster. There have been complaints about botulism in horses eating big-bale silage and these are justified where the bale has at any time been punctured and air (and 'germs') have gained access. The silage often smells sour (as opposed to simply unpleasant!) but in the early stages of contamination may appear normal.

Reject any bale which has any puncture in it or which appears to have been resealed. Resealing does not get rid of the contamination; the germs have already gained access and are doing their worst. Carrying these bales is a problem; one type of carrier has a large spike which is pierced through the centre of the bagged bale; the bag is obviously broken which lets in air and starts off the trouble. The farmer/merchant may then seal up the hole thinking that all will be well, but this is truly a case of shutting the stable door after the horse has bolted.

Some years ago, trials with resting horses and non-Thoroughbred broodmares were carried out at the Irish National Stud (and have since been done elsewhere) which confirm that horses do well with silage as part of their ration when working, or as the whole ration when resting, but many horse owners still prefer to avoid it. It is not easy to handle, is very messy and the scares over botulism have put off many owners. Be that as it may, silage can be a most useful feedstuff for any horse if of good quality and not contaminated, either as a main product or as a hay replacement.

Hay is best cut when the grasses have plenty of leaf but have not gone to seed. Such hay will have a high nutrient quality, but if allowed to grow on till the plants are that little bit taller and the seeds have formed, the nutrient content will fall considerably. You might get that extra inch on the bottom of the stalk but will lose out on the feed value. Go for flower heads which were still flowering when cut, and with plenty of leaf, all else being equal. The type of hay is perhaps less important than the quality and nutrient content – seed hay of inferior quality is not so good as mixture or meadow hay of superior class, yet you may have to pay more for it!

Oats are the cereal grain traditionally fed to horses in the western hemisphere and in Australasia, and are very suitable for horses: they have a reasonable proportion of fibre because of their significant husk, they are palatable and digestible and because they have the lowest weight for their volume of other cereals, variations in quantity in those yards which feed by the scoop instead of weighing their feed can result in less serious anomalies than with other grains. Barley, for instance, 'weighs heavy' compared to oats.

It is highly inaccurate to feed any food, particularly concentrates, by the scoop instead of taking the trouble to weigh everything and make sure you are feeding the correct amount. It can result in either serious deficiencies or 'overdosing' of that particular food and is uneconomic and wasteful.

Some horses do become undesirably hot-headed on oats, just as some people can take alcohol and others can't! And like alcohol, familiarity with the source of the problem does not always create tolerance in the consumer.

Oats have an undesirably high content of a chemical called phytin which can prevent calcium in the diet being absorbed by the horse's digestive/circulatory system. Cereal grains in general are low in calcium and high in phosphorus (the reverse applies with hay, hayage and straw) and the high phytin content of oats just makes matters worse.

Barley is often a much more acceptable feed for many horses than oats. Roughly, $^3/_4$lb (.3kg) of barley equals 1lb (.4kg) of oats and many horses become less 'dizzy' on barley and lose the minor skin problems such as dullness and itching which some horses do show when fed oats. Although oats *can* be fed whole (though they may not be properly masticated and therefore be insufficiently digested) this is not advisable for barley. Barley grains are smaller and harder than oats with less fibre, and should be rolled or bruised before feeding. Much barley sold for animal feeds these days is pre-cooked and sold flaked, extruded or micronised. It contains less fibre/roughage than oats.

Maize is a starchy food suitable for putting weight on thin animals or providing extra energy. However, it contains little protein and this is of low quality, and the fibre content too is very low. Therefore, it must not be the staple grain ration, but be simply part of a ration (say up to a quarter) in which some form of fibrous roughage has been added. In Britain it is normally fed flaked or micronised but in other countries whole grain is fed. Maize is in fact the same grain as our breakfast corn flakes.

Coarse mixes are justifiably popular these days, particularly for novice owners who do not want the responsibility of balancing a ration themselves – and for experts who recognise that this is, in any case, a job for a scientifically qualified nutritionist! Those mixes available are of high, reliable quality and are a definite boon to the modern horse-keeper.

They consist of a variety of ingredients and are properly balanced, the analysis being on the bag or label for all to see. Most horses love them, but some can be choosy about which brand they prefer. Coarse mixes have a binding agent such as molasses or syrup added which takes out the dryness and makes damping unnecessary. However, this also means that they do not keep terribly well in warm weather, so small establishments should not buy large batches. It could be worth having a large, old fridge in the feed room in which to keep such things as coarse mixes, molasses and so on; set it on low – remember you only want to keep them cool, not cold.

With coarse mixes, then, the analysis is worked out by the feed company, and different grades of energy level are available according to the type of horse or pony you have and what work it is doing. The energy level is much more important than the protein content for this purpose, protein having previously been considered the criterion by which a feed was judged. All the owner has to do is feed the required amount since the ingredients are all present, and the vitamins and minerals all in balance in a good make.

Although *cubes or nuts* have the same practical advantages as coarse mixes, when they form the main part of a diet some horses do get very tired of them. This does not seem to happen with coarse mixes which generally seem to be more palatable.

Bran is a bulky roughage food which used to be (and still is in some quarters) considered an essential part of the routine of any stabled/sick/convalescent/recently-brought-up/soon-to-be-turned-out horse, and bran mashes were considered to be easily digested, palatable and bland. In fact they are the exact opposite.

More seriously, bran is excessively high in phosphorus and low in calcium. This causes weak, porous and sometimes enlarged bone, making the horse prone to bone stresses such as splints, fractures and general 'soreness' from concussion it would normally be well able to withstand. In mature horses the process may not become immediately apparent, but a diet with a consistently reversed calcium:phosphorus ratio will cause trouble in the long run. In youngstock and broodmares carrying foals it can quickly cause problems, as its effects are accelerated due to bone still being formed. There should always be more calcium than phosphorus present, usually a 1.1:1 ratio.

Bran is also an expensive food and likely to become more so as its popularity as an ingredient in human foodstuffs and high fibre diets increases; and I feel some merchants play on the fact that horse-owners of the 'old school' feel they cannot run a 'proper' yard without bran. In fact, bran is something you can easily do without, and would be better off not using.

An alternative to a bran mash is a mixture of dried grass or alfalfa (such as the product marketed by Dengie) and soaked sugar beet pulp. Sugar beet pulp has a high calcium, low phosphorus content so is ideal for adding to cereal feeds in any case, and so does dried grass/alfalfa, so either on their own or as part of a cereal diet, they are excellent products for any yard to have available. Dried alfalfa, depending on the brand, can have high protein levels so you may need to adjust the rest of the concentrate portion of the diet, but this should be easy with expert advice.

Roots are welcomed by just about every stabled horse – they represent a succulent treat, and the most popular seem to be carrots. Apples are also favoured, and some horses like to crunch up a whole turnip. Carrots and apples should be thinly sliced so they do not become stuck in the oesophagus (food pipe) and cause choke. Choke in horses is not connected with the trachea (windpipe) as in humans – it represents a blockage of the oesophagus, which is extremely uncomfortable for the horse. Food, if consumed, comes back down the nostrils with saliva and the horse makes frequent attempts to swallow. This is not a first-aid situation; call the vet if it happens to your horse.

Sugar beet pulp has for some time justifiably been a popular feed. It is a succulent, and helps balance the calcium:phosphorus ratio of the diet; it is loved by most horses, particularly the molassed type. It comes in loose shreds, as pulp or in cubes. The product, particularly the cubes, must be *thoroughly* soaked in cold water. The shreds and pulp must be soaked in at least twice their own volume of water but the cubes, which are compressed, need to be soaked in three times or more their own volume of water. Shreds are sometimes fully swollen in 12 hours but I prefer to leave them at least 18. With cubes, 24 hours' soaking is not too long – this is easy to do if you make it a habit to put them to soak at the same time each day. Check with your hand right down to the middle of the bucket that the water has reached well in and that everything is squelchy and really well soaked before mixing with your other feedstuffs.

With roots, the normal recommended daily amount is 4lb (1.8kg). Much of this is water and fibre, and in cases where extra roots need to be fed – for horses with respiratory problems on hay substitutes – this amount can be increased to about 10lb (4.5kg), split evenly with the rest of the ration.

As with supplements, it is essential that manufacturers' recommendations be followed when using ready formulated feeds. Read any literature you can get on the product and follow the instructions. It is particularly important that feeds are not mixed together or with straight grains: for example, if a suitable amount of a coarse mix for your horse is, say, 8lb(3.6kg), do not give instead 'for a change' 4lb(1.8kg) of the mix, with a bit of barley, a few oats and a handful of cubes, the total to make up the recommended weight. This will thoroughly unbalance the resulting feed and could cause problems.

Keep to a consistent diet so that the horse's digestion has the best chance of making the best of its food – and your money.

PHYSICAL CONDITION AND FEED QUANTITIES

By far the most accurate way of deciding how much of what to feed your horse is to feed according to bodyweight. A weighbridge is ideal, but they are few and far between. Instead, you can obtain a fairly accurate idea by measuring your horse round the girth with an ordinary tape-measure (or a piece of string and then measuring that) and then reading off your horse's probable weight on the accompanying table. Alternatively you can obtain a special tape such as the Equitape (available from many good equestrian suppliers or from an independent consultancy such as the Equine Management Consultancy, 20 Victoria Road, Bulwark, Chepstow, NP6 5QN).

Cobs can be particularly difficult to assess and it is recommended that wherever possible their weight should be checked on a weighbridge.

Table 1 PONIES

Girth in inches	40	42.5	45	47.5	50	52.5	55	57.5
Girth in cm	101	108	114	120	127	133	140	146
Bodyweight in lb	100	172	235	296	368	430	502	562
Bodyweight in kg	45	77	104	132	164	192	234	252

Table 2 HORSES

Girth in inches	55	57.5	60	62.5	65	67.5
Girth in cm	140	146	152	159	165	171
Bodyweight in lb	538	613	688	776	851	926
Bodyweight in kg	240	274	307	346	380	414

Girth in inches	70	72.5	75	77.5	80	82.5
Girth in cm	178	184	190	199	203	206
Bodyweight in lb	1014	1090	1165	1278	1328	1369
Bodyweight in kg	453	486	520	570	593	611

(Based on work of Glushanok, Rochlitz and Skay, 1981)

Overfeeding is one of the main dangers in horse management, and if anything it is safer to slightly underfeed, particularly in horses not able to take their own exercise but dependent on the 'man made' sort.

Feeding can be purely for maintenance, ie to keep a resting horse or one in light work 'ticking over', for work which is moderate to strenuous, for breeding or for growth. Expert guidance will again be needed in the case of emaciated horses or sick ones.

The exact amount you feed your horse will depend on many factors, and any information given in a book or brochure can only be regarded as a guide, if a fairly accurate one. The horse's workload, the climate, his type and constitution, whether or not he is clipped, his temperament and general health all need considering, and the final amount decided upon for any set of circumstances will depend on the observation of the person in charge of his management. That old saying: 'the eye of the master. . .' again! Also, if the horse's circumstances change, even from day to day, such as an enforced or intended rest or conversely, more work than intended, the diet should change accordingly. Always, the work should increase before the feed and the feed should decrease before the work.

A maintenance ration for a horse would be about 2 per cent of his bodyweight, maybe $2^1/_2$ per cent, but for ponies and cobs no more than 2 per cent. For youngstock and lactating or late-pregnancy broodmares, maintenance would be 3 per cent of bodyweight. For example, if your horse, according to your measurement, appeared to weigh

1000lb(453.5kg), feeding him for maintenance at 2 per cent would mean giving him 20lb(9kg) of food daily, or 25lb(11.3kg) at $2^1/_2$ per cent. For resting or light work, this could be fed entirely as good quality roughage (hay or equivalent) depending on the individual. If some concentrates are fed, up to one third of the total weight could comprise concentrates.

Medium work, say two hours fairly active hacking per day, dressage, show jumping, light hunting, could be performed on, again, a $2^1/_2$ per cent of bodyweight ration, but the proportion of concentrates to roughage could be narrowed, so feeding up to half the amount as roughage and half concentrates. Many horses will manage hard work quite adequately on this ratio. For those who need more concentrates it may be considered suitable to give two thirds as concentrates and one third as roughage.

Some experts recommend that horses in hard, strenuous work (racing, three-day-eventing, hard hunting etc) have only one quarter of their ration as roughage (hay) and three quarters as concentrates. Although horses consuming fairly large amounts of concentrates often slacken off on their hay consumption of their own accord, this is getting to a point where many horses would feel that this is not enough hay. As ever, much depends on the individual.

In a few cases where horses need a good deal of food in general to exist and work satisfactorily, up to 3 per cent of the bodyweight could be fed, but it may be better to keep to $2^1/_2$ per cent and add a cupful of corn oil, soya oil or animal feed grade linseed oil to make the feed more 'energy dense', rather than overload the possibly reluctant horse with too many concentrates. Vitamin E and selenium should also be supplemented in such a case.

Exposure to cold weather also increases the amount of food needed, because it is obviously more difficult to maintain the body temperature. Outwintered horses should be given a constant supply of roughage, concentrates as needed on a regular basis and possibly a feeding block of vitamins and minerals in the field to help them maintain condition and keep them warm. The digestion of food takes energy which creates warmth. A hungry horse feels cold, whereas a well-fed one with some food always inside it being digested feels much warmer.

The condition of the horse is also important in deciding how much to feed. If you measure your horse when he is in fat condition, his weight according to the table will indicate that he should have more food than is really appropriate. Conversely, if the horse is too thin, his measurement may cause you to feed a lower amount than is really needed.

The places where horses noticeably put on or lose condition (fat) are along the crest of the neck, on either side of the withers, behind the shoulder muscle just above the elbow, on the sides, flanks and in

*Cross section through the pelvic region,
showing the outline for a very fat horse and
a very thin one, as used in condition scoring*

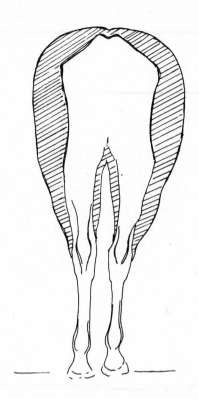

*The areas of the horse where fat accumu-
lates and which are used for assessment in
condition scoring*

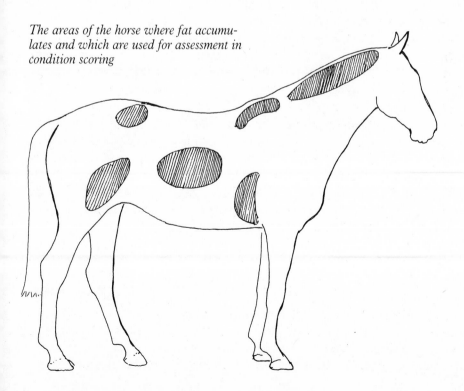

the loin area. If you can see the horse's ribs easily, if his withers and hipbones and even his spine protrude significantly and if he appears 'cut up' between the thighs, then he is surely underweight! Even horses who are naturally lean characters should not look like this. On the other hand, if you can't even feel your horse's ribs let alone count them, if you can't begin to guess where his backbone or his hipbones are because of the rolling fat covering them, he is obviously too fat! Common sense and educated judgement are needed. The diet can always be adjusted as you go along, but remember not to make any sudden changes. Don't chop and change but try to keep the horse on as settled a diet as possible.

Apart from deciding on the *amount* of feed to give, the *type* as regards energy content is also important. You should look for products which state on their analysis labels that they contain 10-12MJ (megajoules – a scientific measure) of DE (*digestible* energy – the horse is not able to digest *all* the energy in his feed) per kilogram of the feed. This is adequate for horses in moderate to hard work. For ponies, cobs and horses resting or in light work, 8.5-10MJ of DE per kg is about right.

· WATERING ·

So far, little has been said about the water in the diet which is probably more vital than food itself. Most feeds contain some moisture but the horse obviously needs more than this.

The horse's body is very roughly three quarters water, young bodies containing more than old ones. Water is needed in most body processes, and the whole body is full of fluid – inside the cells, between them, in the blood, milk, digestive juices and lymph; and sweat and urine are, of course, mainly water.

These days, most yards keep water constantly with their horses either in ordinary containers such as buckets, or by means of automatic waterers which do save a great deal of work in large yards. If these are used, though, it is best to use the kind with a meter so you know how much your horse is – or is not – drinking. Water intake is a good guide to general health and condition and if your horse suddenly starts drinking a lot more or less than usual you will know there could well be a problem.

Depending on work and weather, a horse can drink up to about 12gal (54.4l) per day, and occasionally more in hot weather and during hard work. Most stable buckets only hold 5gal (22.7l) so unless someone keeps an eagle eye on the supply this means that many horses are going slightly short of water much of the time. The horse doesn't have to be thirsty to be slightly short of water. If he goes to the bucket and it is empty or dirty he will not drink and may not worry too much about it, but ultimately this shortfall may cause slight dehydration; if he has a constant supply of fresh, clean water he will drink whenever he thinks about it.

The way to test for significant dehydration in a horse is simply to pinch up a fold of skin on the neck and see whether or not it slips back down again at once. If it doesn't, the horse could be dehydrated, although some endurance competitors allow a parameter of up to four seconds for this to happen. Milder dehydration could be manifested by the horse looking slightly lacklustre and sluggish, with dull eyes, and perhaps small, dry droppings and loss of condition. In more advanced cases, apart from the 'pinch test' described, there could be several symptoms: less urine passed (or too much depending on the root cause), the eyeball appearing to sink in the socket, weak pulse, and the horse obviously depressed and feeling ill.

In the 'old days' horses were either taken to water or it was brought to them, and this still applies in many traditional-style establishments such as some military and police stables. The rule was, and is, water before feeding because it was feared that a large draught of water could wash partially digested food out of the stomach into the intestinal tract and cause colic.

However, it is now felt that water could actually stimulate the production of digestive juices and it is certainly a fact that many horses, on being brought home and expecting a feed, will refuse to drink at all until they have eaten. I owned a horse like this, and he would persistently take short drinks (two or three swallows) while eating, in the same way we might sip a glass of water or wine. If you took his water away he would not actually refuse to eat but was obviously unhappy about it.

Professor George Waring of the University of Illinois at Carbondale spoke to a group of the Equine Behaviour Study Circle a few years ago and cited the case of a mare who dunked her hay in her water before eating it. If the water was removed she would not eat her hay at all. She did not, however, try to dunk her concentrates.

If water is always available, I feel it does not matter at all if the horse drinks during and after feeding because a horse so kept will not, anyway, drink large amounts. Horses' natural feed, grass, contains a lot of moisture, and it is generally felt that horses do digest feed better if it is slightly damped before feeding. This is contrary to the advice of hitherto which said not to damp feed because this diluted the digestive juices and made for poorer digestion. You only have to watch a horse tackle a dry feed, and watch the same horse eat a damped one, to see that the latter is more comfortable and easier to chew and swallow.

It should be remembered that wild and feral equidae (horses, ponies, zebras and asses), often do not have water always nearby (unless they live in the Camargue!) but may have to trek to the nearest watering sources, which they do night and morning. They drink long draughts then but only twice a day. If this practice is followed in domesticity, rest assured that your horse will come to no harm – but I still feel safest recommending that you do it *before* you feed!

It is also important to realise that horses will take a seemingly long drink and will then raise their heads for a rest and perhaps look round. If you wait with them they will often put their heads down again to drink, and a very thirsty horse may even repeat the process a third time. If we drag him away during the first rest, the horse will not have slaked his thirst and we shall be depriving him of water. If we do this repeatedly at both of the day's waterings we could be inadvertently dehydrating the horse ourselves. Usually, horses will leave the trough themselves when satisfied, and we should certainly wait for them to do this.

Another helpful point to remember is that even a very thirsty horse may not drink for several seconds (up to half a minute) when first offered water and may then spend a good two minutes drinking. At one swallow, it will take in about two thirds of a pint/one third of a litre. You can see the swallows by watching the underside of the neck as the horse drinks so you can check approximately how much the horse has taken in; this is useful to know at times, such as if he is hot after competition when his water intake must be small and gradual.

Although horses appear to come to no harm if they drink very cold water, they do drink more if it is a comfortable temperature. This is particularly important in winter when even stabled horses may restrict their own intake because of this. Water heating kits are available from some equestrian suppliers and agricultural merchants, which can be set to keep the water at about what is loosely termed 'room temperature' (about 20°C [68°F]) – not exactly warm but encouraging to drink.

Summary

●Food is used to maintain body temperature at about 38°C (100.4°F), for growth and repair of body tissues, to provide energy for life and work and to put on condition (store food as fat), the first two being the most important.

●The digestive system works best on a 'trickle feed' system, ie by digesting large quantities of naturally fibrous feed most of the time. Fermentation of cellulose is very important and for this process a healthy, stable population of gut bacteria is essential – disturbances such as several hours without food, sudden changes in feedstuffs and routine etc, kills bacteria and results in poor digestion or serious digestive disorder.

●Dental checks every six months to ensure that the horse can grind up his food effectively are essential.

●Feed supplements can be very potent: ensure that your horse really needs one; never mix supplements unless advised to do so by a vet or nutritionist; and never feed other than the recommended amount. Feed a little of the supplement in each feed to ensure consistent digestion.

●Never mix branded products, either one with another or with 'straights' such as oats, as this can significantly unbalance the diet.

●For horses with respiratory problems, soak hay thoroughly for at least four hours; hot water softens the hay.

●Be careful to introduce hayage products or silage gradually, mixing them with the original forage first, as with any feedstuff. Never use a bagged product (hayage/silage) if the bag is punctured or damaged – this can cause dangerous toxins in the product. If the horse eats its hayage ration too quickly, you can create that all-important *ad lib* supply and feed more by using a lower energy grade product, and by feeding it in special nets with smaller holes so the horse takes longer to eat.

●Do not over-estimate the importance of bran: it has a severely reversed calcium: phosphorus ratio, containing far too much phosphorus and too little calcium. Cereal grains also have this failing (to a lesser extent), so the addition of bran can cause a worsening of an already undesirable situation in horses on a high concentrate diet.

Summary

• Foods which have a higher calcium than phosphorus ratio, include grass hays so a largely hay/hayage diet represents a safer balance, also dried grass/alfalfa and soaked sugar beet. Sugar beet pulp/shreds/cubes *must* be soaked before feeding, the cubes in particular for 24 hours, otherwise the product can swell up inside the horse.

• Feed no more than 4lb(1.8kg) of concentrates in one feed – if the stomach receives too much food at once it cannot function properly. Hay/hayage can be fed *ad lib* since it passes through the stomach more quickly than concentrates, being digested further down the digestive tract in the large intestine; an *ad lib* supply keeps the digestive system working as it should.

• Keep the horse on a stable diet for optimum digestive efficiency – keep to the same ingredients in each feed, varying only the amounts and proportions according to the horses's work/rest régime. Thus the digestive bacteria receive a constant supply of food which is essential to their survival and therefore to the health and wellbeing of your horse.

• Feed according to bodyweight, not height, and allow for type, work, constitution etc; the tables will provide a fairly accurate guide to the amounts needed. Use an appropriate energy level diet.

• Water is best kept available all the time; like this the horse will consume only moderate amounts which probably aids digestion rather than hinders it. Large draughts are probably best taken before feeding concentrates. Allow horses watered at troughs plenty of time to drink, rest and then drink again, to ensure adequate intake.

PRACTICAL CONSIDERATIONS

· *PREPARATION* ·

Many owners find preparing their horses' feeds one of the most enjoyable tasks of horse management. They take great pleasure in watching the horse tuck into a carefully prepared feed after the anticipation of 'what's coming', and preparation *is* important for efficient digestion.

However, some practices can be detrimental to the nutrient content of the feed and one of these is cooking food, which can destroy many heat-sensitive nutrients and therefore significantly reduce the value of the feed. The practice of cooking feed was originally to make it more digestible, but with today's pre-cooked and processed feeds available, this is not necessary. Horses often do like cooked feeds, however, such as boiled barley, but remember that the vitamin content will be damaged by the high temperature – if you wish to add a supplement, wait till the feed has cooled down before mixing it in.

When feeding supplements in ordinary feeds, half fill the container in which it is to be mixed, then add the supplement, then the rest of the feed; this ensures that it is evenly mixed and that a powdered supplement does not blow away.

If cooked feed is on your menu, simply cook a normal feed, preferably by steaming – this is better than making a separate mash with different ingredients from normal in it which of course constitutes a sudden change of feed.

A feed can be warmed up by adding black treacle diluted and melted in very hot water, or just damp the feed (a good practice in any case) with hot water. It is *not* advisable to soak sugar beet in hot water with a view to giving a hot feed – it has been found to ferment very quickly indeed and can cause serious digestive disorders.

All feeds should be mixed and fed in conditions which will not put the horse off eating. For instance, wash your hands before handling feed as any unpleasant smells such as droppings, liniment or your own cheese and onion sandwiches will be transferred to the feed and some horses would then refuse to eat.

Take the time to watch your horse eat and drink so you can spot any abnormalities; is he happy with his feed container or is it rattling and putting him off? Is it too deep, in an unfavoured corner, too high for him or too low? Normally the top of the manger, if fixed, should be level with the point of the horse's shoulder. Feeding from the ground in a domestic stable can cause problems because unless the container is a free bucket, horses can catch their feet in low mangers, and dirt can easily get into them.

Water should be offered in two containers in separate corners. One bucket will only be sufficient for a very few hours (and certainly insufficient for overnight or all day while you are at work) and also, if the horse does a dropping and the two are standing together, some will be bound to fall in both buckets leaving the horse with no drinkable water. Stand the buckets in the same, separate corners each time so the horse always knows where to find them.

Food being prepared in advance can be mixed but not damped or cooked as this could well turn it sour and cause those ever looming digestive problems. If pre-mixed feeds are left overnight, cover them with a heavy object (such as a plank the width of the container) so tats and mice cannot help themselves and contaminate the rest of the feed.

· CLEANLINESS ·

Obviously, containers and mixing utensils with old, caked-on feed stuck to them harbour disease. Feed equipment should be thoroughly cleaned each day. If soap is used to remove oils, rinse very thoroughly. Water buckets should be scrubbed out at the same time as mangers to prevent the accumulation of slime, and it is much better to empty them and refill when needed rather than simply top up water which may be thoroughly stale and flat, and already have old saliva, bits of dirt and other debris in it. Auto-waterers with drain plugs are obviously easier to clean than the other sort. If your horse is a quiet eater, he could eat from a clean piece of sacking on the floor, but choose the cleanest corner.

Long mangers in field shelters should not be overlooked but regularly cleaned, and field troughs too need emptying periodically and scrubbing out before swilling out and refilling. It is not necessarily true that fish in a trough mean that the water is clean enough to drink, and in any case their presence will put off some horses from drinking. 'Natural' water sources such as ponds and some streams are rarely, these days, pure enough to drink from, since they are either stagnant or contaminated with chemicals from agriculture and industry. It is far safer to provide water in well-maintained troughs or other containers, either automatically filled or from a hosepipe. If you do have an apparently suitable water source, have it tested: contact your vet or your local Equine Services representative for the Agricultural Development Advisory Service of the Ministry of Agriculture, Fisheries and Foods, whose address will be in your 'phone directory; but be aware that water that is pure enough to drink on one day may not be on the next.

· STORAGE ·

Feeds of all kinds do deteriorate in feed value and general quality if improperly stored – feed supplements are particularly sensitive. Do not buy supplements which have passed their 'sell by' date, which have been stored in sunlight or damp, or in hot or humid conditions (and don't keep them in such conditions yourself), or which have been damaged or opened packages. Don't buy more than you can use within the recommended viable period (check with the manufacturer if in doubt), and reseal the pack properly after each use to reduce the presence of air.

Roots keep best in cool, dark, airy conditions with the soil on. Rinse them just before feeding to remove soil and any residual chemicals. A plastic mesh laundry bin is suitable as storage for small yards.

Concentrates are best stored in galvanised bins with the lids kept down and preferably locked to prevent accidental access by horses – and others! If storing them in sacks, keep them off the ground and *dry*. Plastic dustbins are good (although rats *can* chew through them) if the lids are kept firmly on – perhaps by means of a long pole poked through the lid handles and wedged into holders at each end of the line of bins, like a sliprail.

Hayage/silage products should be delivered in undamaged sacks – if they are damaged at all do not accept them. Open one sack or bale at a time to prevent waste and deterioration: they can be stored outdoors where they won't be damaged by rodents. Use silage within 12 hours.

Coarse mixes and any product containing molasses keep best in cool conditions. In summer, unless you have a natural stone-built feedroom, you could buy an old, tall fridge, remove the shelves and keep your sack or two in that. Large yards should buy no more at a time than they can use within a few days and, again, it is best to open one sack at a time.

Hay can present practical storage difficulties. It should also be kept in well-ventilated, *dry* conditions; old-fashioned hay lofts kept hay truly dry (provided the roof was in good condition!) but too often today we see hay stored in open barns with simply a roof and no sides which does little to protect the bales from driving rain and can cause considerable deterioration and wastage. Use your imagination to create dry storage conditions, and if buying new hay pay particular attention to ventilation to prevent it becoming mow-burnt. Even older hay (and don't be persuaded to buy 'good' two-year-old hay because its feeding value will have dropped greatly by that age) needs reasonable ventilation, dryness and preferably off-ground storage. Pallets or planks on bricks (provided a cat can get under) are helpful here.

One often sees hay and straw stored round the sides of indoor schools or outdoor manèges. This is very poor management because the rising dust from the flooring will penetrate the exposed bales and contaminate them, to the detriment of the health of any horse eating such forage. Hay and straw should also be stored downwind of stables, particularly where there are any horses susceptible to respiratory problems – otherwise the spores from it can be blown into the stables, affecting the horses.

· FEEDING HORSES IN COMPANY AND ALONE ·

Many horses can be put off feeding by a higher-ranking neighbour or colleague. Stabled horses, even when they cannot see each other, can suffer in this way, and horses living out can be chivvied away from their rations. Give horses amenable neighbours and stay to ensure fair play when giving outdoor horses concentrates. Horses appear to prefer a personal space of about 20 yards/metres around them when eating 'man-provided' food, and this is important when putting out hay. Have at least one more pile than there are horses, but spacing is perhaps even more important. Horses fed in shelters should be watched to see each is eating peacefully. If not, the underdogs should be fed separately, you may even have to bring them in for the purpose.

Summary

●Make sure they have cooled down to a comfortable temperature, and do not add supplements until cool as the heat can destroy vitamins. Do not soak sugar beet pulp in hot water as it can then ferment extremely quickly and cause serious digestive disturbance.

●Be careful to feed in clean conditions to prevent transfer of unpleasant smells which can put horses off eating. Feed containers can be sterilised, if necessary, by using a baby steriliser such as Milton.

●Take the time to study your horse for several minutes, regularly, while it is eating and drinking to ensure it is doing so freely and easily. With regard to possible dental problems, watch for apparent hunger yet reluctance to eat, difficulty in chewing or swallowing, quidding and unfinished food, and an air of anxiety while eating.
●Check natural water sources for pollution and stagnation – the presence of fish and other waterlife is no guarantee of purity

●Feeds are best stored in cool, dry, well-ventilated conditions, away from dust, driving rain or pollutants such as exhaust fumes. Hayage/silage should be rejected if in damaged sacks, as should any feed which looks mouldy or smells bad.

●Outdoor horses like a personal space of about 20yd(m) while eating. Stay for a while to ensure that each horse is eating and drinking freely.

PASTURE

Pasture management is a very specialised subject and present day 'experts' are few and far between when it comes to horses as opposed to cattle. ADAS do now have some representatives trained in equine requirements, and some seed firms and merchants are gradually becoming more aware of horseowners' needs, although they concern themsleves mainly with studs. The fact is that the worst sort of grazing you could offer your horse is that used for dairy cattle, even if a farmer allowed you to use it. Such pasture is far too nutritious and high in nitrogen to be safe for horses, who fare much better on clean but low nutritional value grass such as sheep or dry-cow pasture. Many endurance horses live mainly on such pasture; however, horses in other disciplines do not seem to enjoy the same management, for some reason.

Grass mixes can be arranged to suit the needs of various categories of horse, be it ponies, breeding stock or working, athletic horses; if more owners took advantage of recent advances in our knowledge in this field their animals could benefit and also their bank balances, as well-cared for grass of the right sort is far cheaper, even taking into account field care costs, than bought-in forage and concentrates.

Old-fashioned meadows which were used for both hay production and grazing are now almost non-existent. However, meadow hay can still be produced as a special seed mix (usually on request), and the wide variety of grasses present in such a mix is nearer the horse's natural food which comprised a varied, interesting sward with a wide range of nutrients in the different grasses and herbs. Herbs are usually missing from the more specialised grass mixtures sown for seed hay, mixture hay, legume hays (clover/lucerne (alfalfa)/vetches) and particular species' hays such as timothy and ryegrass. Herbs are nonetheless a most valuable addition to a horse's diet, often rich in important nutrients missing from grass, and can with advantage be added to a mix. Otherwise, a special herb strip can be sown in the field.

· GRAZING HABITS ·

Horses' grazing habits are well known and documented. They designate some areas of their paddocks for grazing, and others for lavatories which they never graze even if the 'dining' areas have become virtually bare. Like other animals, horses are revolted by their own droppings; they wander over to the lavatory, and rather than pick their way through existing droppings, they dung on the edge of the area which grows larger and larger, decreasing the eating areas more and more. The grass in the lavatory areas grows long, lush and rank and is constantly fed by the droppings, while the eating grass is constantly cropped sometimes down to the bare earth and is never fertilised. Thistles, nettles, ragwort, docks and other poisonous things proliferate, particularly round the hedges and fences, and eventually the land is all but useless, providing nothing but an exercise area for the horses. What a waste of a precious resource!

· TYPES OF PASTURE ·

Anyone who ventures around the country must appreciate the vastly differing types of soil there are, from the red clays of the midlands to the rich loams of the south east, the shallow poor soils of the uplands and the sandy soils of the Cotswolds, plus the variations which can occur in any region even from field to field. Soil type largely governs what grows best on your land. Herbs in particular can be regarded as indicator species, in other words the presence of a particular plant indicates what kind of soil it is growing on and the expert will already have a good idea of the chemical and mineral analysis of the land.

Yes, we're back to analysis again because until we know what our soil contains we cannot with any certainty prepare a seed mix or even try to improve the grazing – sowing plant and grass seed unsuitable for the soil will not result in success! It is not such an old wives' tale that limestone underlying the soil results in plenty of calcium in the grass, very favourable for the formation of strong young bones – such paddocks are therefore still favoured for bloodstock studs. However, this does not mean that other soils cannot produce equally good horses, given an all-round balanced diet.

· IMPROVING AND CARING FOR LAND ·

Horse owners who do not have their own land may feel like skipping this section. Understandably so, particularly if they are only able to rent land by the season – but I hope they will at least skim through it if only to find out the basic elements of pasture care which will certainly help them to care for their temporary plot, and to know what to look for when searching for 'somewhere to turn him out'.

Finding rented land is extremely difficult in some areas, mainly because horses' 'wasteful' (some would say selective) grazing habits are anathema to farmers. The only land which is usually available is that normally grazed by horses anyway, and that, except for a few privately owned establishments (leaving aside well-run studs), is normally patchy in the extreme with long, rejected loo areas and bald grazing areas, worm-ridden, weed-infested and virtually useless from a food production point of view. However, even a little basic care can improve such land and make it safer and more pleasant for your horse.

Firstly, *drainage* needs attention because wet land is cold and starved of oxygen and will never produce valuable grass. If the land supports tufts of spiky marsh grasses or even rushes, or seems very rough and rutted even in summer, this is a sign that it is naturally wet land which will be waterlogged for much of the year, and therefore useless except for mainly exercise in summer.

It is certainly not worth installing a drainage system in land which is not your own or for which you do not have a long let, because it is an expensive operation. If you *are* going to have the land for some years, however, go ahead and have it properly drained – this involves drainage pipes being installed underground which empty into a convenient ditch or other outlet which will have to be maintained to be kept clear.

Soil analysis comes next. Here again ADAS can help you, as can the local representative of a fertiliser firm (who will subsequently expect you to purchase their products), or an independent agricultural consultant such as the Equine Management Consultancy Service mentioned earlier. Once you have the analysis, you will know what to apply in the way of lime and fertilisers to create a healthy, balanced soil. Your expert should also assess what herbage is already growing in the field, tell you what should be encouraged and what should be got rid of either by spraying, repeated topping (cutting or mowing down) or digging up. You need a blend of a variety of grasses, some clovers (wild white clovers rather than red) and herbs. Grass species are changing and improving all the time and expert advice really is needed as to what will be best for your land and your animals' lifestyle, and according to what is already present or absent.

Horses do tend to gallop about their fields and hooves can do a good deal of damage, particularly if shod. For this reason, horse pastures are better with a covering of old turf – the springy mattress of turf and roots will cushion the impact with the ground and protect the land itself. This should *not* be ploughed up and started from scratch except in extreme cases. Having a field ploughed and reseeded means it will be out of use for at least a year and the 'mattress' will be destroyed. It is normally better to remove unwanted vegetation and fertilise according to your analysis, and provide a seed bed by giving the field a tough harrowing with a pitchpole harrow to thoroughly tear out old, dead grasses and roots and aerate the soil. The chain harrow can then be run over the field, the seed mix sown and the land possibly rolled to level and consolidate it. A field so treated in spring may be ready for light grazing the following autumn and normal use the next spring. If the work is carried out in the autumn, light grazing could start in the spring and increase throughout the summer (in line with a grazing/resting rota).

If nitrogen has been applied, a hay crop must be taken off the land before horses are grazed on it, as the resultant growth of grass will be too nutritious for horses and especially cobs and ponies, and you could end up with digestive disorders and laminitis. If you do not wish to use the hay yourself you could always sell it and put the income towards other hay and feed or into your land management kitty.

Once the land has been improved, it should be incorporated into a proper rota as all land needs resting for at least three continuous months out of every year if it is to remain in good heart. Fertilisers will also be needed periodically, according to the advice your consultant has given.

Ideally, land should be divided up into at least three paddocks so that each can be used, treated and rested in turn. If you want your land to provide a significant amount of your horse's nutritional requirements, you will need about two acres (.8 hectare) for the first horse on it and half as much again for each subsequent animal. Take note of which are the two driest paddocks and try to arrange your rota so that these are alternated for winter use; or simply set aside the driest with a good grass cover for winter.

Put the horses to graze in paddock 1 for two or three weeks and when it starts to look patchy, some areas being noticeably shorter than others, move the horses to paddock 2. Paddock 1 should now have cattle put on it (this should not be too difficult – most farmers are glad of a bit of free grazing for their youngsters or dry cows). The cattle will eat off the long grass rejected by the horses, not be offended by their droppings, and will use the horses' grazing areas for *their* lavatory, so adding much needed natural fertiliser to those constantly depleted areas. If you cannot obtain cattle, sheep would be better than nothing. If you cannot arrange anything at all, you should, at any rate, top (mow) the long areas and then harrow the whole paddock. Harrow the lavatory areas carefully so as to break up the droppings and help the sun and air desiccate both them and the worm eggs (see next section), but do *not* spread the horse droppings to the horses' eating areas. These should be harrowed separately to avoid contaminating them with worm eggs and with the droppings themselves. Perhaps the farmer whose cattle are enjoying your free grazing would do this job for you? If you are having difficulty in arranging it and cannot do it yourself, your ADAS representative should be able to put you in touch with a contractor who would take it on.

The paddock should now be closed off to rest and grow again. When paddock 2 starts to look patchy, move the horses to paddock 3, and give paddock 2 the same treatment, and carry on rotating like this throughout the growing season.

When other treatments such as spraying and fertilising are being done, horses usually need to be kept off the land to prevent possible poisoning – this may be from one day to a few weeks, depending on the characteristics of the product being used, and whether there is significant rainfall, so your rota will have to be carefully arranged so that the land gets its treatments and your horses their freedom and grazing.

Grazing horses with cattle in the same field is policy on many good studs and can be a sound practice, provided the cattle are free from brucellosis and ringworm, and are dehorned. It does depend on what the cattle are being additionally fed, however, as some substances such as hormones and nutrients which are toxic to horses could be passed out with their droppings onto the land which the horses will be grazing. Discuss this with your advisor and check with the owner of the cattle as to their diet. For the same reason, spreading your land with cattle manure – a good fertiliser which disguises the smell of horse droppings therefore encouraging the grazing of previous lavatory areas – could produce problems if the manure is so contaminated.

Other farm manure, particularly from pigs and poultry, can result in too rich a growth of grass for horses and should be rejected for horse paddocks.

· WORMS AND HORSE PADDOCKS ·

One of the reasons for putting cattle on horse paddocks is so that they will hopefully eat the worm larvae in the horses' lavatory areas and help to significantly decrease the worm population on the land. This is also a reason for picking up droppings daily. Worm larvae will have migrated from the droppings onto the surrounding grass within 24 hours, so unless they can be picked up daily it is a rather pointless exercise. It is a truly gargantuan task to do manually on a daily basis for any but a very few horses, so most owners end up leaving the droppings on the land.

The worm larvae of the most infective species crawl up the blades of grass and stay around the top, hoping to be eaten so that they can mature. If cattle eat them they will, of course, be killed, but if horses eat them they will cause trouble – so it is one of nature's safety mechanisms when horses decline to eat the long grass (which will contain larvae) in the lavatory areas of their paddocks. In overcrowded paddocks, however, there is a good chance that some worm larvae will be eaten, an excellent reason for not overstocking paddocks, for picking up droppings if at all possible and for grazing with cattle or sheep.

Many owners spread their own muck heaps on their paddocks, so providing a good, free source of natural fertiliser. If this is done, make sure the muck used is really old and well rotted (at least a year old) as otherwise the smell will make the paddocks unpalatable to the horses. The heat in the pile should have killed off any worm larvae in that time as well, and owners who practise this report that their paddocks grow healthy grass which their horses appear to relish. It should be spread in the autumn on paddocks resting for the winter and in the spring on the winter paddocks which will not be used till much later in the year.

The problem of pasture and worms can be greatly minimised if horses and ponies are methodically and frequently wormed *all year round* to be on the safe side. Worming will be covered in Chapter 11, but basically, if you worm your stock every four to eight weeks throughout the year, the numbers of infective larvae passed out in droppings will be minimal. With the newer wormers now available containing ivermectin, you could manage with worming only 12 weeks or so, depending on your circumstances and according to veterinary advice, as these products kill the worm larvae while they are still migrating in the bloodstream, whereas other wormers only affect mature worms which have returned to the intestines.

· ALTERNATIVE GRAZING AREAS ·

Many horse owners are so short of somewhere to turn their horses out that they are tempted to use any spare land, orchards and sometimes roadside tethering places. There are obviously dangers in such areas. Spare land is usually badly fenced if at all, full of dangerous litter and pollutants and in areas where vandals can reach the animals.

Orchards are not usually available unless they have fallen into disuse, but even then excess windfalls can bring on a digestive disturbance of serious proportions. Low branches are most dangerous for horses and chemical pollutants can remain on the trees and grass.

Ordinary woods and spinneys are valuable for cover but often harbour snares, traps and poisonous plants, not to mention protruding tree roots which can trip and injure animals playing about. Although we cannot wrap horses in cotton wool all the time, these are obvious dangers which must be considered and eliminated as far as possible before turning horses out.

Tethering horses and ponies, donkeys and mules, is subject to legal requirements preventing the animals being tethered in such a way as to cause unnecessary suffering. If this method of grazing is used, the horses should wear a stout headcollar or neck strap and be on a swivel stake so that the rope does not wrap round and round the stake, imprisoning them in one tiny area – they seem quite unable to un-wrap themselves but stand stoically until someone puts matters to rights. The area chosen should be safe from vandals and provide access to ample food, shelter and water. Although horses prefer to have company, they should not be tethered where enemies can reach them. If two or more are tethered together they should not be able to touch each other, and should be far enough apart to prevent kicking matches.

· POISONOUS PLANTS, HERBS AND TREES ·

One of the hazards of grazing horses at all is that they may come across poisonous things which can certainly kill them; despite an apparently bitter taste, some animals do acquire a taste for these with often tragic results – yet another reason for taking time to watch what your animals like to eat.

Good pasture management dictates that poisonous growths be removed from the paddocks, but it is impractical to check every square metre of ground every day for something poisonous appearing – and if it does the horses will probably find it before we do.

Fortunately, most horses only try out poisonous plants when they are very hungry and the nasty taste of most of them will be a deterrent. One way to dissuade them from experimenting is to make sure they do not become so hungry that they will try almost anything (except the long grass in their loos!). Keeping the land productive with a not-too-nutritious species of grass will serve its purpose of providing freedom, exercise and enough food to keep hunger at bay. On bare paddocks, feed the animals before turning them out and/or give hay in the field.

Ponies and cobs are prone to laminitis and can develop this distressing condition almost at the whiff of a blade of grass due, probably, to some metabolic sensitivity which we do not fully understand. It could be that such animals can never be turned out but must be fed strictly controlled diets and only turned loose in surfaced pens or yards. Starvation diets however, are now not recommended.

Many horse and pony owners cannot recognise many poisonous plants. It is imperative, however, that *some* effort is made to learn what they look like in order to safeguard the horses' safety and health. Short of a practical lesson from an expert, an excellent booklet from any HMSO branch (see your telephone book) called *British Poisonous Plants* Book 161, ISBN 0-11-240461-8, is probably the most comprehensive one available and will really help you recognise dangerous things. Meanwhile, here is a list of some of the more likely ones you will come across, in alphabetical order:

Aconite

Box

Bracken

Bryony

Buttercup

Charlock

Dodder

Foxglove

Giant hogweed

Hemlock

Horse/mares tails

Ivy

Laburnum

Marsh marigold

Nightshades

Oak

Privet

Ragwort

Rhododendron

Rushes

Thorn apple

Yew

Where trees or shrubs cannot be safely removed, they should be fenced round so that horses cannot possibly reach them. Many garden plants are poisonous, so check the individual geography of the area and fence the horses away from gardens. Take the trouble to ask neighbouring householders not to throw garden rubbish into your field, too, and explain why.

Methods of removing poisonous plants vary from spraying, hand pulling, forking or digging up, to constantly cutting down, particularly before they go to seed. Many are more palatable dead than alive, so they should be taken right out of the field and burnt in case the horses eat the wilted plants. For the same reason, watch for them in hay, too.

Ragwort seems to be proliferating alarmingly. With its bright yellow, daisy-like clusters of flowers and ragged leaves, it is now a familiar sight on roadsides and particularly motorway embankments. As a naturalist, I am pleased to see it as a food plant for the lovely cinnabar moth and other insects – but its place is not in horse paddocks. Although local councils do have the authority to make land-owners remove it from infested land, many of them do not bother, so it is becoming more and more familiar all over Britain. If a horse does eat ragwort, it has a progressive, cumulative effect on the liver and is ultimately fatal. Once ragwort gets a hold in a paddock it can reproduce from its rootstock and is very difficult indeed to eradicate permanently. Expert advice on the most up-to-date method of removal (probably repeated spraying and forking up) should be taken and followed.

Unless you are certain what your horse is eating, it may be best not to let him graze out hacking as hedgerows alongside lanes are a real stronghold for poisonous plants. Once you become familiar with the more common plants, however, you will be able to allow the horse his treat in confidence.

· HYDROPONICALLY PRODUCED GRASS ·

An increasingly popular way of producing grass is by means of a hydroponic unit. These enable you to grow a nutritious mat of grass or cereal with just water and sometimes added nutrients (plus warmth and light) but with no soil, and there are units to suit very small yards to ones suitable for large establishments. Many owners are finding this an excellent way of providing nutritious succulents for stabled horses, especially in winter, and claim feed and veterinary bills are reduced because of the increased wellbeing of their horses.

Even the smallest units, however, can cost over £100, which the one-horse owner may find discouraging. If you are prepared to put up with some inconvenience in your home or have a heated greenhouse, you can grow your own grass fairly simply. You will need trays, or containers such as supermarket vegetable containers (provided they do not have holes in the bottom), polythene ice-cream packs (no lids) or any other fairly shallow container which will hold a little water; seed and, of course, light and warmth – you will *not* need soil. You can buy your seed from any seed merchant and can choose from grass seed, wheat (very popular apparently), barley, oats or maize.

Just set out your trays, scatter your chosen seed in a thin layer on the bottom, sprinkle about a quarter to a half cup of water evenly on it – and wait. Do another tray the next day, and another the next and so on, so you have a constant supply; the first should be ready to feed in about 10 to 14 days depending on the seed. Water the trays with the above amount of water daily. Apparently wheat, barley and oats are the most successful. Open bookshelves are useful for stacking your containers.

Do check with a nutritionist or your vet if you are at all worried about this method of feeding greenstuff to your horse. It is a homespun method originally described by equestrian author Janet Macdonald in *Equi* magazine some years ago, and I know several people who have since tried it successfully.

If you wish to buy a proper unit, you will receive full instructions with your equipment and may well find the initial outlay and small amount of daily labour well worth it to provide your horse with nutritious, cheap, welcome, natural food every day.

The amount fed depends on preference but a couple of trays a day for one horse seems to be in order. Feed the whole growth, roots and all. And if you are worried about the nutrient content – have it analysed!

Summary

●Pasture is a largely wasted resource among most horseowners. Grass mixes can be formulated for any type or category of horse or pony, and the resultant crop represents an economical and nutritionally sound feed source.

●For advice on land improvement and management, contact your local Equine Services department of the Agricultural Development Advisory Service, a division of the Min of Ag, Fish and Foods (details in your telephone directory). Alternatively, contact an independent consultant eg the Equine Management Consultancy Service (address see p.00), or obtain free advice from a seed and/or fertiliser company (but use their products!).

●Horses generally fare best on grass with a fairly low nutrient content; grass to which nitrogen has been applied is too rich and should have a hay crop taken off it before grazing horses. A mix typical of old-fashioned meadows with a wide variety of grasses and herbs, is best.

●Horses' are selective grazers – they have eating and defecating areas which can keep the worm burden in check, though may be wasteful from a food production point of view.

●Cattle make complementary grazing partners for horses: they eat the 'loo' grass rejected by horses (and therefore their worm larvae) and drop their manure on the horses' eating areas, thus providing fertiliser. Make sure the cattle are dehorned and free from brucellosis and ringworm; beware of substances in cattle feed such as hormones and other nutrients which when passed as manure can have adverse effects on horses.

●Soil type largely dictates what grass you can grow. Soil analysis is essential if subsequent treatments and fertilising are to improve the properties of your soil. Drainage, land rotation, topping, harrowing and resting keep the land productive and in good heart. A hay crop can always be sold.

●Worm your horses every four to eight weeks to prevent infestation; modern wormers are effective against migrating larvae, so you may need to only worm every 12 weeks, on veterinary advice.

Summary

Use only well-rotted horse muck at least a year old on your own paddocks, otherwise its smell will contaminate your land.

●Beware of using waste land, orchards and roadside verges for grazing. If you tether your horse or pony, ensure that it has access to shelter and water, is on a swivel tether and cannot be reached by human vandals or bullying equines.

●Beware of poisonous plants – learn to recognise the most common and eradicate them ruthlessly. Never let your horse become so hungry that it will experiment with these normally bitter-tasting plants; if necessary, feed before turning out.

●Laminitis animals should have only the poorest quality grazing, and then a special watch must be kept for poisonous plants. Alternatively, turn them out in special surfaced yards or pens and feed a strictly controlled diet on veterinary instructions.

●Hydroponically produced grass is a useful succulent in winter and for stabled horses all year round.

Checklist

✓ 1 The only way you can get an accurate idea of what your horse is eating is to have his diet checked and/or formulated by a qualified nutritionist or veterinary surgeon, taking into account the laboratory analysis of hay/hayage, concentrates, supplements (if used) and other additives. By having a diet formulated, with sufficient flexibility to suit your horse or pony's varying circumstances throughout the year, and by having your feeding programme updated yearly (or more often if necessary), you will keep abreast of what is best for your particular horse in an ecomomical, effective way.

2 Keep to the standard rules of feeding but relate them to your particular horse. Common practice is not necessarily correct, for instance. . .

3 . . . three feeds a day with hay night and morning does *not* constitute 'little and often'.

4 Making sudden changes is bad practice and includes: missing out feeds; feeding different ingredients in each feed; mashing horses; and allowing them to become unnaturally hungry by leaving them for several hours without food, particularly overnight. Such practices will have an adverse effect on the gut bacteria, resulting in serious colic or at least impaired digestion, a below-par horse and wasted resources.

5 When feeding specially compounded feeds never add 'straights' or mix brands as you could seriously unbalance the diet. The same goes for supplements which are often very potent in small amounts.

6 Feed your horse according to his bodyweight at an appropriate percentage and energy level. Check his weight regularly and adjust his intake accordingly; use your practical judgement.

7 You can do very nicely without bran.

8 Always ensure that your horse has a constant supply of water and good quality hay (meadow or mixture hay) or an appropriate grade of hayage. Overnight is often a crucial time, when horses run out of everything: leave two buckets of water and, if in doubt, two full haynets – horses do not gorge hay and will simply leave what they do not need.

9 Always increase the work before the concentrates, and decrease the concentrates before the work. If the horse has to stand in for any reason, cut the concentrates right down (otherwise azoturia, lymphangitis and laminitis may result), but not out completely – the bugs need their feeds, too!

10 By feeding a constant diet you will help your horse maintain optimal digestion, and therefore good health and physical performance.

5

BEDDING

Mucking out and bedding down are amongst the more mundane tasks in caring for a horse or pony, but their importance is often under-rated. The type of bedding used and the way it is managed can significantly affect an animal's comfort, health and performance, and this means athletically working animals and breeding stock, both of which are in high-profile categories and subject to considerable stresses. A working horse can be highly stressed indeed and everything should be done to minimise that stress, increase its comfort and conserve its resources if it is to give of its best. Broodmares in the last three months of pregnancy and the first three months of lactation are also on a plane of maximum physical output, because this is when the foetus/young foal makes most of its demands. And the youngster itself is at a most critical period of life when development is at its most rapid. Discomfort or threat to health can impair this development and the loss may never be recouped in later life – indeed it can lower a horse's potential for health for the rest of its life.

THE NEED FOR BEDDING

Bedding provides the horse with a cushioning layer to lie on when stabled and prevents injury on a hard floor. It helps keep a horse warm, and provides a 'buffer' when the horse stales – many horses will withold their urine if they think they are going to splash themselves; and it keeps horses cleaner and drier by providing material for the urine to drain through. Many people believe that it benefits a horse's feet and legs to stand on bedding rather than on a hard, bare floor, but although I feel it must be more comfortable for them, there is no actual evidence that physical benefits do occur.

HARMFUL EFFECTS

Poorly managed bedding, or bedding of unsuitable materials, can, however, cause actual ill-health either in the form of allergic respiratory responses to fungi and mould spores or as a skin reaction to chemical residues sprayed on when the bedding material was a growing crop or tree and remaining on the product you buy.

Respiratory health, in susceptible individuals, is probably most harmed by straw bedding. As is well known now, even top quality samples of straw of any kind carry *some* mould spores which may be invisible to the naked eye, but float around the airspace of the stable, are breathed in and can cause the distressingly familiar symptoms of coughing and breathing difficulties.

Skin reactions, taking the form of apparent burns, rashes and blisters, seem to occur most with wood shavings. The trees from which these are made are sprayed, by Common Market Law, with various chemicals meant to enhance growth and tree health, but which remain in the final product to the detriment of the health of horses or ponies with skin sensitive to those particular chemicals.

Bedding which is not kept properly clean can, in extreme cases, become nothing but an indoor muck heap, creating a putrid, stinking atmosphere. Ammonia is produced (among other things) from the decaying of organic matter, not only the bedding itself but actual droppings and urine. And ammonia is caustic, a heavy gas which hangs around the lower part of the box in particular and is breathed in in considerable quantities by a horse lying down to rest or sleep (which a stabled horse will probably do for several hours out of 24). Even when not lying down, the ammonia is in the air and is obviously breathed in all the time the horse is indoors. He cannot stand with his head outside *all* the time and some stables with full grilles or even single bars across the top opening prevent a horse doing so at all. These effects occur to some extent with even a well-managed bed, as it is obviously quite impractical to completely change the bedding every time a horse stales, but are more significant in poorly-managed beds.

DRAINAGE

Drainage is a subject of some differing of opinions. The older style stables floored with grooved stable bricks are now few and far between, and, in my experience of them, were not as effective as they were cracked up to be – they were slippery and did not drain any better than more modern floors. Old-style stalls (tie-stalls/standing stalls) slope slightly to the rear so that urine can drain into a channel in the aisle behind; old-style loose boxes (box stalls) often had a centre drain to which the four sides of the floor sloped slightly. The main complaints against these is that they became easily blocked and if the grid (which was supposed to *stop* them becoming blocked but didn't) became dislodged horses could get a leg down and injure and frighten themselves – and if there is one place a horse needs to feel secure it is in his stable.

When concrete became all the rage, it was recommended that a herringbone pattern of drainage grooves was put into the floor, which, again, sloped slightly towards some outlet in the bottom of an outside wall to allow the urine to run into an outside channel and away into a drain. This type of floor is still very common – and not much urine at all runs into the channel. Concrete is in fact a cold material which absorbs the urine (and therefore the smell) and is never really dry when the box is in use.

Various kinds of natural floorings can be used which generally work very well – these can consist of ordinary earth, clay, chalk, fine shale or anything similar, tamped well down. The urine just drains straight through and I have never known hygiene problems occur with them. However, local authorities differ in their requirements on hygiene and may not allow them but insist on 'proper' drainage systems.

Wood is useless as it rots easily, wears quickly and is slippery when wet; but good floors can be made of ordinary house bricks laid on their sides with a space of about $^1/_2$in/1cm between them – the urine drains through to a fine gravel bed which in turn is laid either on rubble or just the earth.

A flooring which works beautifully is loose weave asphalt laid on small pebbles over rubble. This is warm and the urine drains away completely through the layers. It is essential that the top asphalt layer is coarse/loose weave – it must under no circumstances be tamped down but simply lightly smoothed level, otherwise it will clog together and its drainage properties will be nil.

Cross-section of stable flooring showing (from the bottom up) rubble, medium sized stones, coarse gravel and loose-weave asphalt, for easy drainage of urine and saving of bedding. It is essential that the asphalt is not tamped down but merely lightly smoothed off by raking, otherwise it clams together and the whole purpose of the flooring is negated

If you are stuck with a concrete floor, there is a system of tough plastic drainage tiles called the Ridry Stable Flooring System which could solve all your problems of coldness and excessively wet and wasted bedding, provided you use straw or, ideally, long-shredded paper. It is marketed by Mrs Janet Cross of Cobbacombe Farm, Huntsham, Tiverton, Devon and consists of perforated interlocking tiles which form a slightly raised platform on the floor. The bedding is laid on top and obviously the urine goes straight through the tiles to the floor and drains away (down those herringbone grooves presumably), leaving bedding to dry out quickly and not remain wet underfoot.

With any drainage flooring (as opposed to, say, ordinary concrete) you save a great deal of bedding and labour, and avoid the problems of excessive ammonia build-up in the airspace.

Stable drains themselves should be very regularly cleaned out as they will readily clog with bedding and other debris – depending on the number of horses they serve, they should have washing soda put down them weekly or monthly, then be swilled down with very hot water. At least twice a year get them properly cleared out.

ELEMENTS OF A GOOD BED

The horse likes a dry bed to lie down on – although horses roll in mud they choose the driest spot they can find to lie and rest. The bed should also be thick enough to protect the horse from a hard surface and from floor draughts. This question of floor draughts is a vexed one. Ventilation experts say air inlets should be at ground level because incoming air will be cold and from a higher level it will 'fall' on the horses and chill them; and at ground level it should help disperse the ammonia gas. However, a ground draught will not be at all pleasant for a horse lying down, except in hot weather. A urine outlet in the bottom of the wall will act to some extent as an air inlet, so I'd leave it at that!

A good bed should be easy to maintain, should not cause respiratory or skin problems and should be reasonably economical, something aided by proper flooring. Furthermore the material should not scatter too easily, and its disposal should be convenient.

MATERIALS

Straw of various kinds, different grades of wood shavings or chips, sawdust and paper are all fairly readily available, as is peat.

Straw is still very popular, particularly among the 'old school' who, probably rightly, feel that there is nothing quite like a thick rustling bed of golden straw. Unfortunately, however good the quality, that golden straw probably contains fungi and mould spores which can cause respiratory problems. Even the horses which do not exhibit an allergic response are susceptible because the spores are foreign bodies and cause the body's defence mechanism to be activated which uses up resources, however minimally. Some maintain that straw should therefore not be used at all, even for non-susceptible horses.

In the good old days before combine harvesters, straw used to be a very efficient drainage bedding, ie the hard, rounded, shiny stalks did not absorb the urine but filtered it down to the floor. Nowadays, straw is not only much shorter but is mangled and crushed up during harvesting and can no longer be called proper drainage bedding. It does, however, make a springy, resilient, firm and warm bed when properly managed and its manure is easy to sell.

Shavings are an extremely popular bedding and are now probably even more commonly used than straw. Nurseries and market gardens are now obliged to take shavings manure as they find it more and more difficult to find straw manure. Shavings are not as easy to manage as straw when done properly – the bed is often allowed to remain very damp because too much dirty, wet material is left in. It is said that bedding should be not too dry because it is good for a horse's hooves to be on a slightly moist footing; however, in the case of a horse's bed, the moisture is not just water but decomposing urine, which is caustic and definitely *not* good for a horse's hooves.

Shavings do scatter more easily than any other bedding and because of this they need to be really thickly laid down – about 1ft(30cm) – which is hardly ever the case. Once the bed is established, with a used underlayer, they become more stable; but this should not be an excuse for leaving in a great deal of dirty, damp material, which is what often occurs.

Sawdust, when properly managed, does not, contrary to popular opinion, heat up and become maggoty! In use it is very similar to shavings but is more stable. Any bedding will heat up and become maggoty if not kept clean. Again, a good thickness, about 6in(15cm) minimum, is needed.

Paper is becoming more and more popular and despite problems in some areas in getting rid of it, its use seems to be on the increase. There are several brands, and all makers claim their product is 'sterile', in other words contains no chemical residues or mould spores, and, indeed, it should form part of the 'clean air regime' of COPD horses. It scatters easily till established but creates a warm, comfortable bed – a thickness of about 9in(23cm) is best.

Peat is often recommended as a bedding material yet I have never met a single person who, having given it a fair trial, liked it. I have never personally had any success with it and cannot recommend it at all.

There are two kinds on the market as bedding – sedge peat and sphagnum moss peat. Sedge peat is at a more advanced stage in the rotting process from vegetation to coal than is sphagnum moss peat; it really just resembles brown soil. Sphagnum peat is lighter in colour and weight-for-volume and is often still recognisable as the moss from which it came.

All peat is very absorbent, but particularly sphagnum peat, which can apparently absorb nine times its own weight in water. I can well believe this because I have always found it quite impossible to keep a bed even passably dry when using it. The stable drainage made no difference whatsoever.

Peat is also a cold bedding. This may be an advantage if the weather or climate is hot, but I believe its disadvantages far outweigh this one possible point in its favour. And contrary to popular opinion, it is dusty – you can actually see the peat dust in the coats of horses bedded on it. Nor is it easy to work with, I found, which could well result in many beds being improperly managed, and droppings and wet patches being overlooked.

The last straw for me was when I went to my horse's box one winter's morning and found his bed was frozen yet his water wasn't! I immediately shovelled the whole lot out and put it on the garden compost heap, for which it is admirably suited.

Although it is not cheap, peat does have two further uses: because it is so absorbent, it is good for spreading on muddy areas as it soaks up excess moisture like a sponge (although your used bedding is as good, and also free). It is also good to restore moisture to brittle hooves: fill a small pen or loose box with peat and soak it, and stand the horse (preferably shoeless) there during the day.

· HEALTH CONSIDERATIONS ·

If straw is not a suitable bedding for animals with respiratory problems due to the fungi and mould content, it can hardly be recommended for breeding stock either, particularly foaling boxes. Shavings and sawdust are both slightly dusty and therefore not ideal (although better than straw); but dust-extracted shavings can be very good. Both these wood-based products, however, can have chemical residues on them from sprays used on the trees, which can cause skin problems in some animals.

From a health point of view, shredded newsprint (not the more luxurious magazine-type paper) is probably the best, as the process involved to make newspaper-quality paper renders it practically sterile –

and the inks, too are all carbon and vegetable based, so no adverse effects should occur there, either. Many insurance companies give premium discounts to clients whose horses are bedded on paper (and/or which eat hayage) as it is a reliably 'healthier' material than others.

Research at the Animal Health Trust's Newmarket establishment indicates, at the time of writing, that paper bedding should only be used on a semi-deep litter basis and not deep litter, because the natural decaying process which occurs with any bedding – all of which are vegetable based, of course – needs bacteria and fungi to break down the material, and a build-up of these in the stable can cause problems. In fact, the makers of the principal paper bedding in the UK, Diceabed International Limited, recommend that their product be used on semi-deep litter anyway. As usual, when people misuse any product, problems can arise.

For those who, for various reasons, wish to stay with straw, there is now on the market a hay and straw-cleaning machine marketed under the name of Dust Cure (see p266) which removes dust and mould spores almost entirely and is apparently very successful in enabling these products to be used once more for 'windy' horses.

The type of straw does not make much difference to its qualities as something to lie on, but many horses have a nibble at straw and in such cases oat and barley straw are less likely to cause digestive disorders than wheat straw. Oat straw is a good feeding straw, in fact, and barley straw is rendered more acceptable nowadays because modern harvesting processes remove the prickly awns.

Another product of interest to those concerned to keep a hygenic bed is the Stable Boy Barn and Stable Deodorizer (see p266) which consists of porous, fine granules which you spread on the stable floor before laying the bedding. The distributors claim that it absorbs ammonia and 'other noxious gases' and subsequently lets the remaining water evaporate off, allowing the granules to continue working. Lime was popularly used in the past but it can stain white socks and, more importantly, burn the skin if it comes into contact with it.

BEDDING SYSTEMS

The three systems with which readers will be familiar are full mucking out, semi-deep litter and deep litter proper.

Full mucking out is unboubtedly the most labour intensive and time consuming method but the most hygienic. Obviously, all droppings and very wet, soiled material are removed, the floor swept all over and rinsed down, preferably, the slightly dirty material put down again, preferably after the floor has had time to dry off (perhaps during the horse's exercise), the remaining clean bedding laid on top of that and fresh material brought in to top up and bank the sides.

This system is successful with straw, shavings and paper but not so practical with sawdust, although certainly possible.

Semi-deep litter is the system most commonly used with shavings, sawdust and paper. Here the droppings and very worst of the bedding are removed daily, the clean bedding from the banking raked in to fill in the gaps and fresh stuff brought in to top up and re-bank.

With shredded paper, however, the slightly damp and soiled material should be turned aside and tossed to allow it to air and dry out, which makes it more economical – this is *not* a way of salvaging the worst material, which should be removed. Once aired, the bedding is laid again in the usual way and fresh material, as needed, brought in.

Semi-deep litter is a good system for working owners who wish to save time during their working week, and do the more extensive mucking out at weekends.

Deep litter can be a successful system with any of the four materials under consideration. Here, only the actual droppings are taken out, you strongly resist the temptation to remove anything else or to dig down in the bedding to see what's happening underneath, and, in a very few weeks, your bed is a firm, springy cushion with no smell or detectable dampness. Although I have asked several vets and other experts exactly how the system works I have never had a satisfactory explanation! In practice, *any* of the four materials can make a good deep litter bed provided you are absolutely meticulous about removing droppings. Unfortunately, for the working owner away from the horse all day, this can be difficult – but not impossible, especially if the horse is out all or part of the day. If you can persuade someone else to skip out during your absence, you will find the system easier to maintain.

You do need an airy, well-ventilated, well-drained box for deep litter, even in winter. Otherwise, and especially in summer, you may find the floor of your stable stinking and swarming with flies and the airspace only a little less so, and your poor horse will be in abject misery.

It is up to you how often you remove everything and start again. I knew one highly-respected horsemaster who kept two horses on wheat straw and who said he could not remember the last time he took the whole lot out, and had no idea what was going on in the bottom layers of his horses' beds! However, I can vouch for the fact that the beds had no smell, were dry, and as comfortable as spring interior mattresses. As with a compost heap (an unfortunate but apt comparison) the bottom layers rot down in situ, but as these decrease, the depth is maintained as more material is put on top. When such beds are taken out, if properly managed they are usually dry and crumbly underneath and certainly do not have any rotten, choking smell or fumes.

MANURE USES AND DISPOSAL

Possibly the most difficult bedding to dispose of is paper, but at least one manufacturer, Diceabed International Limited, issues instructions as to how to make *Roganic*, an ecologically safe fertiliser and soil conditioner, out of their used product. This is quite feasible, and paper is a valuable part of any compost heap.

Straw is always easy to get rid of, to market gardens and other sources, particularly mushroom farms; as also sawdust and shavings, which although said to deplete the land of nitrogen, are much easier to dispose of than some years ago.

· THE TWO-PILE SYSTEM! ·

A good way to muck out, whatever bedding system you operate, is to first take out only the droppings – as far as practically possible – and make one compost heap of these (including droppings from the field shelter and paddocks). Then take out the dirty bedding and make another heap of this. Droppings alone (almost) make a highly saleable manure, obviating the common complaint among private purchasers who may buy the product that 'horse muck is nearly all straw (or whatever), not real manure'. You retain the used bedding material which you can use in several ways around your premises: topping up exercise areas and manèges, soaking up mud in badly poached areas of your paddock and walkways or making an exercise ring during a hard winter. It can also be used to supplement the beds of calves or cattle housed during winter.

Whether or not you use this two-pile system, the way you store your muck/used bedding can depend on where you live. In a country area it may not matter at all what you do with it. In a residential area, its storage can be critical, particularly if you have antagonistic neighbours. In this case, it is probably best to muck out straight into plastic sacks such as those the bedding came in, or in which your hayage arrived, or old fertiliser sacks. Seal the bags at once either by tying or taping the necks securely or, not so satisfactorily, stapling with a strong stapler. Then spread the word that local gardeners can have it free if they collect it – this way, you will make many friends and not have a muck heap/problem at all!

If you are selling your muck to a local nursery or market garden, they may well supply you with a trailer or other container – when this is full, they will take it away and leave an empty one in its place. Alternatively, you may make a normal muck heap and they remove it onto their lorry with a mechanical grab or fork lift. Such firms usually want fresh manure rather than old, well-rotted stuff.

If you want to use your horse manure on *your* land, do make sure it *is* well-rotted otherwise its smell could contaminate your paddocks and spoil your horses' pleasure in grazing. Worm eggs and larvae may still be viable, too.

You should, in such a case, have three muck-heaps: one rotted and ready for use, one rotting down, and one in use. If, when your pile is finished, you compact it down and enclose it (with any old material such as old doors, or asbestos sheets) it will rot better and quicker. However, working owners in particular will probably not be able to spend too much time looking after their muck heaps when the horse himself needs attention! Provided it doesn't actually sprawl all over the place, there is absolutely no need to form your heap into a neatly squared-off brick.

Wherever you site your heap, trailer or container, you will save yourself a lot of time and hard physical work if you can put it in a dip in the ground; alternatively, rig up a strong, gently sloping ramp up which you can pull your barrow (easier than pushing it up in front of you) to a platform at the top. Then all you have to do is turn the barrow round and tip it down into a container or onto the heap. All this will save you a great deal of effort and time, and should not be too difficult to arrange with a reasonably competent handyman's help – you will bless the day you installed it.

Anything you can do to save pointless manual labour is *efficient* and *effective* – *not* lazy – and you should be constantly on the lookout for ways to cut down work so that your labour and time are put to more valuable and rewarding uses such as actually looking after and being with the horses. There is no virtue in hard work for its own sake; but if you can get as much necessary work as possible done by the fewest people in the shortest amount of time, *that* is effectiveness. Bedding and its management is one of those jobs which is vital to the horse's health, comfort and wellbeing yet which expends, in many establishments, the most time and energy. The concept applies to *any* task. The important point is to get a job done well, *not* to spend a lot of time and sweat doing it.

Summary

- The management of bedding is vital to the horse's health, comfort and wellbeing, and therefore ultimately to his performance.

- A good bed increases the horse's comfort, encourages it to lie down and rest, and protects it from the hard floor. It provides extra warmth in winter, acts as a buffer for urine and helps keep horses cleaner.

- Badly managed bedding of bedding or unsuitable materials can cause respiratory, skin and horn disorders.

- Some form of drainage is necessary; drainage floorings should be given much more consideration than they are, both for economy of bedding and the maintenance of a healthy atmosphere.

- The bed should be dry. Some people believe a damp bed is good for the hoof horn; this dampness, however, is largely urine, which gives off caustic ammonia as it decomposes which is most harmful to the horn (and skin).

- Probably the healthiest and most sterile bedding available at present is shredded newsprint. The elements of a good bed, whatever material is used, are that it should be dry, not the cause of health problems, it should not scatter too easily but form a springy, resilient cushion beneath the horse's feet, it should be fairly easy to manage and economical in use and not present disposal problems.

- Bedding systems are: daily mucking out which is the most hygenic but time and labour intensive; deep litter which can be very successful given good drainage, ventilation and meticulous removal of droppings; and semi-deep litter, a good system for working owners who wish to muck out fully only at weekends – this is the normal system used with shavings, sawdust and shredded paper.

- Muck out into two piles: one almost entirely droppings, which you can sell as 'concentrated' manure (at a higher price); and the other used bedding, which can be used around your premises for various other jobs.

Summary

●In residential areas store your muck in old plastic sacks, sealed; most muck heaps can be removed by contractors such as mushroom farms or market gardens.

●If you use your muck on your own land as fertiliser, make sure it is well-rotted (at least a year old) to avoid contaminating your land with the smell and possibly with worm eggs.

Checklist

✓ 1 Remove *all* droppings from the horse's bed.

2 If the stable smells at all unpleasant too much dirty bedding/droppings have probably been left in.

3 A bed should provide a cushion on the floor of the box – if you are aware of a hard floor there is not enough bedding down.

4 Choose a bedding material which is suitable for your horse. It is positively damaging to your horse's health to stick rigidly to straw, for example, as bedding if it makes him cough his head off.

5 Mucking out and bedding down are both vitally important. If they were considered equal with, say, feeding and fitness, then management problems and health disorders might be less. And finally. . .

6 If you would not be happy to spend time on your horse's bed, lying down, taking a nap and rolling around in it, don't expect your horse to do so!

6

HOOVES AND SHOEING

EVOLUTION, STRUCTURE AND FUNCTION

The horse's hoof is one of the most specialised structures in the animal kingdom and is characteristic of a specialised running animal. It is hard yet yielding, capable of withstanding considerable wear and stress yet able to be damaged, and the horse or pony without four sound feet on a fairly permanent basis would not have long to live. In the wild it would probably fall prey to some hunting animal, and in domestication it may be put down as being no use to its owner and a liability otherwise. (If the condition is painful and cannot be controlled with painkillers, it may, indeed, be kinder to put down the animal anyway.)

The horse's first recognisable ancestor, *hyracotherium* (formerly *eohippus*), had four toes on its forefeet and three behind. The number of toes gradually dwindled to one due to genetic mutations as the animal adapted to a changing environment, in this case from swampy forest to largely open, grassy plains where speed was necessary to escape predators if the species were to survive. These predators still have multi-toed claws and paws, and can run as fast as or faster than the horse and its relatives the ass and zebra, but they are nonetheless not as specialised to run as the horse. They do not have the endurance or such hard-wearing feet as the horse. The single toe combined with the long legs and lack of muscle in the lower legs all make for a high speed and especially endurance due to relative lack of muscle fatigue.

The structure of the hoof is fairly familiar. Briefly, it comprises a horny casing for most of it (wall and sole) lined inside with horny leaves or laminae interlocking with which are fleshy, sensitive laminae. Above the horny sole is the sensitive sole, and likewise above the horny frog (an adapted vestige of the soft main pad of a dog or cat's paw) is the sensitive frog. The heels appear from the outside as fleshy bulbs at the back of the foot; inside is the digital or plantar cushion.

The bones of the foot comprise firstly the crescent-shaped pedal bone which articulates with the short pastern bone. Behind this joint is the little navicular bone. Joining with the short pastern bone is the long pastern bone and the cannon bone joins at an angle with that. This joint forms the fetlock joint and behind the fetlock are the two little sesamoid bones.

The bones have attached to them at strategic points the tendons and ligaments which cause so much trouble in athletic horses, and the joints are cushioned by bursae or joint capsules which are 'sealed units' and contain synovia or joint oil for lubrication. The articular or joint surfaces of bones are covered with smooth, protective gristle or cartilage similar to the material at the ends of our noses. All in all, the system works very well in the healthy, working horse who is not over-worked or abused to the point where damage occurs.

The flexor tendons running down the backs of the legs attach to the bones of the feet and, when the muscles in the forearm or thigh from which they run contract or shorten, they inevitably bend or flex the joints. The extensor tendons running down the fronts of the legs extend or straighten them out again.

From the underside, the foot of the horse is not, obviously, a smooth plate of horn. The ground or bearing surface of the wall round the outside surrounds the sole, which is of thinner horn and which rises slightly. The wall horn turns inwards at the heels, running towards the toe and forms a ridge on the ground surface called the bars. There is then a groove between the bars and the frog (the lacunae) and then comes the frog itself, made of tough, rubber-like horn. The frog itself has a small cleft in it near the heels.

This uneven surface helps the horse negotiate various ground surfaces with minimal risk of slipping, despite the fact that he cannot actually grip the ground.

The foot, then, is a highly specialised, sensitive yet tough structure. The bones are encased in sensitive, fleshy tissues carrying the foot's blood supply and the whole is, in turn, encased in horn.

When weight is placed on the foot, the whole foot expands slightly, especially at the heels. This squashes the sensitive parts, and also the tiny blood vessels in them (the capillaries), forcing the blood out of them and on up the veins of the legs. Blood cannot return down veins because of a 'one-way system' of valves, so when weight is taken off the foot again, fresh blood comes to the foot capillaries down the arteries, filled with nutrients and oxygen and ready to exchange these for waste products. The waste products go back up the leg with the blood in the veins when weight is once more put on the foot, and so it goes on with every step your horse takes. The arteries and veins meet in the highly intricate mesh of tiny capillaries in the foot.

Previously, it was thought that the frog was the main blood-pumping mechanism of the foot, but now the belief is that it is the action of weight on the whole foot, not just the frog, which is important. There are some circumstances when the frog does not touch the ground in fact, such as in a newly shod horse standing or working on a hard surface. Oriental breeds such as the Turcoman (Turkmene) and Caspian have small, hard, almost atrophied frogs, yet have very sound, tough feet.

You can easily test whether your own horse's frogs touch the ground by putting chalk or even just water on them, then walking him on a hard, dark surface, such as smooth tarmac. The chances are that, unless he is in need of shoeing, they will not, and no chalk or moisture will show on the ground.

This expansion and slight flattening of the foot and sole is obviously vital to blood circulation in the foot and to the health of the foot and legs. Although the horse will move around slightly in his box, this is insufficient on its own to enable adequate blood circulation, so here is one more reason for sufficient exercise to be given, either at work or by turning loose.

The shoe can make or mar the function and health of the foot. Because most of the expansion takes place at the heels, this area is the 'loosest' part of the shoe. The nail holes are nearer the front of the foot than the back, and only in cases where there is difficulty in keeping a shoe on is a nail placed near the heels. Even so, shoes do inevitably restrict the

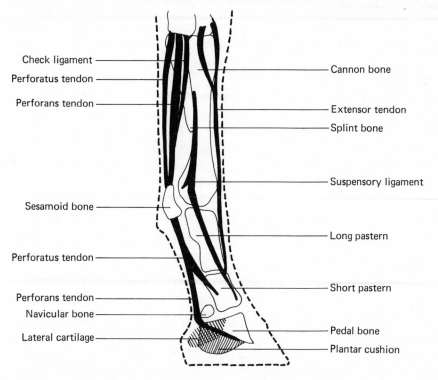

Simplified diagram of side view of leg and hoof showing anatomy

expansion to some extent, which often results in the feet actually reducing in size, as can be seen when a horse brought up from a rest, unshod, is shod once more: shoes a size larger are usually needed for the first few shoeings, because the feet, unhampered by being gripped between nails and shoe, have been able to expand and function naturally and the foot has returned to its more natural size. Horses should have at least two periods a year off work with no shoes on, even if only from the point of view of foot health.

FOOT BALANCE AND ITS IMPORTANCE

The front feet bear most of the horse's weight (about two thirds) and are more circular in shape than the hind, which are more nearly oval, longer from front to back than side to side. Horse's feet are measured by placing a ruler across the widest part of the foot across the sole, then measuring again from the point where the wall turns in to form the bar to the centre of the toe. In the front foot those measurements should be the same. In the hind, the latter measurement will be slightly longer because of the more oval shape. These measurements tell your farrier what size shoes your horse takes.

They also tell us other things. In the front foot, provided the foot is obviously not broken and therefore out of shape, if the measurement from toe to heel is significantly longer than that across the quarters, the toe of the foot is probably too long – this condition often goes with heels which are too low. A foot this shape is prone to uneven, excessive stresses which can impair the blood supply and lead to laminitis and navicular disease because the unnatural pressures impair the normal blood supply.

This condition is actually quite common and can be due entirely to faulty trimming, and fitting shoes which do not go right back to the heels, known as short shoeing. It can also be due to owners leaving their horses too long between shoeings; the foot continues to grow, pushing the shoe forward with it, and there is no support at the heels. Corns and extra strain on tendons and ligaments can also result.

Shoes should be fitted full length, ie right back to the heels so as to provide proper support; if the horse is going to be doing fast work on soft ground, the heels of the fore shoes can be tapered or pencilled to prevent being trodden on and pulled off by the hind feet. A careful watch should be kept by eye and measurement to ensure that the toes are not insidiously growing too long.

A properly balanced foot should conform to certain proportions: when looked at in front, you should be able to imagine a straight line dropping right down the centre of a horse's leg and foot, terminating at the toe;

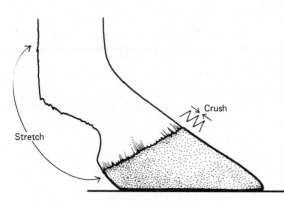

*Diagram indicating
the stress areas in a foot with a
long toe and low heel*

Crush

Stretch

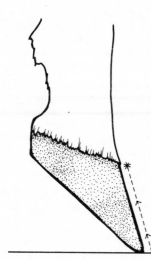

*The above-shaped foot 'breaking over' in
action, indicating the excess pressure
directed up the toe to the coronet,
resulting in a crushing of the horn-forming
structures in the coronary corium*

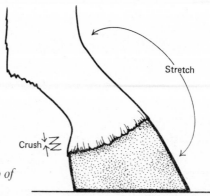

Stretch

Crush

*A hoof of the opposite conformation to
that shown in the illustration at the top of
the page, showing the stress areas*

from behind, the line should bisect the heels, but allow for the horse family's natural tendency to very slight cow hocks and turned out hind feet. The angle of the cannon/pastern and foot in the forefeet should be about 45°, and about 50° in the hind.

In addition, when looked at from in front, both sides of the horse's coronet should be the same height from the ground and the slope of each quarter the same. From the back, the ends of the coronets should be the same height with similarly sloping quarters.

Looking from the side, imagine another line passing down the centre of the pastern: this should reach the ground half way along the foot. The front wall of the foot and the back wall of the heel should both be parallel to that line.

If you fail to see this straight-line pastern/hoof conformation, your horse's foot is not correctly balanced. If it appears to sag down at the coronet or the line running down the pastern from the side reaches the ground too far back, the toe is too long. If the coronet bulges upwards and the line reaches the ground too far forwards, the toe is too short and the heels may well be too high.

Faulty feet can cause faulty action. On the other hand, faulty action resulting from badly conformed legs can cause faulty feet due to uneven pressure and stress on the feet. This whole question is complex and important. Even if you yourself are happy with the way your horse looks and goes, it is worth getting an 'outside eye' periodically to look over his conformation and action. It may just spot something you had not seen due to familiarity.

Very little can be done to correct faults the horse was born with, after it is six months of age, but acquired ones may be a different matter. They may need putting right very gradually, but if any correction is possible, it may be very well worth the trouble and the wait. In any case, the horse might not be out of action – you will simply notice a gradual improvement in his way of going.

If the faults are natural to the horse, it may not be worth upsetting matters by trying to make him conform to convention. This could, in fact, introduce stresses and strains which are unnatural to him as an individual and may cause unnecessary trouble and pain. Ask yourself (1) does he go quite sound and level, willingly and freely, and (2) does he hit himself? If the answers are 'yes' and 'no' respectively perhaps he is best left as he is. If you are still unsure, or if the horse often seems slightly lame or pottery or goes 'feeling', you should certainly discuss matters with your vet and/or farrier.

Correct conformation helps a working horse cope much better with already substantial stresses – nowadays he must work more intensively, and more frequently at fast paces than he would naturally, whilst carrying the weight of a rider or pulling a vehicle. Maintaining the correct balance of his feet, within any individual constraints he may present, goes a very long way towards maximum performance with minimum stress.

THE NEED FOR SHOES

A highly respected master farrier once said to me, 'the best shoe is no shoe'. Despite that, shoes *are* often very necessary to today's working horses, since work on hard or rough surfaces wears away the foot quicker than it can regrow. Furthermore, if the horse moves so that one part of his foot hits the ground before another, that part is initially taking all the weight and stress and will wear down faster than the rest. In response, the foot might put out more and stronger horn in just that area. This might work well, from the horse's point of view, but sometimes there is an over-compensation and a distorted foot can result, which sets up a chain reaction: it affects the stresses within the foot, the horse's action, his weight-bearing and placement on other feet and limbs, which then become overstressed in turn and may also compensate likewise – and so it goes on.

A competent, conscientious farrier is a godsend, particularly if he is not only technically competent but good with the animals, professional and businesslike. Having well-made, suitable shoes fitted by such a craftsman can do away with all the problems mentioned above and prevent them occuring in the first place.

On the other hand, a not-so-competent farrier can do a great deal of harm, not only by frightening and sometimes immediately laming a horse, but by faulty workmanship (usually incorrect trimming) which, over a period of time, may cause malformation of the feet resulting in serious foot disorders and leg problems.

Many areas of the UK are very poorly supplied with good farriers and although the Worshipful Company of Farriers and the Farriers Registration Council are working hard to change this situation, many owners either have to travel their animals out of their region to get them shod and trimmed properly, or pay extra travelling expenses to 'import' a farrier. The latter is not always possible because good farriers are usually so busy they do not want to travel excessively. Many also feel that they may be 'trespassing' on another farrier's area, which I find highly counter-productive – it does not occur in the veterinary profession, and owners are, after all, free to choose whichever vet or farrier they want. Obviously any professional can likewise be choosy, but 'area' should not come into it when the wellbeing of animals is at stake.

The situation is so bad in some regions that I personally know three owners in different parts of the country, and have heard of several others, who have taken to working their horses without shoes or using shoe substitutes, and trimming their horses' feet themselves according to the standard guidelines (see p136). This situation is obviously far from ideal, and it is recommended that those in a similar situation contact the Farriers Registration Council (see p263) for the name and 'phone number of a good farrier in their area. The profession wants to put matters right as a whole, but cannot help you if it is not aware of your problem.

TYPES OF SHOE

The type of shoe which is in almost universal use for pleasure working horses is based on the hunter shoe – without calkins and wedges which have long been obsolete since the advent of studs – which usually covers the ground surface of the wall entirely. It has fullering (a groove) on its ground surface into which the nail holes are stamped and into which borium can be welded (borium is a hardener which, as it 'wears rough', helps prevent slipping). There are toe and quarter clips for fore and hind hooves respectively, and the shoe is concaved out from its bearing surface to its ground surface; the heels are tapered or pencilled to a blunt point rather than finished off square. The farrier will put screw holes in the heels (for studs) for you, if you ask him.

The whole point of these features is to give ground purchase to a horse doing fast work while at the same time reducing the chances of it treading on a shoe and pulling it off, or having it sucked off in holding mud. The fullering gives grip, the concaving out reduces mud suction and the tapered heels reduce the likelihood of the heel being trodden on. In addition, the stud holes allow for studs to be screwed in, as needed – and there are very many different designs. The holes should be packed with oily cotton wool between use to prevent their becoming filled with grit and dirt which ruins the thread.

These shoes, although primarily meant for mud, are in use all year round. The fullering also makes the shoe lighter than would be the case with a plain stamped shoe (such as are still used for heavy horses), and the shoes are, in any case, available in light, medium and heavy weights.

There are many more variations of shoe: featherlight racing shoes (known as plates) made of aluminium; race exercise plates for racehorses working between races; and the plain stamped heavy shoes for working heavy horses. The basic pattern shoe (as it is still called) can be adapted in many ways to suit individual horses' (and owners') requirements. Three-quarter shoes can be made, and feather-edged shoes to minimise self-inflicted kicks and treads, also rolled toes for horses who stumble, and any number of special surgical shoes. In countries other than Britain, usually in trotting or bloodstock racing circles, grabs or grips are often added to give the horses extra purchase when cornering or when racing on dirt tracks. These are simple strips or wedges of metal or patented metal alloys (according to the manufacturer) which are either forged with the shoe or rivetted on, sometimes into the fullering, as needed.

In Britain these have not caught on, partly because few of our 'natural' racecourses have such tight turns as foreign tracks, and partly because we race on turf, whereas tighter turns and dirt tracks are quite common abroad. Grabs or grips do their job, but they also restrict the spread of force by stopping much of the slide of the hoof during fast action. Because of this, although they help keep the horse on his feet on a tight turn, the force which would normally be dissipated is transmitted to the feet and legs, which means more stress and greater risk of injury.

I once had an interesting conversation with an American veterinary surgeon employed in the American bloodstock industry. He was of the opinion that grabs increase foot and leg problems significantly, particularly torsion (twist) injuries, because of their inevitable restriction in order to help the horse stay upright. When I asked him what was the alternative between torsion injuries and horses slipping and falling, he said: 'Turf tracks and gentler turns, like you have in Britain. For God's sake, don't change your racecourses!' I think it unlikely that we will, traditionalists that we are.

Horses are obviously individualists and often have slightly different shoeing requirements. Attempts continue to be made to improve on metal shoes which have to be nailed on. Recent tests with synthetic (polyurethane) shoes, which are fixed by means of adhesive, have shown that the stresses and strains which take place in a foot wearing one of these are much closer to those of a natural, unshod hoof, than in fact wearing a nailed-on metal shoe. So far, the ones tried in practice have not been satisfactory; the adhesives have not been strong enough and the shoes themselves have been weak and slippery.

I do feel that many owners put heavier shoes than necessary on their horses thinking that they will last longer. In fact, what happens is that the extra weight of the metal causes the horse to drop its feet that much harder, wearing the metal that much more and putting so much more jar and stress on the hooves and legs. Medium-weight hunter shoes are all that most horses will need, not heavyweight, and many horses, particularly those in light work or working on softish ground with a minimum of time on rough, gritted surfaces, would do well with just lightweight shoes or even race exercise shoes. Show horses frequently wear very light shoes so that their natural action is not hampered. In some yards, it is the practice to have the horse wear medium-weight shoes when not showing, and the day before a show have light plates put on, so the horse, unaccustomed to 'fairy feet', shows a more extravagant action in his class.

Most books say horses should be shod on average every six weeks – I feel that the natural growth rate of your horse's horn and a discussion with your farrier could well change that. Horses whose horn grows quickly could well need shoeing more frequently, but those with naturally slow-growing horn would have feet full of holes if you tried to shoe them every six weeks.

While a horse may be perfectly shod one Monday, by the next Monday he should be shod again from the point of view of fit of the shoe. The horn is growing all the time, but the shoe and nails are not adapting to it because they are rigid metal. If the horn grows a millimetre, the shoe is a millimetre out of place. This *is* rather pedantic, but an inescapable fact. You can imagine the effects of shoes left too long on constantly growing feet – horn growing over the edges of the shoe, causing concentrated stress from the edge of the shoe on the bearing surface of the wall; heels pulled forward into the seat of corn ready to bruise the sensitive tissues underneath, and lessening heel support; clenches risen which could tear the leg of the horse who hits himself; a loose shoe ready to be torn or sucked off, breaking the horn as it goes.

Economies can be made by welding borium into toes and heels, or wherever needed, to prolong wear or correct uneven wear. Then the same shoes can be replaced after trimming, maybe even two or three times. This prevents those damaging unnatural stresses and strains on feet left too long between shoeings because 'his shoes aren't worn out yet'. From the farrier's point of view, it must be soul-destroying to do a good job on a horse only to know that his efforts to keep the horse comfortable and sound may well be for naught because the owner will try to squeeze every last day out of one shoeing. Whether a horse has slow or fast-growing horn, whether he wears his shoes evenly or unevenly and whether he works on the hard or on the soft, there are solutions to both ordinary and extraordinary problems, if we take the time and trouble to take advantage of a good farrier's knowledge and advice, and really learn each horses' idiosyncracies and way of going as well.

· *SHOE SUBSTITUTES* ·

As well as synthetic shoes (see p140), there have been on the market for some years now boots of various makes aimed at obviating the need for shoes. The intention is obviously not to put farriers out of business! It is to make life bearable for those who cannot find a good farrier, who cannot shoe their own horses (which means nearly everybody) or whose horse has lost a shoe but cannot be spared from work or a training routine. Indeed shoe-boots, for want of a better expression, are most useful to have around.

Many people do, indeed, trim their own horses or get their farriers to do so, and use the boots anyway in preference to shoes. Other owners report difficulties such as coronet and pastern or heel wounds from the friction caused by some makes of boot. Others seem to be rather difficult to fasten. Different makes vary, so try out what you have available till you find something suitable, just like trying shoes for yourself. Because the boots are removed after work they do represent significant economies, although I have only ever seen a horse do gentle work in them, in other words I have not seen them in use, say, across country.

They are certainly useful for keeping medications in place on the hoof.

THE SHOEING PROCESS

The two main methods of shoeing are still all-hot shoeing and all-cold shoeing, and the advantages and disadvantages of each are well known and documented. Hot shoeing is still regarded as The Thing by many people, but most racehorses are cold-shod and a really good job can be done this way – if you have a really good farrier. Most farriers have regular clients and get to know the individual horse's feet very well. Even after just one shoeing, a farrier with an eye for his job and a professional attitude will ensure that he has suitable shoes for that horse ready at home for the next call, and a close eye on foot changes can be kept so that adjustments can be made as necessary.

Against hot shoeing is that not only does the hiss and smell frighten some horses, but also the fact that hot, burnt horn is depleted of moisture and so shrinks. The shoe is made to fit, then after a few days the horn, having probably been subjected to moisture again, swells and yet the shoe obviously does not – and the fit is just as obviously affected. This does not happen in cold shoeing, and perhaps the fact that such a precise fit cannot be obtained in cold shoeing is mitigated by this disadvantage in the hot process.

There is an in-between method which I feel could be used much more widely. A particularly caring farrier used it some years ago on a horse I had who disliked hot shoeing. He would make the shoes hot in the yard, after first checking the horse's feet in the usual way. Then he would cool the shoe down before trying it. He would note any adjustments needed, heat the shoe again, alter it, cool it down and try it again, and so on till he was satisfied. It did not seem to take him any longer than the conventional hot process, he got just as good a fit (with no dried, burnt horn) and the horse was relaxed and co-operative. What more could anyone want?

DOING WITHOUT SHOES

Most horses' feet benefit from at least one period a year without shoes, but I am sure more people could work their horses without shoes if they gave the subject a little consideration.

Shoes are needed mainly to prevent excess wear, but if you exercise mostly on softish ground, with some on *smooth*, hard ground, why not try your horse without shoes? This could work very well if you are having farrier problems, and could be better for your horse's feet than having him shod by an indifferent farrier.

It will not work if your horse is exercised mainly on hard, gritted roads or stony going; if he puts his feet down very unevenly, causing excessively uneven wear; if his horn is naturally of poor quality despite a balanced diet; or if you cannot learn to trim his feet yourself. If none of these things apply, then going barefoot could suit you and your horse very well. Even if you do have a good farrier, most are so busy I feel he is unlikely to object and his services will still be needed to periodically check and trim the feet.

In any case, the decision is not irrevocable. If it does not work you can always have the horse shod again.

Assess your horse honestly. The first thing to put right, if it is wrong, is his diet. He produces his horn from the food you give him, so in order to produce top class, tough, pliable horn he needs proper feeding. Check his diet with your vet or nutritionist and make sure that it contains adequate amounts of methionine and biotin, both of which assist in the development of healthy horn, also vitamin E with selenium.

If the horn needs improving before your new venture, remember it takes about a year for new horn to grow down from the coronet to the toe, four or five months at the heels, so you may really need to plan ahead. As soon as the message reaches the brain that tougher horn is needed, the body itself will respond by causing this to happen, provided the diet permits it.

If your horse has rather flat soles, you will always have to be careful on which hard surfaces you work him as he will feel pebbles that much more than a horse with more arched soles. However, on smooth tarmac and concrete he should be alright.

Wet conditions soften horn. If your horse lives out and the grass and ground are going through a constantly wet period, you could find that his horn softens up to such an extent that it cannot stand the wear and tear of working unshod on hard surfaces. You may not know till you try, but it is something to watch out for.

If you decide to go barefoot, wait till the horse needs shoeing, then have his shoes taken off and his feet *lightly* trimmed by your farrier (or yourself!), just enough to balance the feet normally, not to remove excess growth as this extra horn will give added protection in the early days. See that the edges are well rounded off to help minimise chipping and cracking, particularly around the toe.

Remember, the feet are adapting as well as the horse himself. If you do have to go on hard surfaces, walk or lead and do not abandon your campaign because your horse flinches the first time he steps on a little stone. Be careful where you take him and if you come to any unavoidable stony or rough place do dismount and lead him for that stretch. Treat the whole thing like a fitness programme and start with half an hour a day, *very* gradually building up to your normal amount of exercise. Of course, if you are working almost entirely on soft going anyway, this should not be necessary.

If you wish to use a hoof dressing to assist horn quality, discuss brands with your vet and farrier. Most are simply oils which lie on the surface of the horn and pick up dirt. Only those with lanolin or glycerine are actually absorbed into the horn – and don't forget to apply the dressing to the ground surface, too. *Cornucrescine* rubbed into the coronet acts as a very mild blister (not enough to cause discomfort) and encourages the blood supply to that area (from where the horn grows, of course), and can speed up horn growth. The quality, however, can only come from the nutrients in the blood itself, which depends on the quality of the diet.

As two thirds of the horse's weight is carried by the forefeet, you may find that your horse or pony always needs shoes in front, depending on how he as an individual reacts. Since this will still leave his hind feet shoeless, it may be an ideal system for kickers who are often denied the chance of being turned out with other animals because of the damage they can do; this damage is considerably lessened when the hooves are free of metal shoes and may make the idea of turning out the animal more acceptable.

If, after a fair adaptation and trial period you find your horse or pony is consistently footsore, reluctant to move freely or his horn keeps breaking or wearing too fast, either he is quite unsuitable for this way of working or your workload on hard surfaces is too demanding and, if you wish to make full use of him, he will have to be shod in fairness to him and so that you can use him as you wish. However, if hard surfaces can be largely avoided, there should be no need for this.

Keeping your horse unshod but properly trimmed, you may find it a good plan to use a shoe-substitute boot, just during work. The boots are specifically intended to be removed when the horse is not working, not to be kept on round the clock, so you may find this combination is just what you need.

Shoes will almost certainly be needed if you work your horse on slippery mud at fast paces, such as hunting – then he will probably need the extra purchase of shoes and maybe studs too, if he is not to be in danger of slipping and falling.

GENERAL FOOT CARE

Whether shod or not, because feet are so important they should be at the top of your daily jobs list when it comes to horse care. Really, they should be picked out and the shoes and horn checked before and after each ride, and at least once a day when the horse is not working, but few people seem to do this. When picking out the feet, press the frog firmly with the back of the hoofpick to see if the horse flinches – if he does, he could have thrush developing. Keep an eye out for softening, rotting horn, a nasty smell and a dark discharge coming from the frog. Watch out for any cracks, worn patches or discoloured horn which could indicate bruises, especially in the seat of corn where the bars turn in. Although not all foot lameness is accompanied by heat in the foot, un-even temperature here is one indication of something wrong, so check the temperature of the feet with the backs of your fingers (more sensitive than the inside of your hand) and compare the feet. You might as well check the legs at the same time.

In some countries it is the practice to pack the feet with clay or other earth, or with specially prepared products, so as to keep in the moisture (or a lanolin dressing on the sole), and keep damaging droppings and urine away from the underneath of the feet. If the weather is unusually dry, some horses may benefit from this, but in Britain few people do this now and I have never found it necessary if the feet are generally well cared for and the diet correct.

Washing the feet, too, is the subject of differing opinions. Some yards always do it, others never do. If you do, at least make sure the heels and pasterns are properly dried afterwards to avoid chapped skin and infection.

Summary

● It is the flattening and expansion of the foot as a whole, rather than just frog pressure, which is important for foot health and circulation. When weight is placed on the foot, it flattens slightly which squeezes the fleshy tissues together and pushes blood up out of the foot; when the weight is released, fresh blood comes into the foot. It is this function which ensures blood circulation in the healthy foot, so obviously adequate exercise is needed.

● Allow a horse at least two periods a year turned out with no shoes to allow the foot to function completely naturally without the constriction inevitably applied by shoes. It will often be found that the horse's feet have increased in size.

● Correct foot balance is important in ensuring the even transmission of stress in the limbs and feet – otherwise uneven forces could lead to injury, or impaired blood supply which can result in foot diseases.

● If a horse does not have naturally balanced feet, corrective trimming can be professionally done, but before the animal is six months old after which age the bones may be too mature for significant correction to be made. Previous faulty trimming and shoeing can be gradually corrected in mature horses.

● Today's shoe is largely based on the traditional hunter shoe but with tapered/pencilled heels, and with stud holes if you ask. Shoes range from ultra-light aluminium racing plates to plain stamped heavy-horse shoes. In some countries, grips/grabs are used to assist foothold where dirt tracks and tight corners exist, but it is now believed that many more leg injuries, particularly torsion injuries, result from them.

● Many animals could probably manage perfectly well with either lighter shoes or no shoes at all.

● Any shoe must be taken right back to the heels – the foot must not be 'shod short' as this causes gradual foot deformity and tendon strain, also laminitis and navicular disease.

● Shoe-substitute boots are used by some owners; trials with synthetic adhesive shoes show that the forces on the foot more closely resemble those in the unshod foot than in the conventionally shod foot.

Summary

- Hot shoeing is generally regarded as preferable, though the horn shrinks slightly, obviously affecting fit. A good farrier can obtain a very good fit with cold shoeing. A good in-between method is where the shoe is made and altered hot but checked cold.

- Working without shoes is quite feasible provided that: the ground is soft, and if hard it must be *smooth*; the horse's action is more or less perfect; his hoof horn is of good quality; and the feet are trimmed to maintain correct balance.

- The feet and shoes should be picked out and checked twice daily, also before and after each ride. Once a day may suffice when the horse is not working and is unshod.

Checklist

Important factors in foot care and health

✓ 1 Your horse or pony's feet will most benefit by a correct diet, and expert trimming and shoeing. No amount of hoof dressing applied externally will markedly affect the quality of the horn, which depends mainly on diet.

2 Ensure that your horse is shod full length, so that the heels of the shoes extend right back and support the heels of the hoof – this prevents the heels 'sinking' and the toes lengthening, but not by over-shortening the toe to 'force-fit' a short shoe.

3 Decide with your farrier, according to the rate at which your horse grows his horn, how often he should be shod, and make a regular booking for those intervals. Leaving shoes on too long is one of the prime causes of foot problems and other deformities.

4 Check and pick out the feet and shoes twice daily and check the frog area for thrush.

5 Do not go fast on hard surfaces: excessive concussion can split horn and injure the sensitive parts of the feet, and this can impair the all-important blood supply; it also bruises and overstresses the limbs, particularly joints. Hoof pads may lessen concussion but could result in early loosening of shoes – discuss with your vet and farrier. Pads should *not* be seen as a licence to work a horse fast on hard ground.

6 Do not leave studs in when not needed, particularly on only one side of the foot, as this can significantly upset the balance of the foot and produce uneven stresses up the foot and leg.

7

GROOMING, CLIPPING AND TRIMMING

STRUCTURE AND FUNCTION OF SKIN AND COAT

Skin is something we often take for granted, and associate with appearance when in fact it has several other vital functions.

It forms an elastic, tensioned covering to almost the whole body except the hooves, and these are covered with horn which is a modified form of skin. Hair is a version of skin, and the same ingredients in a diet affect all three – if the skin is not healthy, the hair growing from it will not be, either.

Skin is in two main layers, the dead outer layer called the epidermis and the sensitive under layer called the dermis. The skin is formed of cells which are constantly being replaced; these are made mainly of a hardened protein substance called keratin. The epidermis consists of flakes of dead cells which help protect the more sensitive under layer and which are constantly being shed into your horse's coat, being seen as the dandruff which is groomed away. Live cells from the dermis take their place, and so the skin is constantly being renewed, this process being more effective in the young than in the old. In older creatures, skin becomes less elastic and loses its 'body' due to the breakdown of collagen (another protein), and elastin – the skin starts to sag, it often becomes dryer and wounds take longer to heal.

The dermis contains nerve endings, which inform the horse of pressure and pain, and tiny blood capillaries which nourish and cleanse it and which also play an important part in temperature regulation. When the horse is too hot they expand, allowing more heat-carrying blood to flow through them so that the excess heat can radiate out, through the skin, to the outside atmosphere. When it is cold they constrict, conserving heat.

The dermis also contains oil glands which secrete sebum, a natural lubricant which conditions skin, makes it water-resistant and helps in temperature control. The sebum is secreted from tiny glands in the hair follicles or roots, so it forms a thin film over both skin and hair which grooming helps distribute. The sweat glands, also in the dermis, secrete sweat through different openings commonly called pores. Sweat contains some waste products so helps with elimination, and it also helps with

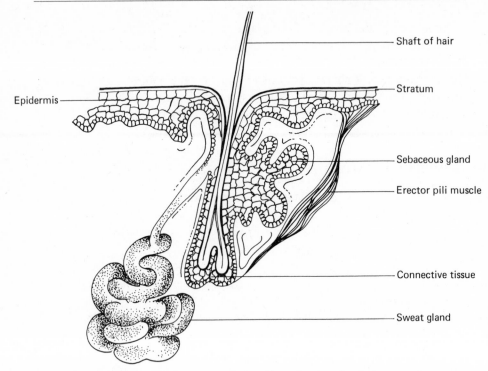

Shaft of hair

Stratum

Epidermis

Sebaceous gland

Erector pili muscle

Connective tissue

Sweat gland

Simplified diagram of cross-section of the skin, showing the hair root, the erector muscle which raises the individual hair, the sweat gland and the oil gland

temperature control by cooling the body down through the evaporation of the liquid sweat. Sweating itself does not cool down the body; cooling happens only if the moisture, and the heat it contains, can be evaporated off into a cooler, dryer atmosphere.

When the atmosphere is hot and humid, the moisture and heat from the sweat may have nowhere to go, as it were, the surrounding atmosphere itself being already loaded with heat and moisture, and the horse can seriously overheat; this mainly affects those horses working fast over extended periods, such as in the speed and endurance phase of a horse trial, and long distance horses, even though their work is slower.

The dermis is also where the skin's colouring matter, melanin, is found. This is known to have a strengthening effect on skin – the more melanin the darker will be the skin (and usually the coat), and the more resistant it is, particularly to the effects of wet and sunlight. This is why horses with large white patches are more prone to rain scald or rain rash on those areas, and those with white socks have the same sensitivity to mud fever. White noses often suffer from photosensitisation in summer, a combination of sunlight and high nitrogen in the pasture.

Some horses do grow white hairs from black skin. I knew a lovely leopard-spotted Appaloosa whose spots were liver chestnut and the rest of his coat white, but his skin was evenly chocolate-coloured all over. He had four white socks, but only his front ones were over pink skin, and they were the ones which occasionally succumbed to mud fever. The pink in the skin is caused by the blood which shows through due to the lack of melanin.

True albino animals have pink eyes as well as all pink skin, due to lack of colouring in their irises, and they often appear to have poor eyesight.

The thickness of skin varies with breed and type, the more 'cold-blooded' types such as heavy horses and ponies – our own native breeds, or Haflingers for example – have slightly thicker skin than, say, Arabs, Caspians and their crosses. On the back of a Shetland pony, skin can reach a thickness of about 6mm (almost $1/4$ in) particularly in winter when a natural, slight thickening often occurs; however, in an Arab or Thoroughbred horse in summer, and on areas where skin is naturally thinner such as the insides of the legs, it can be very thin indeed, about 1mm ($1/20$ in). Skin is generally thicker on the upper areas which need most protection (top of the neck, back, loins and quarters) and thinner on, for example, the belly which needs less protection from the weather but needs increased sensitivity.

Skin is aided in this protection/sensitivity function by the hair. Besides the coat hair there is the mane and tail, the antennae or 'feeler' hairs round the eyes and muzzle, the tiny hairs on the edges of the lips which help the horse delicately feel his food, and the leg hair which sometimes amounts to quite thick growths known as 'feather'; there is also the way the coat grows and changes with the seasons.

Generally, the coat hair is cast in spring and autumn and a thinner and thicker coat respectively grown in its place. Hair forms a very good insulating cover, not only trapping a layer of air next to the body, but each hair itself is hollow. In winter, this helps keep the body-warmed air next to the skin so the horse feels warmer, air itself being a poor conductor of heat. Tiny erector muscles at the base of each hair can contract, raising the hair, so the air layer can be made even thicker, when needed.

In summer this function is not so vital and in fact the horse may well need to cool himself down; the summer coat is therefore shorter, and lacks the softer almost woolly underlayer of the winter coat. Less air is trapped so heat finds it easier to escape from the skin, through the coat and into the surrounding atmosphere.

The function of the winter coat is affected by wind and wet (rain or sweat), and clothing. All these flatten the coat, or part it in the case of wind, enabling the warm air to escape. Water is a good conductor of heat, so a wet coat conducts heat away from the body quite rapidly and the horse can become chilled. In winter particularly, this may result in his having problems keeping up his body temperature to the required level of about 38°C (100.4°F) as heat is being lost more quickly than it can be created by the body's resources. The horse could then develop hypothermia and even die; it does not even need to be wet to cause this. Severely cold, dry weather, especially combined with wind, can also cause it.

Wind, wet and cold combined are a horse's greatest enemies in winter. The wet flattens the coat, the wind carries the heat away and the horse is subjected to a severe chill factor which it may not be able to overcome. In these conditions a proper shelter and probably a waterproof rug are essential.

Horses can withstand dry, cold *still* weather very well – in fact, putting a rug on a horse in these conditions will be of little benefit as it will flatten the coat and largely remove the good effect the warm-air layer has in an unclipped horse.

Both winter and summer coats grow in swathes or 'pathways' in such a way as to facilitate the drainage of moisture; this is particularly noticeable in the flank area. Other drainage features include the coarse, long hairs which sometimes grow under the lower jaw and on the lower legs, and which sometimes grow in the winter coat of more commonly-bred animals (known as cat hairs). These are also a sign that the horse has been feeling cold.

The leg hair is often subject to variance of opinion among horsemen as to whether or not it acts as protection against mud fever and cracked heels. It is certainly true that if a horse or pony does get mud fever, the condition is very much more difficult to treat through long hair, which has to be removed for effective treatment to take place. However, it does no harm to neaten up the hair with scissors and comb, but leaving a little downward-curling tuft for drainage, and it certainly does not bring about mud fever in a horse who does not seem susceptible to it. A registered mountain and moorland breed is not normally trimmed anyway, so leave the hair on.

With animals who *have* shown a susceptibility to mud fever etc, I have found it safer to trim the hair or even clip the legs with the coarse blades of the clipper, and apply a preventative substance daily such as liquid paraffin (mineral oil), rubbing it well into the skin. Any preventative dressing is bound to have a greasy base, so it will be necessary to wash it off (and the accumulated dirt) with luke-warm water and baby soap or mild medicated soap, before applying a fresh dressing – otherwise the dirt will simply be rubbed into the skin along with any mud fever bacteria present and may actually set up the disease. The bacteria like airless conditions, which the oil provides once they have infected the skin. However, on *healthy* skin, the oil protects it and helps prevent infection. Petroleum jelly (Vaseline) or zinc and castor oil cream, are too thick to be really practical, I feel, whereas liquid paraffin is thin enough to be used on the belly, around the sheath and between the upper hind legs, too, to protect these areas which receive most of the kicked-up mud in winter.

Mane and tail hair help protect the horse rather more than we may think. The mane gives some heat-retaining protection to the neck in winter which due to its long, thin shape loses quite a lot of heat quicker than would the abdomen, which is a more rounded, barrel shape with a deep central core. In summer the mane and forelock give limited protection from flies.

The tail can be very important in preventing heat loss in winter from the thin skin between the buttocks. If similar horses are wintered out in identical conditions, it has been shown that those with pulled/shaved tails lost 20 per cent more body condition (weight) than those with unpulled tails. Horses naturally stand with their tails and quarters towards the direction of the wind and rain. The natural tail hair spreads out and covers the sensitive buttock skin and retains much heat. Deprived of this protection, the heat escapes and the body has to use up more energy (provided by food) to make up the loss. In severe weather, this may not be possible and condition may well be lost.

From the point of view of turnout, I much prefer to see braided or plaited tails than pulled ones. They give the impression that more care has been taken over the horse's turnout and, of course, allow the hair to remain for that vital natural protection. For casual occasions, a well-groomed, clean tail, full at the top and banged at the bottom, racehorse-style, complements the horse's natural physique and personality much more effectively than the artificially pulled tail. Any tail, of course, is important in helping the horse get rid of flies in summer.

Most people take pride in a smartly turned out horse, at least for special occasions, and even if it is unclipped in winter, they tidy it up by judicious trimming. The antennae or feeler hairs around the eyes and muzzle are often clipped off, although in Britain at least the practice fortunately appears to be becoming less common. These hairs are richly supplied with nerve endings around their roots and are intended to help the horse avoid bumping his sensitive head, particularly in the dark when horses are quite active, and to sense when objects are near. They serve the same purpose as a cat or dog's whiskers, and no one in his right mind would deprive his dog or cat of these hairs – yet so many people think nothing of doing so to their horses.

Clipping off these hairs can seriously upset and disorientate some animals, putting them off their feed and making them feel insecure. I do hope the practice of leaving them *on* will spread faster and be the trade mark of people who care more for their horses' well being than for an unkind fashion. It is a mark *against* those who clip them off.

As a matter of interest, the official instruction handbook *Horse Management* of The German National Equestrian Federation, says on this subject:

> The protective hair inside the ears and the feeler hairs on the mouth and nostrils must never be pulled out or cut off.

Although the British Horse Society and Pony Club's *Manual of Horsemanship* does say the hair inside the ears should be left as protection, it unfortunately makes no mention of the muzzle hairs. It would be good to see this inserted in a future edition.

Like hoof horn, the condition of the hair is a good indicator not only of general health but of the horse's diet. As may be expected, the same correctly balanced diet with appropriate amounts of methionine, biotin, vitamin E and selenium, will help produce healthy, effective coat hair. A teacupful of corn oil or soya oil may be added to the daily diet (gradually introduced like all nutrients) as an extra aid to coat health and appearance, particularly in those animals living out or suffering from any skin or coat disorder or with simply a dry, dull skin and coat.

DIFFERENT TYPES OF GROOMING

The term 'grooming' covers all the different processes we apply to the skin and coat of a horse to clean him, promote his comfort and assist the effective functioning of his skin; it can cover such processes as brushing (with a variety of brushes), hand rubbing, massaging with hands, wisp or tapee (massage pad), and sponging areas such as eyes and dock. For practical purposes, the following definitions are used:

· QUARTERING ·

This is where the horse is tidied up before work; if he is rugged up (blanketed) it is done without removing the roller or surcingle (when using a round-the-girth surcingle or roller) – his rugs are unbuckled at the front and thrown back, then replaced and thrown forward from his hindquarters, so that all four of his quarters are brushed over without removing his clothing entirely. Of course, this results in his saddle patch and girth areas not being done, but if the horse was 'put to bed' clean the previous night it should not matter. If not, any dried sweat and mud should certainly be removed from these areas before a saddle is put on or the horse could be rubbed sore.

Modern rugs have surcingles which cross under the belly, and sometimes leg straps: these can simply be undone and draped over the back, and the rugs folded back and forward while the whole horse is done.

In quartering, the stable stains (dried droppings) are removed with the sponge or water brush and the horse gone quickly over with the body or dandy brush to smooth his hair and remove bits of bedding from coat, mane and tail. The damp patches then have a chance to dry before work. The eyes, nostrils, lips, sheath or udder, and dock area (between the buttocks and under the tail) are all damp-sponged and, in winter, dried with an old towel, and the feet are picked out. Some people apply a tail bandage at quartering to smooth the top of the tail, unless the horse's work is imminent.

· STRAPPING ·

This term indicates the thorough grooming given after work when the horse has dried off but when the skin is still warm and pliable and more receptive to being cleaned. It involves initial removal of mud and sweat with the dandy brush, a thorough brushing with the body brush, which is frequently cleaned with the metal curry comb, and a final going over with the stable rubber to remove any residual dust which may have settled on the coat during body-brushing. The feet are again picked out (and in some yards washed) and any sponging done, which certainly refreshes the horse.

Exercise will have 'toned up' the skin and loosened any dirt and dandruff in the coat, making its removal easier. The task can be pretty hard work, but is made easier if you learn the knack of leaning your weight on your brush arm, which should be held stiff and slightly bent at the elbow, instead of using your arm and shoulder muscles to push the bristles through the hair to the skin. This is most tiring and an unnecessary waste of energy. Particularly if you have several horses to do, you should conserve your energy for other work; but you can still get the job done effectively by using your body weight.

It is generally set out in text books that you should use your left arm when doing the nearside of the horse and vice versa. However, it is far better to change arms if you get tired than risk only half doing the job because you feel you should 'go by the book'. There is also no need to give more than six firm strokes of the body brush in one place, thoroughly cleaning the brush on the metal curry comb after every two or three. Over-grooming can result in irritated skin which, in fact, throws up extra grease and dandruff in response as a protection.

· WISPING OR 'BANGING' ·

This is the massaging of the muscular areas of the horse with a wisp made from a plaited rope of hay, plaited binder twine or, less satisfactory, straw. The object is to make the horse use his muscles by flinching them in anticipation of the wisp's landing on his coat. There is some difference of opinion as to whether or not the process actually develops muscles: some say that the only muscles which flinch are those immediately un-der the skin, the long, flat, subcutaneous ones which are not meant to be particularly 'chunky' anyway. In my experience, however, wisping does make a noticeable difference in a horse's physique, skin and coat when done properly.

The wisp, slightly damped, is brought down with a firm, but not rough, bang or slap onto areas such as the sides and topline of the neck, the muscles behind the shoulder and above the elbow, the back, quarters and thighs. Areas to be avoided are sensitive or bony ones such as the legs, shoulder blades, loins and hips. Wisping, in theory, also squeezes extra sebum out of the sebaceous glands and distributes it along the coat and skin and the appearance of a regularly wisped horse does seem to confirm this.

I have found wisping particularly useful on grass-kept, working horses who should not be body brushed too much, as it seems to improve not only muscular development and skin tone but cleans the horse without removing too much natural grease. It also helps keep the skin and muscles toned up on horses who, for whatever reason, are on restricted exercise or even stable-bound. Needless to say, sick horses should not be wisped – they should be messed about as little as possible, just quartered, sponged and feet picked out.

If a proper hay wisp is not used, a horsehair-stuffed leather pad called a tapee can be used instead, but it is not as good.

· HAND RUBBING ·

Like all grooming, this is enjoyed by most horses if done with sensitivity. The legs can be rubbed briskly (usually only upwards to assist circulation) with a final downward stroke to smooth the hair; this is particularly beneficial in horses who, no matter how much work they get, stock up (get filled legs) when standing stabled. The body can be hand rubbed with the flat of the hand, the 'heel' of the hands and the fingers, feeling the muscles for any tense 'knots' or tender spots – watch the horse's reaction to see if any discomfort or pain is felt. This hand rubbing or massage should be relaxing and even therapeutic, similar to an athlete's stint on the table after a workout. Muscular areas should be concentrated on, such as the upper legs, neck, shoulders, back, quarters, and loins and thighs.

· SET-FAIR OR BRUSH-OVER ·

This is often combined with wisping in the evening, again to stimulate the skin and promote circulation and to freshen up the horse; the rugs are usually changed for night clothing at this time. Stable stains can be removed, the mane and tail tidied and maybe laid with the water brush, sponging done and the feet picked out again.

All this might sound like a lot of grooming to give a horse in one day but a regularly worked, regularly groomed horse is fairly easy to keep clean, much more so than one who is out of work and whose skin is therefore not so clean or toned up. I hate grooming a freshly brought up horse and in fact I usually cheat, and wash him first to save me a lot of time and sheer physical effort!

Electric grooming machines are a boon to large yards and busy owners. The most effective are those which combine rotary brushes with a vacuum facility which sucks the dislodged dirt out of the coat and into a container such as a cylinder or fabric bag. They are so efficient that some makers actually advise purchasers to use them only once or twice a week to prevent the removal of too much natural grease from the coat; often all you need do on the other days is quarter and maybe wisp (plus, of course, sponging and picking out feet), and massage if you favour it.

· SHAMPOOING ·

A very few decades ago, it was considered almost a sin to wash a horse, at least in private stables, yet as far as I can discover it has always been done in military establishments and, to a lesser extent, commercial ones using horses for deliveries and so on. Nowadays, some people go to the other extreme and wash their horses and ponies far too often, particularly showing enthusiasts.

In natural conditions, horses do get rained on quite often; they also roll in mud, which is thought to help make the skin a less 'desirable residence' for skin parasites and, when it dries on solid, to protect the horse against cold winds. A mud pack or clay-based skin treatment has a drying, astringent effect on skin; outdoor horses are in roughly the same position, but stabled ones, of course, are not, although they may become wet with rain during work. They do not have the opportunity to rid their skin of excess grease, so we do it for them by grooming and sometimes washing them.

Shampooing horses presupposes soap of some kind, as water on its own will not break down grease. This is where things can go wrong, however, as soap-based products are often over-used. Unless a horse is exceptionally greasy (as opposed to just dusty or muddy) there is no need to use soap. In fact, using soap too often dries out the skin too much and can make it uncomfortable, takes the natural bloom off the coat, and makes the hair too soft. Naturally lubricated hair has a firm, substantial look and feel to it with a deep, sleek gloss. Hair which has been washed with soap/shampoo and maybe dressed with conditioner is too soft and slippery, does not cling to the skin or have the same depth of sheen to it. The coat hair is more difficult to manipulate for such things as quarter marks and 'cosmetic brushing' to enhance good points and disguise poor ones, and mane and tail hair is more difficult to trim, plait and lay.

If you do use soap, it is essential that it is *all* rinsed out otherwise soreness and skin problems could result. The type of soap is also significant. There are special animal shampoos on sale in most tack stores, you can use human shampoos (although avoid the perfumed ones), anti-dandruff ones being as effective on horses as on humans, baby soap, mild medicated soap or mild washing-up liquid.

It is a real advantage to have both hot and cold running water in your yard, with a mixer tap so that you can get the temperature just right. I always use lukewarm water, or actually warm water in winter – if you wash or rinse down a hot horse with freezing cold water you might cause muscle cramps and even muscle-fibre damage, particularly if water strays onto the loin and quarter muscle masses. It is always safest to cool the horse down first and then rinse off sweat with lukewarm water which can do no harm whatsoever. In winter, hosing down a muddy horse with bitterly cold water cannot possibly be comfortable for him.

If you cannot arrange for a mixer tap and hot running water in the yard, get one of those instant water heaters fitted to the cold water pipe, which heat the water as it is passing through so you only heat as much as you need; set the thermostat to blood heat (38°C (100.4°F), buy a decent screw fitting for your tap and hosepipe and you have a very useful facility for a relatively small outlay.

One commonly-quoted theory is that if you wash horses with *warm* water you open the pores in the skin and enable mud, particularly clay which has fine grains, to get in and cause soreness. Using cold water is said to keep the pores closed and so is safer. However, cold water in itself can cause problems. When I am muddy, I wash myself in warm water, I rinse down my muddy dogs with warm (clear) water, I hose off muddy horses with warm (clear) water and as far as I am aware, Rugby players do *not* take a cold bath after a match but a steaming hot one. So this theory does not seem to withstand a practical test – nor does the related one, which maintains that you must let mud dry on the legs *then* brush it off, otherwise you will cause mud fever because the water will wash the mud grains into the pores.

In my experience, one of the surest ways of causing mud fever is to do just that – leave the mud on till it is dry then brush it off or, even worse, pick off hard clay with your fingers or rub it off with a rubber or plastic curry comb. These methods are calculated to irritate and scratch the skin, and even the tiniest abrasion is enough for the mud fever bacteria to get in and start to work.

Whenever your horse is wet – from rain, from washing, or simply from hosing off – he could develop sore, chapped skin susceptible to infection if he is not dried properly. If you dry the horse *properly*, particularly in cold weather when the chill factor is a consideration, there is no reason why you should have problems. Except in warm conditions (summer weather or a box with a heat lamp) never let your horse stand around wet and exposed to draughts; otherwise he could become chilled or chapped.

Scrape off excess water with a sweat scraper or the sides of your hands, rub him down with old towels and/or straw, get him used to being dried off with a hand-held hair dryer (taking the normal precautions about having a properly earthed appliance and circuit breaker) and either thatch him or clothe him with an anti-sweat rug, a modern 'breatheable' rug made of permeable fabric and/or another rug on top if the weather is chilly or actually cold; pay particular attention to his legs especially the heels and the backs of the pasterns. Dry these thoroughly and bandage them and, if they are often washed, rub in a lanolin-based skin cream or liquid paraffin (mineral oil) if the hair is quite short and you are worried about over-dry skin.

Even in winter, you can safely rinse down or shampoo your horse if you do one section at a time. Fold back the rugs and do the neck and shoulders quickly, scrape them and cover them at once with a blanket clipped together under the neck with a large bulldog clip to keep in body warmth, while you do the back and barrel. Give them the same treatment and finally do loins and quarters. This way the horse is mainly covered while having his bath and will not become chilled. Once his neck and body are done and he is thatched or clothed, do his legs (unless someone else has been doing them meanwhile). Do this under cover away from draughts, and keep his neck covered, as horses lose a considerable amount of heat from their necks. Use old towels to rub him down under his clothing to speed along the drying process. If you have a heat lamp in one of your boxes (they are very reasonable to buy and run and are a great help in winter) you do not need to clothe the horse at all, just rub him down thoroughly including his legs, stand him in a deep, clean bed and he will dry off very quickly.

Steaming him clean with hot, damp towels is also a good system: get a large bucket of very hot water and add just a few drops of shampoo if the coat and skin are very greasy (as in some cold-blooded or warmblood horses). Wear rubber gloves yourself and soak a towel in the hot water, wring it out very thoroughly and rub the horse clean one section at a time, regularly rinsing and wringing out the towel.

Summary

●The skin is vital for maintaining body temperature, for the excretion of waste products via the sweat, and in the sense of touch. Hair and horn are modified forms of skin and a correct, balanced diet is essential to maintain their health.

●Skin is in two main layers: the upper layer or *epidermis*, composed of dead skin cells; and the lower layer or *dermis* made up of living, sensitive cells. The dermis contains the hair follicles, the sweat and sebaceous glands and the nerve endings, plus blood capillaries which by dilating or contracting, help regulate the amount of heat carried in the blood. Sweat glands secrete *liquid sweat* which contains the waste products of metabolism and which also cools the body when it evaporates. The sebaceous glands secrete *sebum*, which lubricates the skin and coat.

●The dermis also contains *melanin*, a colouring agent: The less melanin a horse's skin contains, the less resistant is his skin to outside elements such as sunlight, water, bacteria and abrasions.

●The hair insulates the body by trapping a layer of warm air next to the body – if the hair is flattened by wet or windy conditions, or by clothing, this layer of air will be less effective. Leg hair can actually encourage mud fever by creating airless conditions, and also hamper its treatment.

●Tails left full at the top significantly help outdoor horses withstand cold winds and rain.

●The antennae or feeler hairs around the horse's muzzle and eyes are important to his sense of security so should not be trimmed off. They should never be *pulled* out as this would be extremely painful for the horse.

Summary

● The grooming process includes: quartering; full strapping; wisping; hand rubbing. All grooming should be done sensitively.

● Soap is only needed when washing if the skin and coat are excessively greasy; otherwise simple rinse with clear water is usually quite enough to remove general dirt. Using soap too often dries out the skin and removes too much of its natural protection; it also makes the hair too soft.

● Use lukewarm water, or water at blood heat. A mixer tap, an instant water heater and heat lamps are a boon to any yard and are relatively inexpensive.

● Thorough drying is essential to avoid chilling and chapping, particularly in cold weather. The horse can be washed quickly in sections to avoid chills; cleaning the horse with hot, damp towels is an effective method of freshening up a greasy animal.

CLIPPING AND TRIMMING

A horse is trimmed up and clipped firstly to prevent loss of condition due to excessive sweating, and secondly, to smarten the horse up for appearance's sake.

Hair is an effective insulator and the long, thick winter coat greatly helps keep the horse warm, but the horse will get too hot at anything other than slow to moderate paces. The body sweats to lose some heat, but the coat will become soaked and flattened, thus destroying the insulating layer. This may not matter while heat is required to be lost, but what usually happens is that the horse cools down after work faster than the coat dries. The horse then reaches the stage where he is at his normal temperature but is standing in a wet coat, with no insulating air layer next to his skin. Since water (even in the form of sweat) is a good conductor of heat, body warmth continues to pass from his body (if the surrounding air is colder) more quickly than his body can probably make up the loss. This will certainly happen if the horse is exposed to draughts, either in the stable or outdoors, and he could lose so much body heat so quickly that he becomes chilled and hypothermic; in an extreme case he could die.

This not infrequently happens to horses living out in cold, wet weather without adequate overhead shelter so that they can get away from the rain. In persistently cold and wet weather, even a rainy spell lasting several hours could result in hypothermia and they may well become seriously ill at least if they are not dried and warmed up. If they

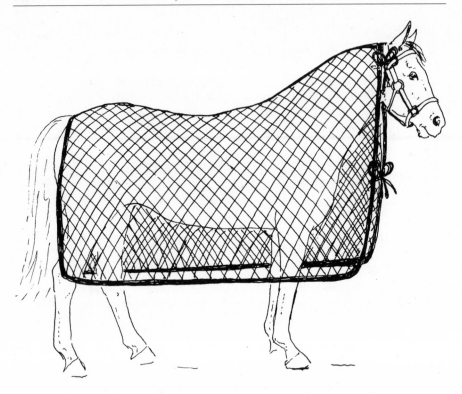

An American cooler which fastens to the browband of the headcollar and ties below the neck. The coolers are not 'see-through' – this one has simply been indicated like this to show the outline of the horse beneath and the fit of the cooler. These are very useful garments

can keep reasonably dry, however, either by means of a waterproof rug, or take shelter in a shed or barn or, if the rain is not too heavy, a thick wood or spinney, they are normally safe.

To counteract these effects – apart from cooling off and drying a sweating horse in winter – at least some of the winter coat can be clipped off. The horse sweats most on the neck, breast, shoulders and flanks. Areas covered by tack and/or harness appear to sweat a great deal but as the air cannot get to them to allow the sweat to evaporate, they actually do become wetter.

The most extensive clip is where the horse is clipped all over, and then the hunter clip where hair is left on the legs and usually on the back in the form of a saddle patch, which ostensibly protects the back from saddle pressure and friction. Strangely, however, a 'protective patch' is not normally left for the girth area! Clipping (usually with specially coarse blades) is sometimes carried out on the legs, too, particularly if the horse is the more common type who grows a thick coat and leg feather; this is partly for smartness and also for ease of cleaning and drying.

In every clip in the repertoire, the hair is always clipped off the belly and breastbone area ie the underneath of the horse, leaving this area practically bare of protection from the kicked-up mud of which it takes the brunt – yet hair is left *on* the legs, supposedly to help protect them from mud. There seems to be little logic in the theory and practice of clipping.

The fact is that there are two sides to the coin (apart from smartness which is down to personal taste and opinion anyway); we clip to avoid loss of condition and chilling due to excessive sweating in the working horse in winter; and by doing so we unavoidably remove some of the horse's natural protection from the elements, of which mud is one. So we have no choice but to make up for the system's shortcomings by extra care of the horse.

I do feel that many people clip their animals unnecessarily extensively. There may be a case for hunter clipping or clipping all out a commonly-bred horse with a very thick coat which is also greasy, but any other horse should be fine with nothing more extensive than a blanket clip. Hunting is one activity where a hunter clip is, in fact, *not* suitable. Hunting consists of bursts of activity and, on poor scenting days, lots of standing about and probably getting cold. In such conditions, horses really should be left with protective coat on their backs, loins and quarters. People who clip out or hunter clip purely because they think it looks smartest are putting misguided opinion, fashion and groundless tradition before common sense and their horses' wellbeing.

With a blanket clip, the hair is removed from the head, breast, neck, flanks and belly, and the tops of the legs – these are all areas which either sweat most or end up with most of the mud, and this clip enables the horse to remain relatively cool, to be dried off quicker and cleaned more easily.

Horses of Thoroughbred and/or Arab breeding have finer coats and can do very well with a 'chaser clip, a sort of high trace clip with the head off as well. There is nothing 'common' about such a clip at all; very many steeplechasers and point-to-point horses are clipped like this, and if it is well done it can enhance the streamlined appearance of a fit horse's physique.

Children's ponies doing little or no work during the week in winter, but working at weekends, can be given a breast-and-gullet clip or a low trace clip. If animals are to be turned out a good deal, or to live out in winter, perhaps we should think twice about clipping their lower regions (belly and underside, and the tops of the legs) because if they do lie down on wet ground these are the very areas which will then be deprived of any real protection.

Horses prefer dry resting places in any case, so out-wintering animals should be provided with a field shelter or open barn, bedded down, so that they can rest in comfort in dry conditions.

Because the summer coat starts coming through sometimes as early as January, it is usually advised not to clip after this time as the appearance of the new coat will be spoilt.

Clipping up the sides of the tail is not appropriate for horses who stand around a good deal during their work, or who are turned out for more than an hour or two each day, because of the heat loss it causes. It is only called for in mainly stabled horses doing fast work who are 'chaser or blanket clipped.

When clipping, the usual precautions should be take. The machine should be properly serviced and maintained, the plug properly earthed, the blades and spare sets really sharp and a circuit breaker used. Wear rubber boots yourself and, if at all possible, stand the horse on a dry rubber flooring material, or at least a dry floor. The horse should be as clean as possible and *dry* otherwise the blades will soon blunt and pull, and also heat up, causing considerable discomfort and an understandably fractious horse. A haynet to munch on will keep him occupied and clothing put on as the process progresses will keep him warm if necessary. When clipping, direct the blades slightly askew to the lie of the hair to avoid 'lines' on the clipped areas.

It is as well to have an antiseptic spray on hand just in case of nicks, although tiny ones may well occur which you don't spot because they do not draw blood. Watch the clipped areas for a few days afterwards to check for sore, perhaps slightly swollen patches which could indicate a tiny, infected wound.

Straight after clipping, the horse can beneficially be given the hot towel treatment which helps get rid of that 'just clipped' look, an electric grooming or a thorough hand grooming to remove any itchiness or sharp little bits of hair, not to mention dust or scurf which have come to light. Turn him out without a rug and let him roll. It is always recommended that the food be increased to compensate for the cold, but this should be done with care to prevent the effects of over-feeding.

· COAT CONTROL WITHOUT CLIPPING ·

You may not wish to clip your horse at all. Perhaps he is difficult to do, or you may not feel competent to do it yourself and cannot find anyone else to do it; perhaps you feel it is not really necessary and/or you wish to turn the horse out for several hours a day, perhaps while you are at work; nonetheless you might also feel you would like his coat shorter, both for appearance's sake and so you can work him more. The solution is to consider encouraging him to grow a shorter than normal winter coat.

This is done by fooling his brain into thinking the weather is warmer than it is, so it will send out instructions to grow a shorter winter coat. Many horses start casting their summer coats by late August. Keep an eye out for this and immediately start rugging up your horse or pony at night with a cotton or linen summer sheet. As September draws on, use a light-weight stable rug, and perhaps a light sheet during the day, too, and increase the warmth of the clothing gradually as the weather grows cooler.

This will prevent the horse ever feeling cold and his winter coat will end up considerably shorter than normal. However, for the sake of his comfort ensure that he is not uncomfortably warm or even sweating. His winter coat will be fully set by the end of November, maybe earlier if he was an early foal, then you can rug him up normally, if at all, depending on how you keep him.

Do not make the mistake of trying to make his stable too warm by heating it or shutting the doors. Provide the essential fresh air he needs in the normal way, and use clothing to achieve your aims.

To prevent the casting summer coat becoming matted into his rugs, use a cotton or linen summer sheet underneath, or even an old bed sheet.

In spring, use the same technique to encourage him to change his winter coat earlier; leave the light on in his stable till about midnight, too – this technique, together with heat lamps, is commonly used to bring Thoroughbred mares into season early by fooling their brains into thinking it is spring.

· TRIMMING ·

Some areas are better trimmed with scissors and comb rather than with the machine, to produce a softer, more natural effect. The hair inside the ears should be left, but close the edges of the ears together and snip off any hair which protrudes, especially at the base. The long hair which may grow under the jaw can sometimes be pulled out by hand, particularly after exercise, or done with the scissors or, judiciously, with hand clippers. Leg hair is best done with scissors and comb, combing upwards against the hair and snipping off hair which comes through the teeth. Leave a little tuft on the fetlock for drainage. If doing legs with the clippers, again, leave a little tuft.

Manes and tails are best pulled in the autumn or spring when the hair comes out more easily, but you can keep on top of them all year round by pulling a few hairs out every week or so when you groom.

Obviously, mane hair should be pulled out from the underneath layer so that the top is left to lie flat. Shorter hairs growing on the crest should be trained flat with a water brush and maybe a neck hood. If you or your horse really hates mane pulling, try using a razor comb available from most chemists. These have two layers of teeth with a blade between them, set down a little so you cannot cut yourself. Comb carefully upwards from the roots on the underside to thin out the mane, or downwards towards yourself from underneath at the ends to shorten it, holding the ends with your spare hand in the latter case.

Long manes which need to be left 'natural' for showing can be tidied up and still look good if you just snap the ends off between thumb and finger with a sharp sideways movement.

If you do wish to pull your horse's tail, the same points apply – do a little each day during grooming and after exercise. Many horses will tolerate having their manes pulled but will not stand for their tail being done. In some countries, tails are shaved rather than pulled, with a reasonable effect if done skilfully, but if this does not appeal to you, why not consider leaving the tail full and plaiting it for those special occasions? There is no point upsetting your horse; and it is not the best horsemastership to have a battle over something as unimportant as this, when there is a perfectly good alternative.

Nowadays, most horses (at least in Britain) have the ends of their tails banged, that is cut off squarely to give a level, full appearance. However, some breed classes stipulate that the tail as well as the mane should be left natural. This is not followed literally – tails sweeping the ground not only get in the way, they become scrappy, dirty and look very silly, too. In such breeds, snapping off the ends gives a natural effect, the length being left to personal preference – just above the fetlocks is a reasonable length. Banged tails are usually arranged so that when the horse is still the tail comes about one third of the way down the hind cannons, being just below the hocks when the horse is in action.

Switch tails, which are tapered at the ends rather than banged, are rarely seen these days.

THOUGHTS ON PLAITING

Fashion once dictated that a horse had seven or nine plaits down his neck, plus one for his forelock. Like all fashions, this is no longer followed and you can have any number you like, odd or even – but still only one for the forelock! In show jumping some competitors have followed the American style of plaiting the mane hair but leaving the forelock free. The style of plait has changed, too; a generation ago plaits were shaped like short sausages – now they are little bobbles or 'button' plaits. Sausage plaits have made a come-back, however, but only in the dressage arena, where many competitors follow the continental fashion of having lots of little, thin sausage plaits down the neck, secured with white adhesive tape – plus one for the forelock, of course.

Some years ago I was judging at a small show and one class was the 'Best Turned Out'. All the children and ponies were immaculately clean if not sartorially correct; one combination in particular caught the eye and was, sadly, the object of some sniggering from the ringside. This was a little girl with ash blonde hair tied in bunches with bright red ribbons. She wore a black velvet cap, black jacket with scarlet lining and a red rose in her button hole and her pony was jet black.

His mane was very neatly plaited with numerous pigtail plaits, in other words she had not rolled them up but left them down, sewn the ends with black thread and finished off each plait with a tiny red bow on the bottom – and one for the forelock. All the bows were perfectly straight and formed a striking red line down the pony's neck. The rest of their turnout was perfectly conventional and correct. I placed her fourth and was reported to the show secretary who promptly asked me back the following year! (No, it wasn't her daughter.)

As we have seen, fashions change in plaiting and turnout as in everything else. Perhaps that little girl was simply years ahead of her time, who knows?

One style of plaiting the mane which happily is becoming a little more common is the crest plait; I feel it suits horses better than any number or style of separate plaits. This is particularly useful for horses and ponies who, for showing in breed classes, must not have short manes; but it could be used on any horse. It enhances the natural line of the horse's

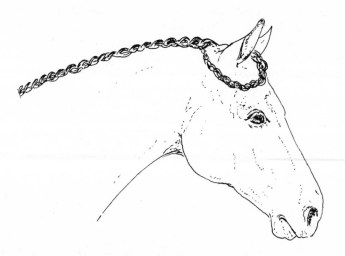

A crest plait, showing plaited forelock taken into mane

crest and, with a little practice, is easier and certainly quicker than the usual method.

The forelock can either be put up in a button plait, left loose or, if fairly long, plaited and brought round the right ear then plaited into the neck hair. The latter is started with three locks of hair just behind the ears like an ordinary plait but instead of plaiting them downwards into a separate plait, you guide the plait along the crest, taking in more hair with your left hand as you go, so you have a single long plait all down the crest. At the withers, continue plaiting the free hair to the ends, sew round the bottom, double up to the withers (as when plaiting the tail, so you have a loop), sew the loop down into a sausage and finish off normally. Some people like to direct the crest plait in a gradual curve down onto the neck itself leaving a 'web' of hair above it, but this tends to flop up and down when the horse is in action.

Crest plaits can be used on any occasion when animals of a registered breed are 'on show', such as when jumping or even hunting.

Plaiting the tail is usually regarded as trickier than doing the mane, whatever style you favour, but with practice it does look good. If you plait the locks under each other instead of over you make a raised plait all down the dock which really enhances the tail carriage, and looks more stylish than the more usual method.

Plaiting is always time-consuming, and many people understandably do it the night before an 'event'. It all takes a good deal of skill and judgement so that the plaits are at just the right tension and not too tight. If they are, they can certainly cause the horse a great deal of discomfort which might result in his rubbing your handiwork overnight and ruining the job. Too-tight plaiting will certainly affect both his attitude to his work the next day and his way of going, which surely defeats the object. So it is really much better to plait your horse on the morning of the occasion, and plaits should be removed as soon as possible after his classes.

Summary

●Clipping and trimming smarten up a winter coat and enable the horse to work hard without losing too much condition through sweating; he can be dried off quicker so that he is less likely to become chilled.

●Warm air forms an insulating layer next to the skin – chilling can result if a long coat becomes wet with rain or sweat and therefore flattened and the warm-air layer destroyed.

●Water is also a good conductor of heat, which means that body heat is escaping perhaps more quickly than the horse can create it – so he may become chilled, particularly if left standing around and/or without clothing.

●Horses out in wet weather need overhead shelter, particularly when rain is prolonged. A well-fitting waterproof rug helps prevent chilling.

●Horses sweat most on neck, brest, shoulders and flanks so this hair is removed in any clip; also the belly hair, since it is easier to dry and clean clipped areas. The hair is usually left *on* the legs, supposedly as a protection against mud which can cause mud fever (a bacterial infection).

●Horses prone to mud fever are better with the leg hair clipped either with coarse blades or with scissors and comb; the legs can then be thoroughly rinsed of mud, dried and a protective substance such as liquid paraffin (mineral oil) applied.

●Few horses actually need an all-out clip or even a hunter clip; blanket or 'chaser clip' is suitable for any hard-working horse, except possibly those with very thick and/or greasy coats.

●Children's ponies doing little or no work during the week and living outdoors can be given a breast-and-gullet clip. Animals living out should *not* be clipped up the sides of the tail or have the tail pulled, to leave protection against unnecessary loss of body heat.

●Judicious clothing from late summer onwards results in a shorter winter coat. In late winter and early spring, the same technique can be used, and the light left on in the stable till about midnight.

●Major hand-trimming jobs, and mane and tail pulling are carried out with greatest ease in spring and autumn when horses are naturally casting their coats, and when the horse is warm.

Summary

- A good effect can be obtained with a razor comb if you do not wish to pull the mane. Snapping off the ends of the hair between thumb and finger to shorten the manes and tails of animals supposed to be left untrimmed.

- The crest plait enhances the crest of the neck and is useful for controlling long manes in animals who are shown in breed classes *au naturel* but take part in other activities, too.

- Do not plait up your horse or pony the night before an event if you can possibly avoid it. Over-tight plaits can cause the horse discomfort, mental anxiety and can adversely affect his action and performance. Remove plaits as soon as possible after competing.

Checklist

✓ 1 Clipping enables us to work a horse hard without his losing condition or becoming chilled, but clothing, shelter and judicious extra feeding must obviously be provided.

2 Unclipped horses can become severely chilled if exposed to prolonged rain since the warm air layer next to the skin will be destroyed as the coat is flattened. The same effect also applies to sweat which will flatten the coat and cause serious chilling.

3 To prevent this, provide overhead shelter and probably a waterproof rug for outdoor horses. Do not let any, whether clipped or not, stand around in winter when hot or even warm and sweating. Try to cover at least the loins and quarters, maybe with your jacket, and keep him walking around so that more body heat is generated to counteract the chilling process.

4 Soap and soap-based products are only needed to break down grease or oil; normally a straightforward hose or sponge down, with clear warm water is quite adequate. Using soap too often can strip the coat of natural protective oils, spoil the look of the coat and cause dry skin. Soap must be very thoroughly rinsed out of the hair.

5 Full grooming can occasionally be skipped with the stabled horse; quartering, sponging and picking out the feet should be done at least once daily, and dried mud or sweat *must* be removed before tacking up otherwise the horse may be rubbed sore.

6 There is no need to clip and trim your horse any more extensively than his work calls for; a blanket or 'chaser clip is quite adequate unless the coat is exceptionally thick or greasy.

· AS A MATTER OF INTEREST ·

✓ 1 If you are faced with a wet, muddy horse to exercise and there is not time to thatch him and wait for the mud to dry, hose or sponge the saddle/harness area very thoroughly, scrape off excess moisture, rub down with old towels quickly and tack up with an absorbent numnah and girth (something like quilted cotton for the numnah and mohair or lampwick for the girth, or one of the new textiles which 'wick' moisture out of the coat and the horse will be quite alright.

2 Washing out the sheath of a gelding or stallion may be slightly unpleasant but it *is* important to prevent possible infection setting in, and should be done every 2-4 weeks. The greasy discharge (known as smegma) is best removed with hand-hot water and a mild, medicated soap. Wear thin rubber gloves and sponge right up inside the sheath, gently but persistently. Rinse very thoroughly with warm, clear water plus a dash of liquid antiseptic with liquid paraffin or mineral oil to help prevent further smegma clinging. In chilly weather, be sure to dry the surrounding skin thoroughly after washing.

3 The areas of the horse most often overlooked during grooming are under forelock and mane, inside ears, under jaw, between front and hind legs and behind pasterns. Groom the various parts of your horse in the same order so that you don't miss anywhere.

4 To check if your stabled horse is really clean, use the old army test: put on a pair of immaculately clean white gloves and rub your horse or pony's coat hard *against* the lie of the hair with your fingertips. Finally, check your gloves. If they are still clean, so is your horse. If they are not. . .

5 It is not a sin to lightly body brush an outdoor horse or pony for a special occasion. Certainly protective grease should be left in the coat but a quick once-over for a weekend show will not do any harm. Wisping plus a polish with an old silk (not polyester) headscarf, and a washed mane, forelock and tail can make your animal look just as good as a regularly strapped, stabled one. Even a hose-down with clear water (no soap) is in order – it will clean him up without removing too much natural oil.

8

PSYCHOLOGY AND HANDLING

THE EQUINE MENTALITY

It seems hard to believe when you watch your old favourite dozing away a summer afternoon that horses are essentially nervous animals – that they are even highly strung, when you see police horse classes and displays at major shows, or watch some bomb-proof schoolmaster pony stoically tolerating his young rider's unintentional abuses and patiently trying to teach his young charge the right way to do things.

But horses and ponies *are* nervous and edgy as a species, because that is how they have survived this long. Even police horses, highly trained as they are to face up to virtual fire and brimstone, can succumb to blind panic in certain conditions, as seen in recent years in public and on television.

The horse family, like other prey animals, has had to be almost permanently on guard for millions of years to avoid being eaten, and this instinct to react instantly when startled or frightened and think later, is still with them. Most horses will therefore run away from trouble, even if only behind the nearest shed or hedge, rather than face up to it. They will fight only as a last resort, although aggressive behaviour can be seen in stallions guarding a harem from a rival or mares defending their own foals from another marauding mare or a predator.

It has been reported that when surrounded by a pack of hunting dogs or jackals, zebras have formed a ring with heels outwards lashing at the predators, and foals and youngstock in the centre, but this sort of communal reaction seems quite rare.

Like other prey animals, horses are not naturally courageous. If they approach a trough to drink from it and perhaps hurt themselves on it, they will tend to steer clear of it in future – the pain is a warning that the object is dangerous and to safeguard personal safety, must be avoided. Hunter animals will often try an alternative course of action to get what they want, rather than practising avoidance. If something frightens a horse in the hedge, he will probably anticipate fright and shy at that very same spot for ever more – his special type of survival instinct seems to programme him to do so. On the other hand, a dog may be frightened by something, but after an initial start he will probably go carefully up to the object to investigate – a horse or pony would not do this unless the incident had been very mild. Normally, there is much huffing and puffing, eyes on stalks and ears pricked and 'let me get away' movements.

So if pain is inflicted on a horse, accidentally or otherwise, he will associate pain with that action, place or situation for a long time to come, maybe for the rest of his life. If we request something of the horse which repeatedly causes him pain or discomfort, he will quite naturally and understandably try to avoid doing it. If jumping causes him pain from a jab in the mouth, a crack on the legs or a slash with the whip, it will be small wonder if the horse turns into a refuser.

Because different types of horses have evolved in different environments, individuals within a particular type or breed may, like humans or any other animal, react differently to painful or frightening situations. Generally, though, horses who are in pain or fear can be relied on to want to run away from it, and to fight to do so if restrained. Horses coming round from an anaesthetic often thrash around because they feel unco-ordinated and are frightened. It is their instinct to want to be on their feet so they can gallop off if threatened, and they often struggle quite violently to achieve this. Similar behaviour can be seen in a horse's reaction to different handlers. A harsh, bullying handler often provokes fear and physical reaction in the animal. A stallion jabbed in the mouth when led in hand (a very common sight) will throw his head up and back and may rear, but the same animal finds confidence in a quiet handler and will lead willingly and co-operatively.

Of course, discipline is essential, particularly with an animal as large, strong, fast and as highly strung as a horse, but discipline does not mean roughness or cruelty, injustice or temper. It must also be administered instantaneously or within a second of any misdemeanour, as horses learn largely by association of ideas. The horse, when unschooled and untrained, has no idea what constitutes right and wrong in our eyes – it just behaves naturally. Nor can it speak English, but it *can* understand tones of voice and recognises a cross or a calming tone, an encouraging or an officially requesting one; this is greatly to our advantage and helps considerably in training.

If a horse is nipping, for example, a cross-sounding 'No' is often enough to let him know we do not want him to do that. Perhaps he barges off when led in hand: if he understands the command 'No' but will still not stop doing this, one sharp crack across the breast *as he is barging* and as you command 'No', should get the message through.

Horses and ponies usually feel more secure in a group, because in the wild being one of a herd meant that becoming a victim of a predator was less likely – solitary animals are the obvious choice of a hunter. This aspect of their mentality can also help greatly in training and general handling. An older, schooled horse is most useful for giving confidence to youngsters – it can give them a lead over a jump or through a hazard such as deep mud, or past a frightening object such as a road digger or even a white cat!

This can also cause problems, as horses not trained to leave others when young, and to work alone, can become impossibly attached to their friends. All youngsters should, after a month or two of training, be made to work away from others, even if still within sight of them, so that they get used to the idea while still malleable in attitude. Mature horses who have never had this training are often impossible to use alone.

THINKING LIKE A HORSE

A fairly close study of equine psychology is important to anyone associating with horses if they wish to get good results and do things safely. The development of the ability to see things from the horse's point of view will help greatly in all general handling, working and training (see p261 for further reference on this topic). Basically, always remember that horses are easily frightened and this will cause you to move quietly and gradually around them, talking to them in a conversational tone to let them know where you are – horses cannot see directly behind them. Always warn a horse of what you are going to do, whether riding, driving, handling or just working near them. Sudden movements, loud noises and anything that will surprise or startle them, should be avoided.

Remember also that horses have lifelong memories of even seemingly small, insignificant happenings and, being natural prey animals, do not consider that a matter is 'over and done with' but that it may very well happen again. I have just been watching Badminton Horse Trials where a horse who had a bad fall at a particular fence two years previously has just refused very firmly at the same fence, despite schooling elsewhere over similar type fences during the intervening period. Two years is a very short time in the memory of a horse. Horses and ponies who have been involved in traffic accidents are often traffic-shy for the rest of their lives, despite any amount of subsequent reassurance and re-training.

If you cause a horse discomfort or pain, do not be surprised if he reacts violently, and do not punish him but reassure him. Because horses in nature eat for roughly sixteen hours a day, do not be surprised if your horse tries to snatch every opportunity to get something edible into his mouth – he is simply doing what his evolution has programmed him to do to survive. Horses soon get to know that they must not eat while working but sometimes the temptation can be too great, particularly if food has been withheld for some time before work and the horse is starting to feel hungry, a state of being which is unnatural to horses.

Years ago an international show jumper belonging to one of the famous d'Inzeo brothers was entering the arena for an important competition, and quickly snatched a large bloom from a display near the entrance. Everyone laughed as he walked round chewing the flower, waiting for the bell. When the time came, he started his round and stopped chewing, but held on to the flower all the way round the course, which he executed effortlessly and calmly; and as soon as he had passed through the finish, he continued his snack. His rider made no effort to deprive him of it.

FIRM BUT FAIR

Most horses are followers, not leaders; they want and respect leadership and usually accept their place in an established herd hierarchy, so discipline is no phenomenon. Herd discipline can be quite harsh; horses obviously hurt each other when they bite and kick, and mares often administer quite hard nips to their offspring to teach them herd manners.

The leader of a herd is usually a matriarchal mare, not a stallion. Horse society is definitely feminist! A stallion is possessive and sometimes acquisitive in ensuring his supply of sexual favours – and favours is the operative word. In the wild, no mare will stand for being mated if she does not wish to be, and most of the scars carried by a wild stallion have been inflicted by mares refusing his attentions rather than by rivals.

Because of this, a horse by nature will submit to leadership and discipline from humans provided he understands it and, although this sounds anthropomorphic, perceives it as fair. Horses do not always understand 'discipline' when administered by humans, because humans often fail to act in accordance with horse rules – they don't use the same body language, and are not consistent with their actions, often failing to act when they should, and acting when they should not. Therefore, we must try to be firm but fair, to be consistent, and request co-operation rather than absolute submission – then we shall obtain better results from a species which is not at all like ours.

VOICE TRAINING

Horses and ponies are taught to respond to the voice during their early schooling on the lunge, and the voice is always used in conjunction with physical aids so that he comes to associate the known voice aid with a particular physical aid; but it seems that the voice is not used as much as it could be later on. Horses are very responsive to the human voice and many people believe it is a serious mistake that although it can be used in any other competitive event, it is not allowed in dressage tests; the horse is supposed to be so well schooled that he responds to physical aids without prompting from the voice, although why this is supposed to be a virtue I have never understood.

Unlike dogs, very few horses are taught to respond to their names and to come when called – a dog who does not respond is regarded as naughty and badly trained yet no one thinks twice if a horse does not do it. Learning his own name should, I feel, be one of the very first things taught to a youngster, like a puppy. However, many horses end up with owners who want a different name, and it would be very confusing for the horse if he were to be given a different name with each new owner. Perhaps it could be made accepted practice that the horse keeps the stable name given him by his first owner all his life, so that at least he knows what to answer to.

Horses respond best to clear, single sounds rather than a running conversation, unless the latter is for the purpose of calming down the horse with its tone rather than its content. He should be taught his name, and the commands 'walk on', 'trot', 'canter' 'back', 'whoa' (not 'stop' which is rather too much like 'trot') and 'over' for moving over in the stable. Each of these words should be said in a distinctive way and *always* in the *same* way so that the horse comes to associate that particular sound with the movement required. The *meaning* of the actual words obviously has no significance to the horse.

Always speak your horse's name when you approach him, particularly from outside the stable to warn him you are there, and when you want to attract his attention; speak before you move around him and speak when you want him to do something. The use of the voice is a great help to us comparatively weak humans when dealing with a large, strong but essentially co-operative animal like a horse. We should not lose an opportunity to speak to our horses and ponies and communicate with them in an effortless way which they will readily come to understand.

BODY LANGUAGE, YOURS AND HIS

Despite the usefulness of the voice, the main method by which horses communicate with each other is by body language. They do use their voices to each other, of course, but body language is more usual, as anyone will know who has watched how horses behave together.

Aggression or displeasure is signified by ears back, cross expression with nostrils drawn back, and maybe coming towards you with muzzle

A head showing a 'kind' eye which denotes a sweet temperament

Alertness and interest shown by the pricked ears and interested look in the eyes

Sour temper shown by backward pointing ears and a generally unpleasant expression

Boredom – again the ears are back and the horse's eyes are not wide and alert. The nostrils are drawn slightly up and back

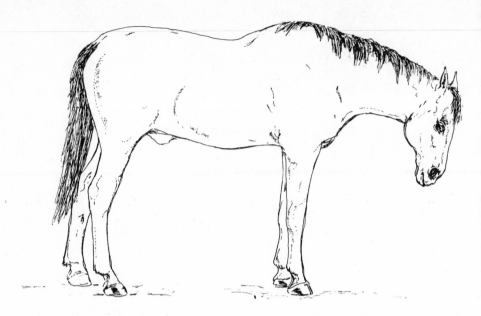

Sick horses often stand apart from others with a generally hang-dog expression, head low, eyes half closed

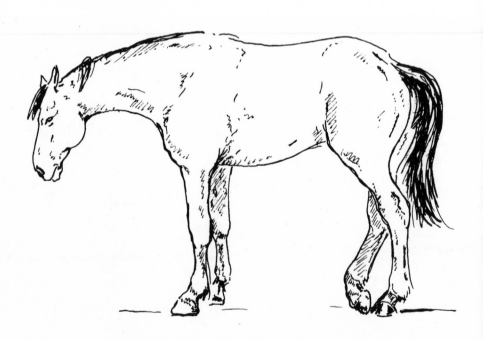

When dozing, horses normally rest one hind leg, alternating them periodically. Their 'stay apparatus' in elbows and stifles prevents them from falling down, so that the horse remains propped up and able to make a quick getaway should danger threaten

One ear on the rider, the other paying attention to what is ahead

Play bucking – bottom up but no kicking out

Should a horse show this kind of expression, with ears flattened back, sour facial attitude and mouth partly open you can be fairly sure he's thinking of biting

A typical stallion strike-out at a rival. Mares and geldings may also use this action, although in them it usually deteriorates into an exaggerated stamp

The youngster on the left is showing submissive mouthing, opening and closing the teeth with the nose extended. They do this to older horses and mares sometimes do it to stallions when they are full in season

extended and head down; the tail may also be switching about. If you see a horse behaving like this either in a competition or elsewhere, you can be sure he is not pleased about something.

Interest and attention are shown by pricked ears, flared nostrils and a prancing gait; his tail will probably be somewhat raised – horses of Arab breeding often turn their tails right over their backs when extremely excited.

Should a horse turn his quarters to you, raise his tail and also a hind hoof you can be sure he is intending to kick you – his ears will be back, and he will have that cross expression again, with nostrils drawn back, too.

Pain and discomfort often have the same physical signs but the facial expression will be one of anguish or even fear – eyes wide, nostrils flared, snorting and puffing maybe, skin and muscles tense. Pain is also signified by patchy sweating. Well known signs of colic include the horse's nipping at its sides where the pain is coming from.

Of all the horse's physical communication aids, the ears are extremely expressive. Pricked ears indicate attention forwards, but ears pointed back can indicate attention to rider or whip. If they are flattened hard back and down, however, this means annoyance and aggression. Ears to the side indicates sleepiness, no particular interest at the moment, or sickness if accompanied by a hangdog expression generally. Doziness and sleepiness have the same ear position, but the head will be lower, maybe having the poll only just above the level of the withers.

Horses will soon recognise what certain human body positions mean. If a horse is charging at you, run towards him yourself with your head lowered: this is said to put off the horse who regards it as confident counter-aggression. Shouting and waving your arms about is also effective.

Positioning your body in a certain way is the main method of communication in the circus ring during an actual performance, when the horses cannot usually hear the trainer for the music. The whip and stick are used here to emphasise position, not to threaten the animals. If we are lunging a horse or pony, we can use the same techniques. Standing in line with the horse's hip as he is on the circle helps keep him moving (it must give a driving-forward impression), whereas changing your position so that you are level with his head often slows him down or stops him; it also helps emphasise what you want if you point the whip at these two points.

Such body positioning is useful when loose-schooling horses – behind and to the side to drive on, in front and to the side to slow down. Using your arms, whether or not holding a whip, emphasises your position.

GENERAL HANDLING

Always move smoothly and quietly around your horse and speak to him appropriately, and remember that even the quietest horse can be frightened into striking out in self-defence. Do not ask for trouble – particularly with a horse you do not know, do not stand directly behind or in front of him for fear of being kicked or bashed in the face. Develop a confident, reassuring feel, telling your horse that you are not afraid to handle him but will not hurt him either. Poking gingerly around with your fingers will not reassure him any more than will rough thumps (called 'pats' by some). I am sure most horses and ponies prefer being stroked to being patted, and certainly dislike hard slaps, supposedly in praise.

Use common sense to maintain safety. Do not let leadropes trail on the floor, do not put things like curry combs down where they can be trodden on, do not work around horses in soft trainers which offer no protection if *you* are trodden on, and try not to let yourself be cornered in a stable. Tie up a horse which does this as soon as you enter the box, and do not go behind him.

When leading a horse, try holding the leadrope (or the reins over his head if he is wearing a bridle) with the back of your hand uppermost and the palm, therefore, down. This may feel slightly strange at first, but your hand and arm will not be so easily pulled away from you by the horse, and to lead, all you need do is turn your fist away from you (ie in a clockwise direction if the horse is on your right) without actually pulling on the rope. Wear gloves, particularly if leading a difficult animal, and put a knot in the end of the leadrope to help prevent it being pulled through your hand if the horse pulls away strongly.

Never wrap the rope round your hand or wrist, or link your arm through the buckle end of reins when leading; if the horse pulls away, your hand or arm might not get free in time to prevent you being pulled over and perhaps trampled on. Your own safety is paramount so let go rather than risk being dragged or pulled over if such a situation arises.

With a normal leadrope clipped to the bottom ring of the headcollar, if the horse does break free he is in danger of pulling himself down should he tread on the rope. To prevent this, some people use a double length rope; they usually have to order this specially or make it themselves, perhaps out of plaited binder twine. They thread the rope through the ring and hold it doubled. Then if the horse does break away and treads on the rope, he will almost certainly only tread on one end so the rope is pulled through the ring and will hopefully fall out completely.

When leading a difficult animal, it often pays to lead it in a bridle or a lungeing cavesson with the leadrope attached to the front ring (or use both) for added control – once the horse learns it can break away it may repeatedly try it – and succeed.

This also applies to tying up horses. In Britain it is recommended by the major examining bodies that horses are tied to a string loop run through the tie-ring or bracket, so that if the horse pulls back the string will break and the horse will, indeed, get free; this is regarded as preferable to its maybe hurting itself in a fall during its struggles. There is, however, another school of thought which maintains that once a horse has succeeded in breaking free, it then knows for the rest of its life that it can do so, and becomes a menace. I once owned a horse like this and he was, indeed, a real nuisance. Those belonging to the second school of thought train horses when young to be tied and to stand.

They usually use a very strong headcollar and/or wide neckstrap round the jowl, an equally strong rope or two, and attach these to a 'snubbing post' or strong pillar, or a wall with a very securely fixed ring or bracket; they also provide soft, non-slip footing such as earth or turf, or a very well bedded-down stable. The youngsters are then left to find out for themselves that no matter what they do they cannot break away. Someone stands by with a very sharp knife to cut the ropes in genuine emergencies, which do not seem to happen very often in these sessions. When the horse has given up his struggle he is praised and rewarded with a titbit or feed, and untied.

It only takes one such session to teach the youngster that when he is tied up he stays that way, and he is reliable in this respect for the rest of his life. Older horses who have learned to break free can be improved, but there is not space enough to discuss this here (See *Behaviour Problems In Horses* published by David & Charles).

As ever with different schools of thought, each tends to be immoveably convinced that his is the best; I leave readers to decide for themselves.

Summary

●Horses are highly strung and easily startled; when frightened their instinct is to run away – they will very rarely fight a predator, the exceptions being stallions defending harems and mares defending foals.

●Horses learn by association of ideas; pain or discomfort experienced during a particular activity will always be remembered, and the animal may become difficult about it in the future, maybe for the rest of its life.

●Herd discipline is natural to the horse, and human discipline is readily accepted if it is firm and fair and given instantaneously; otherwise the horse will not connect the disciplinary act with what he has done wrong.

●Horses are very responsive to the human voice. They learn simple sounds best, up to three syllables; the voice is probably not used as much as it could be by human trainers and handlers.

●Their herd instinct is fundamental; they will always feel more secure an calm in the company of other horses and ponies.

●We should study horses' communication methods more, particularly body language – our own body language or position can influence the horse's actions, which can help in training.

●Human safety should be paramount: try to forsee trouble and avoid it. Carelessness can cause accidents and a frightened, out-of-control horse; normal safety precautions should be observed and handlers should not become blase, however experienced, or however seemingly quiet and trustworthy the horse.

Checklist

✓ 1 Although horses and ponies often seem quiet, trusting and well trained, they can be easily frightened. When in fear or panic, they use their great strength to get free, and their speed to run away from danger; such horses are usually out of control and dangerous, so make every attempt not to frighten them in the first place.

2 Cultivate a quiet, confident air, talk to your horse, warn him of your intentions and show him that there is nothing to be afraid of.

3 Use your commonsense and learn the *correct* way to do the various jobs – this usually avoids trouble.

4 Horses and ponies often appreciate human company and quiet, caring handling confirms their trust. They are also quick to know when to expect rough treatment, and from whom.

Unfortunately it seems that horses really can smell fear after all. Part of the all-systems-go, flight-or-fight response present in many creatures, including humans, involves involuntary sweating. In the sweat produced during frightening situations there are certain substances which horses, with their acute sense of smell, pick up and recognise as representing fear in the person concerned. So it may not simply be your shaking hands or tense body which sends messages out to your horse, but your 'fear smell' too.

9

TACK AND CLOTHING

If you are not careful, you can run up as big a bill paying for your tack and clothing as you paid for the horse himself. Some items are very expensive – saddles can cost several hundreds of pounds, for instance, and a good New Zealand rug is nearly a hundred at the time of writing.

Of course, there is no need to pay a lot, and there is much good merchandise around at reasonable prices. But if you are offered anything new and it is suspiciously cheap, it is either poor quality and possibly dangerous, or stolen; or it may have been imported from the eastern hemisphere where this sort of merchandise is turned out in sweatshops and has often proved to be extremely dangerous, with weak stitching thread, improperly tanned and preserved leather, and generally poor workmanship.

It is far better to buy good quality second-hand tack than poorer quality cheap new items. Most reputable saddlers sell used equipment, and it would be more than their reputation is worth to sell poor quality merchandise. Not many of today's saddlery 'superstores' really come under the heading 'reputable saddlers'; many of them simply act as retail outlets and have no qualified saddler on the premises, nor knowledgeable staff to give customers advice.

Always look for a firm which is a member of its craft association or guild. In Britain, your saddler should be a member of the Worshipful Company of Saddlers and probably also the British Equestrian Trade Association. Both these organisations have distinctive logos which saddlers can display on their premises, stationery and catalogues. If you are in doubt, ask for proof of membership. If you wish to find members in your area, write to both associations (for addresses see p262–3).

Tack and clothing often need repairs and generally checking over – restuffing in the case of saddles, or readjustments of some kind. If you go to an 'unqualified' retail outlet they may not be able to do this work properly for you, nor be able to get it done. Reputable firms can offer good after-sales services, and take a pride in maintaining good equipment and in giving advice.

· WHAT WILL BE NEEDED ·

There is no need to go overboard with your horse's wardrobe. It is nice to have everything, but a lot of equipment is not actually necessary.

However, it is part of your hobby and many owners take as much pleasure in building up their horse's equipment as they do in buying clothes for themselves – in fact, the horse's requirements, imagined or real, often come before their own!

The items you *will* need are: a bridle and bit, saddle and/or harness plus stirrups and leathers, and a girth; probably a breeching if you drive, although many people do without; a stout headcollar as it is not a good idea either to lead your horse about or to tie him up with your bridle; and finally at least one rug – preferably two so you can launder them alternately. You will also need an under rug or blanket if you are going to clip your horse extensively; if you are *not* going to clip and can provide him with really good shelter facilities in winter, you may not need a rug. These items form the basic minimum and you should manage very well with just this range, plus grooming and first aid kits.

You may wish to buy a numnah. This should *not* be because your saddle does not fit and you hope the numnah will make it more acceptable, but because you wish it to give the horse a more comfortable feel on his back; furthermore if the numnah is either absorbent (cotton probably) or made of one of the new textiles which 'wick' moisture away from the horse's skin and into the fabric or out into the atmosphere, it can prevent both soreness from friction and pressure on a wet back. Skin is softened by moisture and is then more susceptible to rubs and pressure. A good numnah can prevent this sort of thing, which is more likely to happen in sensitive-skinned horses in endurance-type pursuits such as long distance riding, competitive carriage driving or eventing.

A discipline with its own specific demands on the horse may need extra equipment. For instance, if you event you will want a couple of surcingles for extra security, probably a weightcloth, maybe a breast-plate and so on; but for 'hobby' riding the basic range already discussed should be enough.

A good quality, well-fitting waterproof rug of some kind would be a valuable addition to this basic range, particularly if you are a working owner whose horse is out during the day while you are at work. These rugs can be an absolute boon, providing the horse with real protection against the debilitating effects of wet and wind during long days in a field with possibly inadequate shelter. If the horse *can* be turned out in such a rug, it also saves you exercising, which can become a real chore on winter early mornings or evenings before and after work.

In summer, some people turn their horses out in summer sheets in the belief that they protect them from flies. To a small extent they do, but flies usually attack face, sheath and dock more than elsewhere and the horse might be more comfortable with no clothing but a good fly repellant. Summer sheets are mainly used on groomed, stabled horses in summer to keep dust out of their coats.

FIT, USE AND CARE

· THE SADDLE ·

Your saddle will be the most expensive item and great care should be taken in its selection. There are four main points to consider:

1 The saddle must fit the horse as regards length and width.

2 The saddle must fit you as regards length and panel/flap size and shape which depends on the length of your thigh.

3 The saddle must be the right type for your work.

4 The saddle must be well-balanced so that it sits you in the deepest part of the seat which should be the centre.

The *sine qua non* of saddles is that they must not touch the withers or spine anywhere along their length. You should be able to fit the width of three or four fingers between the pommel and the withers when the horse's heaviest rider leans backwards and forwards in the saddle – there must be a tunnel of space all the way down the saddle gullet when you look down it from the pommel. If you have a numnah or other saddle pad on, you must be able to pass your whip easily down the horse's back from pommel to cantle. However, if the saddle does not comply with the basic requirements, do not waste your time thinking about anything else.

As for length, the pommel will rest over the back part of the withers. When in this position, the back arch (cantle) must be on the horse's back (it should *not* extend back any further, and rest on the loins). The correct width will ensure that it neither rocks from side to side on the back and bangs against the sides of the withers, nor pinches them, causing bruising and swelling. You should just be able to slide the flat of your fingers over the sides of the withers at the front of the saddle.

When the front legs are extended fully forward you should note whether the front of the panel makes contact with the tops of the horse's shoulder blades; it should not, otherwise it may cause bruising and may affect the horse's action.

Driving saddles are usually the rigid, padded sort and can cause just the same problems (friction and pressure swellings and sores) as a riding saddle, and the same basic rules of fit apply to these.

When you are mounted in the saddle, you should be able to fit the width of your hand both in front of your body and behind it if the saddle seat is the right length for you. If it is too small or too large you will not be comfortable and your riding will not be of the best. Unnecessary slipping about or weight being put onto the wrong parts of the saddle can cause uneven pressure on the horse's back and make it sore.

The width of the saddle can affect the rider's comfort, but there is not much he or she can do about it if the horse needs a particular width – more discomfort is caused by too wide a saddle/horse than the opposite. If the saddle does feel too wide for you, consider a different design which permits a close contact with the horse, with properly recessed stirrup bars and no more padding than necessary between you and the horse – a thick numnah will make a correctly-fitting saddle appear too narrow. A fleecy numnah can add to the horse's comfort but you must allow for its thickness when fitting the saddle. If you already have a well-fitting saddle and wish to use a numnah, perhaps you could consider one of the thin, quilted cotton ones which are unobtrusive but which absorb sweat and are comfortable.

New textiles are now used for saddle pads and numnahs as well as rugs and blankets. Long distance riding's popularity has encouraged excellent developments in fabrics and paddings; these now attempt to keep a horse's back dry, automatically adjust pressure to keep it even despite the unavoidable movements of a saddle in use, prevent the back overheating, provide considerable comfort for the horse, and they are easy-care into the bargain. Probably the worst sort of pad or numnah is the ordinary quilted nylon one. These are not absorbent, can rub and slip in use, and cause excess sweating and overheating – the horse would be better with just his leather saddle on his back.

The style of saddle and your thigh length should also be matched. By far the most common saddle is the general purpose which with its moderately forward-cut flap is suitable for most general riding, whether flat work or jumping. Specialised show-jumping saddles have more forward-cut flaps, and dressage saddles an almost straight cut. Nearly all modern saddles, except show saddles, have knee and thigh rolls to help keep your leg in the right position and support it in action. If, when your stirrups are your normal length for whatever you want to do, your knee comes forward off the flap or is so far back from the roll that you gain no benefit from it, obviously the saddle does not fit you even though it may fit your horse. With a little trial and error and the advice and co-operation of a good, qualified saddler, you will be able to come up with a solution – not necessarily a compromise which never suits anybody.

Specialised equestrian activity will require a specialised saddle – otherwise your general purpose should fill the bill perfectly well. Long distance saddles are now available, with extended bars or 'fans' to spread the pressure; these can cause problems with very short-backed animals, but are useful if you like to go on day-long hacks. Western saddles are

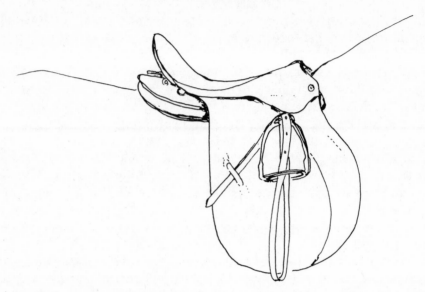

A long-distance riding saddle, based on the general purpose design but with extended, padded bars to spread the load and therefore the pressure on the back over long periods of time spent under saddle. Western and traditional military saddles use the same principles

often used for this sport and, although Western tack is a world of its own, the same basic rules apply concerning even pressure and lack of spine and wither contact.

The balance of the saddle is vital. If it throws you too far back near the cantle your weight will not be on the strongest part of the horse's back: this is just above his centre of gravity, which is just behind his withers, not back towards the loins. The horse can carry you there much more easily, particularly if you ride well and go with his movements. If the saddle throws you too far forward, it will be extremely uncomfortable for you and again your weight will not be centrally placed and you will be unable to ride at your best.

Modern saddles, and particularly dressage saddles, often have gusseted panels under the rear half of the seat; this steadies the saddle on the horse's back and makes the attainment of central balance easier. Look carefully at the saddle when it is on the horse's back and see where the lowest part of the seat is – this is where your seatbones should go. If it is not centrally placed above the horse's centre of gravity, have it adjusted by your saddler if possible, or try a different saddle.

It is also important that the saddle is centrally balanced from side to side, and various factors will result in its becoming unbalanced. If the rider always mounts from the ground and helps himself on by holding the waist or cantle, and perhaps does not have a particularly good spring when mounting, not only can the tree become misshapen but also the stuffing, and the left side of the saddle can become unduly compressed. Using a mounting block is *not* lazy or 'admitting defeat' – it is considerate not only of your saddle but also of your horse's back and comfort. Unevenly compressed stuffing is also caused by lopsided riding.

The saddle may sit crooked on the horse due to uneven muscular development of his back, which is caused by his way of going. He may be protecting his own muscles if he has a sore or strained back, and lameness may cause uneven use of the back muscles and therefore uneven development. He may be bracing himself against bad riding and a rider who rides better on one rein than the other. He himself may well prefer one rein to the other, and this can certainly cause uneven muscular development.

Stand behind your horse when he is saddled and standing square, really assess whether the saddle is sitting straight on his back. If not, get it restuffed accordingly and try to get to the root of the cause.

If a saddle receives a good soaking, perhaps by horse and rider falling in water – either the lake at Badminton or the local duckpond – the stuffing can subsequently become hard and lumpy and may need replacing so as not to risk a sore back.

· THE BRIDLE ·

Probably few articles of equipment set off a horse's appearance as much is an attractive, well fitted and well maintained bridle in which the horse is obviously comfortable.

Whatever bridle you use, you should be able to pass a finger easily under the straps all round, including the noseband; if you can't, it is too tight – and there is a current trend for over-tight nosebands, particularly cavesson nosebands in competitive dressage, in an effort to encourage the horse to keep his mouth closed. However, the basic elements of fit should always apply – the bridle must not rub or cut in anywhere. The base of the ears must be free and comfortable, the cheekpieces of bridle or noseband must not come close to the corners of the eye, the sharp face bones must not be rubbed in any way (this usually happens with the noseband) the breathing must not be restricted and the bit, if a snaffle, pelham or curb used alone, should *just* wrinkle the corners of the mouth. In a double bridle the curb should, of course, be slightly lower than the bridoon otherwise it will interfere with its action.

The safest metal for any bit is stainless steel. Nickel (grandly called 'solid nickel') is weak. It bends, breaks and wears easily. It can even snap without warning, and particularly in snaffles and bridoons will wear away where the mouth piece meets the bit ring, ultimately pinching the horse's lips and causing great pain.

Bits can be bought with vulcanite mouthpieces, but unfortunately these are more common with rings or cheekpieces of nickel rather than stainless steel, although the latter can be found with a little trouble. Rubber mouthpieces are still available, and any mouthpiece can be covered with leather or chamois for extra softness, – I have known them be covered with self-adhesive fabric Elastoplast by more than one professional yard.

Whatever bit is used, it is in practice less important than the sensitivity of the hands on the other end of the reins. A simple snaffle can be an instrument of torture in rough hands; a double bridle with a long cheek can be the means to a sublime partnership in the hands of a true expert and horse lover.

It is not always the case that a thick mouthpiece is best. True, it spreads the pressure, but horses with small mouths may not be comfortable with chunky mouthpieces. As for fit, the bit should protrude out of each side of the mouth for half an inch (about 13mm). Too wide and it will slip about annoyingly, too narrow and it will pinch the horse.

Other items of equipment include martingales, schooling reins, boots and bandages of different sorts. Whatever is used, nothing should cause the horse discomfort but should assist in his management, schooling and work, not create problems. The more we can do without, the fewer problems we shall have.

Exercise bandages are often put on ostensibly for support but their effectiveness is questionable – if they are applied from just below the knee or hock to just above the fetlock, they do not actually support; they do, however, protect against knocks and abrasions (particularly if put on over padding as is usually advised) and probably lessen the vibrations involved in concussion. There are several types of new, impact-resistant paddings now on the market which are practical and economical, being washable and reuseable.

To actually support the leg, it is necessary to apply bandages quite firmly over and around the fetlock joint in such a way as to restrict the action – and this is certainly counter-productive during exercise and work. If a horse or pony needs his legs supporting, he should not be working.

· CLOTHING ·

Horse clothing has improved beyond imagination during the past few years. New textiles can now provide us with rugs which act as a winter rug, summer sheet, under-blanket, turn-out rug and anti-sweat sheet all in one garment. The main feature of such rugs is that the fabrics from which they are made are 'breathable' or permeable, in other words they allow moisture from the horse to evaporate up through the fabric into the atmosphere but prevent rainwater soaking in. Some fabrics actively remove the moisture so horses wearing them dry off more quickly than they would if wearing nothing.

There are many brands and types available; keep an eye open for new developments, because there is no doubt that these rugs are a vast improvement and far more practical than the traditional sort. Natural fabrics such as wool, jute, cotton and linen have their own individual advantages, but caring for them is far more time consuming. Some new fabrics and fillings (notably polystyrene bead fillings) claim to have a therapeutic effect on conditions such as rheumatism, arthritis and poor circulation, and this often seems to be borne out in practice – it apparently is based on the effects of a natural electrical charge emitted by them but which is not detected (in the form of a shock!) by users or wearers.

Modern rug fastenings are also a vast improvement on the old surcingle or roller which encompassed the horse's girth more or less tightly and must also have been more or less uncomfortable. Now we can choose between surcingles which criss-cross under the belly, front leg straps with

The traditional method of rugging up horses with rug, blanket and roller, which cannot be very comfortable for the horse. With the arch or anti-cast roller illustrated, every time the horse rolls he jabs himself in the back, creating sore muscles in the saddle area

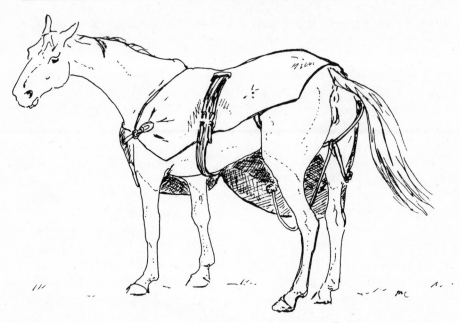

Another old-fashioned and uncomfortable rug, this time a so-called New Zealand. It is not the traditional New Zealand rug which has no surcingle (see photograph on p47). This type of rug slips round, being unshaped, presses on the spine, withers, shoulders, hips and croup and pulls the unforgiving leg-straps up into the tender groin area. Altogether, this is a picture of a horse in absolute misery, yet so often seen

fillet strings and drawstrings, hind leg straps and complete front-to-back harnesses. These are not tightly fastened but rely on their slight tension, careful positioning, and good tailoring to stay on and in place.

The correct shaping of modern rugs is as great an advance as the fabrics and fastenings themselves. Good rugs are tailored along the spine to follow the shape of a horse's back – up for the withers, down for the back, up again slightly for the croup and down a little for the root of the tail. This shaping ensures that the rug sits naturally in place on the horse's back with no significant pressure on the withers (the most vulnerable area), or croup.

Additional tailoring in the form of tucks or darts – round the neckline, behind the elbow, in front of the stifle and/or round the back edge – also creates room for the shoulders and hipbones. All this results in a rug which is much more comfortable for the horse, which stays on and in position and does not cause soreness or irritation from pressure on protruding parts of the horse's body.

So there is no need to buy an unshaped, or only partly shaped kind of rug, as properly shaped ones are readily available in any good retail outlet. If we all insist on properly designed ones, the others will eventually become a thing of the past – to the benefit of our horses.

Anti-sweat rugs (the traditional mesh kind) are the exception – they are so malleable that there is no need for shaping.

Under-rugs should also be shaped, otherwise all your care in choosing your top rug will be largely in vain. Again, these have a variety of fastenings and some stay on with only a breast strap due, again, to good shaping and material which moulds itself to the horse's body. Even if your horse is clipped right out and you feel you need several blankets under a top rug, there is still actually no need to use an old-fashioned surcingle or roller fastening. Modern clothing offers so many different and excellent top rugs and under-rugs that you can buy them with confidence that you *will* be able to keep your horse warm.

· CARE AND MAINTENANCE ·

Some people learn to do simple saddlery and clothing repairs themselves, either from experience, correspondence courses or books; others prefer to have their equipment maintained by a qualified saddler. Either way, maintained it must be for your own and your horse or pony's safety. Get into the habit of automatically checking for undone stitching, cracks in the leather, fraying straps or fabric, broken buckles or clips etc, and get them seen to at once. More than one horse in my own experience has broken a leg in the stable through bringing himself down on a rug which came off but stayed fastened around his neck.

Saddles particularly should be checked where the girth tabs are sewn to the canvas up under the flap; also stirrup leathers around the buckles for loosened buckle tongues and fraying stitching, and the fold in the leather where the stirrup usually goes. If signs of wear are evident, take the leathers to the saddler to be repaired, and maybe to have the buckle end shortened so the stirrup rests on a different part of the leather. Buffalo hide or extra strong leathers are much preferred, for safety, to the ordinary leather ones.

Your stirrups should be half an inch (13mm) wider than the widest part of your boot on each side: any wider and your foot could slide through and become caught, any narrower, it could jam and become stuck, both of which could result in a fatal injury should you become unseated.

It is usually advised that the safety catch on stirrup bars should always be down so that your leather will come off the bar in such a situation, but if your catch is properly oiled and used regularly, you should be able to keep it up and let it do the job for which it was intended, which is to keep your stirrup leather on the bar in all but extreme circumstances.

Fabric items these days can usually be washed at home in an

ordinary washing machine (with a good filter!) but be certain to follow
the washing instructions – high temperatures can melt some fabrics or
fillings, which renders them useless. Do not use biological washing powders or strong detergents as even with umpteen rinses these can cause
skin reactions in some horses (and humans) – use a soap or soda-based
product. Traditional jute night rugs may need washing in a tub or old
bath outside as they are very heavy and difficult to handle when wet.
Woollen day rugs should be dry cleaned; coat the leather straps with oil
and then petroleum jelly (Vaseline) first, and oil them thoroughly again
on return – there is no need to remove them as is sometimes advised.
Woollen blankets normally can be washed at home, in just warm water
and a mild washing product; rinse them in the same temperature water
as you wash them otherwise they may shrink.

Synthetic tack and harness (as well as clothing) is gradually making
an impact on the market, and reduces the cost and upkeep involved with
leather items. Nylon web headcollars have been available for some time,
and nylon or cotton web bridles and harness, although these are harder
to acquire. There is also a permeable, leather-look synthetic material
now being used for Zilco harness, and the Wintec synthetic saddle is
making an international name for itself – very easy to care for (you just
hose it down), and extremely comfortable with an accurate rider-position.
Synthetic tack usually just needs hosing down, or wiping down with a
damp, perhaps soapy, cloth or sponge if greasy, and rinsing. Webbing
gear can be swished in warm, soapy water, and thoroughly rinsed.

Leather tack, of course, must be washed, dried with a chamois,
soaped, maybe buffed up and occasionally oiled, and strictly speaking
this should be done each time it is used; many owners just do not have
time for this – if you are one, at least try to rub over the underside of
the tack, which touches the horse.

Cold water is usually recommended for washing leather as hot is said
to damage it: this is true, but cold water is useless for removing grease.
Use just warm water with a few drops of a mild, soap-based washing-up
liquid in the water, and wash the dirt and body grease off with that. You
need the soap to break down the grease, but use only a very few drops
and there will be no need to rinse the leather again. Get straight on with
the saddle soaping in the usual way.

Glycerine saddle soap is by far the best to use, in my experience, as
it keeps tack supple without the need to oil it regularly. Oiling should
always be carried out on new or neglected tack twice, with a two week
interval; branded leather dressings can be used or, less satisfactory I feel,
neatsfoot oil. Two *thin* coats should be applied, paying particular attention
to the 'rough' or underside which is the most absorbent. Over-oiling, in

fact, weakens the leather by making it too soft and unable to take much strain. It also becomes slimy and most unpleasant to use.

Leather tack in particular, and preferably all tack and clothing, should be stored in dry, fairly warm conditions (about 68°F [20°C]) with good air circulation. If leather tack or harness is not going to be used for some time, it should be well oiled and the metal parts smeared with oil or petroleum jelly too, then covered over with cotton sheets or put in cotton bags. Bridles and harness should, if possible, be undone and stored flat.

Everyday storage is also important. Saddles are best kept on proper saddle racks or saddle horses, and not slung on ropes or poles which press up into the gullet and stretch the seat leather. Bridles should have their headpieces on a rounded bracket (an old saddle soap tin will do, or a wooden block) and not hung on a hook or nail as the sharp fold will eventually crack the leather. Every care should be taken not to scratch the leather as this spoils its appearance and weakens it. Nor can the surface be restored.

Bandages and boots should be stored in a drawer or cupboard; rugs should be aired and perhaps brushed daily and stored on a rack or rug bracket (folding ones are available which store the rugs flat against the wall), or folded and put in a trunk.

Harness should also be kept on a saddle horse or hung from rounded pegs.

Good tack, harness and clothing is expensive and plays an important part as regards your horse's comfort, the safety of both of you and your performance. It is well worth taking care of your equipment.

Summary

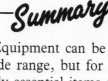

•Equipment can be expensive and there is a wide range, but for basic pleasure riding the only essential items are: a saddle, or harness, bridle and bit; head-collar with leadrope; and perhaps a rug, (also underblankets if you clip). A waterproof turnout rug can be helpful. Go to a retailer who is a member of his craft guild and/or trade association – in Britain, the Worshipful Company of Saddlers and/or the British Equestrian Trade Association.

•Your saddle must: fit your horse, length/width; fit you, length and panel/flap size; be the right design for your work; be well balanced

Summary

from front to back, and side to side, so that it sits you in the deepest part of the seat, which should be the centre. It must not touch the withers or spine anywhere along its length.

●Bridles should fit so that you can pass a finger easily under every part. Take care not to rub the corners of the eyes and the sharp face bones; nor to restrict the breathing.

●Bits (and stirrups) are best made of stainless steel. The bit should protrude on each side of the mouth for half an inch (about 13mm) and should just wrinkle the corners of the lips, the exception being the curb bit of a double bridle which is fitted slightly lower than the bridoon so that it does not interfere with the latter's action.

●A good range of clothing helps effective horse and pony management. New fabrics have resulted in permeable, multi-purpose rugs, properly shaped and with comfortable fastenings.

●All tack, harness and clothing should be kept in good repair for safety and economy. Saddles in particular should be regularly checked for fit and be sent for restuffing if necessary.

●Fabric items can usually be washed at home (follow the washing instructions) although woollen day rugs are best professionally cleaned. Use mild, soap-based products or washing soda (not detergent, and particularly not biological powders, which can cause skin reactions).

●Clean leather items with warm water with a few drops of mild washing-up liquid to break down the grease. Leather regularly treated with glycerine saddle soap does not normally need oiling unless it becomes really soaked. Over-oiling weakens leather and makes it unpleasantly slimy.

●Leather tack is best stored in dry, fairly warm, airy surroundings. Take care not to scratch the surface, and hang it on properly shaped brackets to keep the leather in shape and to prevent cracking.

Checklist

✔ 1 All tack and clothing should enhance your horse's comfort, not cause problems: It must, therefore, be the right type for the job and must fit properly.

2 Ill-fitting equipment will cause warm (inflamed) spots on the skin, raised areas, obvious soreness, rubbed hair, bare skin or, at worst, raw skin. Skin can be hardened off with surgical spirit, but if the skin is actually broken bathe with saline solution, and anyway remove the ill-fitting part. If the horse reacts irritably or violently, he is obviously uncomfortable.

3 With the new, properly shaped rugs, rubbed shoulders and croups are less likely. The old style, unshaped rug can be improved by sewing (inside the rug) stiff felt pads on either side of the withers, and on the back area either side of the back seam (if a round-the-girth surcingle is used). Darts can be added at elbow and stifle to improve shaping. If the rug does rub, lining at the point of friction with old silk headscarves, skirt lining fabric or sheepskin helps lessen the effects but does not remove the cause.

4 Use warm, slightly soapy water for cleaning leather tack to ensure the removal of grease.

5 Dirty tack and harness causes sore skin, and accumulated dirt and grease reduces the life of the leather; at least clean the underside after use. Always wash bits after each use in clear water; thoroughly wash off any metal polish used during cleaning and don't use it on the mouth piece.

6 Check tack, harness and clothing regularly. Rotted and fraying stitching and webbing gives way without warning; so does dry leather, whether cracked or not.

7 Correct storage conditions prolongs the life of your equipment, maintains its condition and keeps it looking good.

8 Clothing should be regularly laundered to help prevent dirt-associated skin disease. Rugs and blankets should be brushed and aired, preferably daily. You will probably need two rugs – one on, one in the wash. Modern synthetic fabrics wash and dry quickly. Try not to swap clothing between animals as this can encourage the spread of skin diseases.

9 Pull out each foreleg after tacking or harnessing up, to stretch forward the skin under the girth. This, plus a clean, smooth girth, is a very effective way of preventing girth galls.

10 Anything uneven under tack and clothing can cause soreness – wrinkled skin, wrinkled fabric, folded up leather, rough stitching, debris such as bits of bedding, dried mud, dried sweat etc. Check that everything fits properly, is clean and smooth and you should have no trouble.

10

EXERCISE AND WORK

Most pleasure horses are kept significantly short of exercise, at least those kept mainly stabled, and those on the combined system who are only turned out for an hour or two each day will be basically short of exercise, too. If a horse is ridden or driven for say, two hours daily, and turned out for a further three, that is still only 5 hours exercise out of a possible 24, leaving 19 hours confined. Fully stabled animals are even worse off, with two hours or maybe even less being their norm.

Many 'classic' stable management books stipulate that two hours exercise per day is the correct amount for a healthy, mature horse, hunting fit. Many horses do seem reasonably content and physically well on this amount, but many more do not. Even if when exercising they are the sort which is keen to get home, they nonetheless show mental and physical signs of lack of exercise and over-confinement – filled legs, restlessness in the box, or dull inertia, standing resignedly with their tails to the door. In others, the frustration and tension of insufficient physical activity and a general feeing of being shut in and restrained can result in stable vices.

This is quite understandable when we remember that horses have evolved to live on the move, walking about in a leisurely manner eating for most of their 24 hours. It is remarkable that so many *do* adapt reasonably well to a life of relative inactivity with at the very most only two periods a day of comparatively intense activity. And even purposeful walking contrasts notably with the slow, wandering amble of horses doing what comes naturally – pottering about to find more grass. Horses living in the wild do not often exert themselves, and they certainly do not exceed a moderate short canter unless harrassed.

However, the horse family is noted for its speed potential, the very thing we find attractive. It is as though we absorb some of that power and speed into our own comparatively, weak, slow body when we ride or drive horses, since ours is *not* adapted for either. Our superior intelligence is supposed to be our forté – although as far as the natural environment is concerned, and all its living creatures, we only seem to use it for short-term gain.

THE NEED FOR EXERCISE

The horse, then, has evolved to need a great deal of mostly gentle exercise if its body is to function effectively and its mind is to feel settled. There is an old adage: 'Slow work is always beneficial, fast work rarely is', and I think if we bore this in mind more we should not go too far wrong. There are times, of course, when even slow work is harmful, such as during lameness, and when fast work is needed, such as when getting a horse fit for work; but basically that old saying is sound. We will not do much harm if we give him several hours walking with some slow trotting every day; but even one hour's fast cantering or galloping could do him irreparable harm even if he were fit.

Exercise stimulates the development of the muscles – their repeated contraction and relaxation, and the movement of the body, manipulates the blood and lymph vessels and improves circulation, the heart has to work harder and faster which again stimulates circulation, and the lungs also must increase their rate of working. Therefore, nutrients and oxygen are carried faster and more effectively around the body, and waste products are carried away and excreted faster. This obviously improves the condition and performance of the whole body.

The horse's body temperature increases slightly with exercise, so the skin becomes more active, sweats more and renews itself more rapidly and effectively.

Exercise, therefore, improves and strengthens the whole body: insufficient exercise weakens it and causes deterioration, according to Nature's law. If there is no demand for something it tends to dwindle away.

Too *much* exercise, however – overwork for the horse's state of fitness – obviously has adverse effects such as stress and strain, loss of muscle power, heart failure (the heart being a muscle), ruptured blood vessels and injury to muscles, tendons and ligaments; it can also have a significant psychological effect which can sicken a horse whether it results from one severe incident or is accumulated over a period of time.

Sufficient rest is essential: it allows the body to recuperate after work, tissue to regenerate, the mind to relax and waste products to be removed, and also energy stores to be rebuilt in the body for future work. After significant work such as a competition or demanding work-out, it can take up to three days for the horse to recover properly – longer if the work was too severe for his state of fitness.

If sufficient rest is not given between competitions, or if a horse is kept working after he has become tired, oxygen and energy will not be

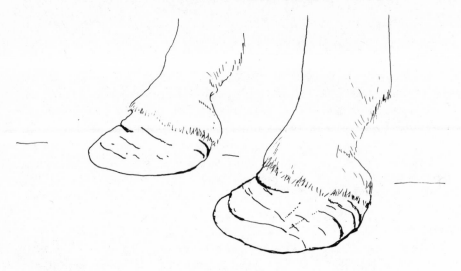

Laminitic feet. Note how the rings grow upwards in the heel region as this area continues to grow. The horn at the front of the foot often breaks under the coronet, where horn production has ceased, and comes away from the sensitive areas of the foot

sufficiently replenished and toxins (the waste products of energy production or metabolism), will build up, resulting in exhaustion, possible injury and maybe collapse.

Insufficient exercise in mature horses causes bad temper and over-excitement, excess energy and crazy behaviour when out, and a host of physical problems: poor circulation, respiration and digestion; obesity, colic and constipation; lymphangitis and azoturia; laminitis and navicular disease, and the feet also tend to shrink. Besides these, the frustration and confinement favour the development of stable vices.

In youngstock, insufficient exercise causes lack of development and stunted growth which may never be fully made up, also susceptibility to disease, delayed maturity and a general weakness of constitution which, again, may never be overcome, plus mental distress.

FIT FOR WORK

The basic process of getting a horse fit will be familiar to readers and is the same for any horse or pony, no matter what work he is doing. It is in the middle stages of a full fitness programme that the techniques change to accommodate the different requirements of the different disciplines.

The first month should always be spent walking and trotting (slowly) in gradually increasing amounts. Certainly the first two weeks should be spent walking, a fairly purposefully walk but not too fast. The horse should be encouraged to take active strides, long and relaxed, with a light bit contact. For particularly demanding activities – eventing, long distance riding, carriage driving – the two weeks could well be extended to three or four. This may sound boring and unnecessary, but it is proven by experience that this month of walking lays the foundations for a stronger, fitter, sounder horse later on in the season, less likely to succumb to stresses and strains.

Trotting should be fairly slow to start with, but up to the bridle, and preferably done on soft surfaces such as verges, or round the paddock or on some prepared riding track or manège; usually, a week or two's trotting is done, the work increasing in length and intensity. The programme will diversify when the canter stage is reached – this is normally the time for specialisation, or for the introduction of interval training, or whatever other system the trainer adheres to.

The traditional method of getting a horse fit consists of increasing the work and feeding, and of giving him his canter work in usually one long, steady stint; in the later stages this will increase to three-quarter speed gallop. Interval training depends on pulse rate: the horse has several short stints; after each it is allowed to *almost* recover to the pre-work pulse rate of very roughly 80 beats per minute (depending on the individual) before it has the next stint. Eighty beats per minute is the approximate rate of a horse walking and trotting about, which it would do to warm up before commencing the more taxing work.

If the horse is allowed to recover completely, the body (including, of course, the heart) is not increasingly stressed and so does not benefit as much as it should – the body will always adapt to stress of any kind by strengthening itself so that it can resist the stressor next time it occurs. This applies to almost any aspect of life. For example, if a horse's body is stressed by an invasion of bacteria, it will produce antibodies (soldier cells) to fight off the invaders, some of which will remain circulating in the bloodstream 'on guard' for when the next invasion takes place; this gives the horse a level of immunity. If the next attack is more severe, the level of antibodies will be increased, and so on.

So it is with work. Increasing amounts of work result in gradual adaptation and strengthening of the body, improved reactions to work by both mind and body and generally better health. Traditional fittening methods do have this effect, but advocates of interval training believe that this method produces a more significant response, more quickly because the body is repeatedly slightly stressed.

This means that the horse does not undergo the undeniable physical stress of training to the same extent and is, therefore, less likely to break down or suffer some other injury purely from the training.

As fitness increases, the stints are lengthened, the pace increased and the recovery time reduced. As a general guide, if the horse has not recovered to the required rate within ten minutes, work is suspended and interval/fast training stopped because the horse is obviously not yet fit enough for this stage of the fitness programme.

The whole subject of exercise physiology in the horse is fascinating, complex and wide-ranging. Several countries are actively researching the physiology of the horse, not only using racehorses who have always led this field, but also today's performance/competition horse. This is prompted by the increase in popularity of horse sports in general, and the increasingly large amounts of money now involved in the world of the competition horse, not only regarding purchase prices but also because of all the ancillary business generated in the form of sponsorship, equipment and services. (For further reference regarding exercise physiology and fitness in horses see p261–2).

Always remember that the importance of the initial 'slow', preparatory stage of a fitness programme should never be under-estimated. It is essential to prepare the horse's body for faster work by *gradual* strengthening and 'toning'. Whether you decide to go for traditional fittening methods or one of the more modern ones, the initial stage is essential whatever you are going to use your horse for. Driving horses, too, can with advantage be ridden and given at least some of their initial work under saddle. Part of it, however, should be given in harness to accustom the appropriate muscles to the work required. The skin of both riding and driving horses also needs to be gradually stressed by the pressure and friction of tack so that it toughens up in resistance.

Methods such as lungeing, long-reining, exercise on a horse-walker or leading in hand do help to get the respiratory and circulatory systems fit, and to some extent the muscles, tendons and ligaments, but they do not exercise the muscles used for carrying or pulling weight, so for at least three quarters of the fittening work the horse should be ridden or driven.

Many people who use their horses non-competitively, say for long, active hacks, also need to get their horses fit. Such horses frequently go down with 'unexplained' injuries which, when investigated, can be put down to the horse or pony simply not being fit enough for the work asked of them. A casual, enjoyable hack to us may be quite a stressful workload to the horse.

Children's ponies in particular are often significantly over-stressed by their enthusiastic young riders. Some distressing sights can be seen on any gymkhana field – ponies, over-fat with heaving sides, sweating and obviously in trouble, yet I have never seen veterinary checks taking place at a gymkhana! Boring though a fitness programme may be to young riders, their adult connections should insist that if any pony is not made properly fit with a correct, graduated fitness programme, they will not be allowed to compete.

There is no mystique about getting a horse or pony fit. Anyone can do it with a little commonsense and with guidance, perhaps, from someone more experienced. Generally, it takes six weeks to make a horse or pony half fit, ie from complete softness to the stage where he is fit enough to undertake about two hours' hacking each day and some schooling, perhaps with low jumps. He should also be fit enough for a half-hour lesson, a showing class or an easy show jumping class. After 12 weeks, he should be fully fit for all normal purposes, hunting, showjumping, showing, hunter trials, one-day events, dressage (which is more strenuous than people realise), and so on. Three-day eventers and endurance horses competing in major rides (50 miles and upwards) have their programmes increased to about 16 weeks, depending on the horse.

Traditional fitness methods dictated that a horse, for whatever discipline he was being prepared, was never tested or worked at the distance and speed to be expected in competition; many researchers believe that this was why so many horses in the past proved not up to the job. They now think that in order to be fit for a purpose – for example, completing a testing cross-country course of a given length in a given time, or travelling 50 miles in one day at an average of 8mph – the horse's body must have actually been subjected to that task so that it can respond to the stress involved and adapt or strengthen itself accordingly. Trainers have always believed that to do this meant working the horse unnecessarily hard and was asking for trouble. 'A horse should never be asked "the big question" except in actual competition', has been the emphatic statement. 'But if you don't prepare him adequately by working up to the required criteria, that question is expecting too much of him,' respond the scientists.

More and more trainers, particularly from racing, eventing and endurance riding, are now co-operating with the scientists, and although our knowledge is very incomplete still, more and more pieces of the physiological jigsaw are appearing as time goes on; before too long we should be able to work our horses with the true confidence born of knowledge which has been tried and tested under genuinely working and competitive conditions.

If you do wish to compete at all seriously, find a veterinary surgeon who is interested in equine exercise physiology so that he or she can do the associated blood tests and profiles, and the muscle biopsies which will tell you whether your horse is likely to excel at speed work for short distances or endurance work, whether you have a sprinter or a stayer, a long distance horse or a jumper who can win against the clock. Any vet can arrange for the tests, of course, but it is more helpful to be able to discuss results with someone who is genuinely involved and interested.

Even if you do not wish to tackle interval training, it will be helpful to know your horse's temperature, and his pulse and respiration rates at rest, immediately after work and while he is recovering. Take them at the same time each day under the same conditions for a week so that you get a true picture of the average readings – this only takes five minutes.

Average at-rest rates for a horse (ponies will be slightly higher) are:

Temperature about 38°C or 100.4°F
Pulse about 34 to 42 beats per minute
Respiration about 8 to 14 breaths per minute (in and out counting as one breath)

· TO TAKE THE TEMPERATURE ·

You can buy digital thermometers which are very accurate but rather expensive, and which give an almost instant reading. They are available through mail order advertisements, good saddlers or possibly your veterinary surgeon. Otherwise, buy a good quality veterinary thermometer from your vet. Shake the mercury well down with a snapping movement of your wrist, moisten the end by either spitting on it or smearing it with petroleum jelly and insert it in the horse's anus with a gentle twisting, side-to-side movement. Press it gently against the wall of the rectum and leave it in place for the time stated on the thermometer. Gently remove it, wipe it clean and read off the temperature.

· TO TAKE THE PULSE ·

This can be done at any point where an artery crosses a bone. The usual sites are under the jawbone, inside the elbow a little way down, above the eye and under or at the side of the dock about a third of the way down. Feel around with your fingers and leave them in one place for a few seconds while searching (do not use your thumb as you might pick up your own pulse instead). Using a watch with a second hand, count the pulse for half a minute and double it to get the rate per minute.

· TO TAKE THE RESPIRATION ·

Stand behind and slightly to one side of your horse and watch his opposite flank rise and fall. It can be very difficult to spot this, particularly in a fit horse or pony. If this is the case, get a mirror and hold it in front of the horse's nostrils to see how often it steams up. He may well hold his breath in surprise first time, but persist and you will succeed!

During a fitness programme, take his rates at least weekly (if you are not using interval training) and you will notice that as his fitness improves they will all be lower at rest than they were when you started the programme. It is very important to know your normal averages: firstly, while the horse is at rest, calm and quiet before morning work; then what they are after normal warming up (the usual walking and trotting about before any fast work); then give your horse your planned fast work and note how long they take to return to the warm-up rates. They should be there within ten minutes, otherwise, generally speaking, the horse is not fit enough to continue at that level.

Britain is a country not normally known for its hot, humid weather, but in the last few years several horses in horse trials and endurance rides have been over-heating. Work involves burning up energy, of course, and this creates heat. In order to lose heat the horse has one major physiological aid, and that is sweating; the sweat then evaporates into the surrounding atmosphere and that creates cooling. Sometimes the sweat cannot evaporate because the surrounding air is already the same temperature as the horse, and if it is humid and therefore loaded with moisture already, there is nowhere for the sweat to evaporate to; in these conditions the horse *cannot* cool down. The horse will keep getting hotter *after* exercise for some little while because his muscles restock with energy and oxygen (this also creates heat) and he can soon be in serious danger of becoming very ill from hyperthermia or overheating, and may even die.

In such conditions it is always speed that causes the trouble. The horse could walk around all day in the burning sun and probably be none the worse, but if he cantered a few miles he could be at risk. Horses and ponies competing in hot, humid conditions *must* be taken more slowly, and organisers of competitions should shorten courses and extend the time allowed to prevent the over-enthusiastic from distressing, and maybe killing, their horses.

Use the horse's bodyweight as a guide to telling when he is at his optimum body condition for work. Keep a note of his weight during your fitness programme, particularly when his fitness seems to be just right for the job in hand – that is your horse's optimum weight. This will help you adjust his work and diet to keep him right, for once he is fit his work can slacken off, since horses can maintain fitness for several weeks, even during a complete layoff. Giving him an easier time – more relaxation, easy hacks, and the chance to graze and roll in the paddock (which I believe he should have every day anyway) – goes a long way towards keeping him *mentally* fit and enthusiastic.

Remember that horses do not have the incentives to work and get fit that we have. They are not interested in prestige, rosettes, prize money or being the best, so may well be less inclined to put up with the physical and mental discomfort suffered by human athletes. They are *horses* and need to be treated as such if they are to remain both physically and psychologically fit to work.

LETTING DOWN AND ROUGHING OFF

Letting a horse down and roughing him off are related processes, and are important in so far as good management dictates that we should never make sudden changes, not only in feeding but in general routine, too. Any change confuses and unsettles a horse to some extent and although there are times when it might be unavoidable – such as when taking him to a competition – generally it is better to avoid it.

Letting down involves gradually slackening off the horse's workload and reducing the concentrate portion of his diet, plus increasing his time turned out. The purpose is to give a fit, working horse a break from the tension of his life both mentally and physically.

Roughing off means actually preparing him for a life more or less outdoors and is a stage further than letting down. Body brushing is stopped, work probably stopped altogether and the horse is left out at grass for increasingly longer periods.

Because a fit horse can retain his fitness for two or three weeks during a let-down, I feel more such breaks could beneficially be given than may be the case with working horses at present. A horse can only retain peak fitness (the sort needed for racing and eventing) for a few weeks, depending on the individual. Horses used for less demanding pursuits such as riding club work are not that fit and can maintain this level much longer. A very fit horse will sooner or later pass his peak and go 'over the top'; he becomes 'overtrained', and suddenly seems, in fact, *unfit*, sweating and blowing after work more than usual, as he may have done part way through his fitness programme.

This is the time for the urgency to be taken out of his routine, for more relaxing and enjoyable work such as hacking, or half a day's hunting if it is winter. This can last for as long as the trainer feels it is necessary. During a long season, even just a couple of weeks on a light routine freshens up the horse without his losing physical fitness.

To rough a horse off, it is necessary to accustom him to living out more or less completely. The process is often far too rushed, particularly in spring when, after a winter stabled, corn-fed and rugged up, the cosseted horse is slung out into the field with very often only a week's adjustment. Like a fitness programme, roughing off should be a gradual process and should follow a couple of weeks' letting down. Otherwise, particularly in cold weather, the horse can become shocked and chilled and not only sick but very thin as well, and so even more prone to chills.

Always pick a mild spell for roughing off, and begin by leaving open his top stable door, although this should be done anyway, and leaving off one blanket or under-rug. Over the next two or three weeks gradually reduce his concentrates to about half his normal ration; be sure he is never short of hay, and very gradually build up his grazing till he is out all day, maybe wearing a New Zealand rug if he is clipped and the weather chilly. It will be much better for him if he has company and a decent field shelter with a bed down, so he can retreat there if there is a bad spell of weather. If he is lonely and cold, he will probably just stand by the gate and start to lose condition.

For his first night out altogether, again pick a mild night, not one that is cold, windy and rainy. Leave the New Zealand rug on and continue with his concentrates and as much hay as he wants. When he is ready he will start to leave the hay but will probably carry on eating the concentrates, so watch both the growth of grass and his condition, and gradually cut those out too over the next week or two, depending on circumstances. As soon as his coat starts to come through and the weather improves, leave off the New Zealand rug first by day, then by night too, and the process is complete. Keep a close eye on the weather and the horse's behaviour and condition, especially if it is still early in the spring, but generally if you have done things gradually there should be no problem.

Roughing off in autumn and winter is obviously easier, as you simply leave the horse out for longer and longer. If the grass has passed the autumn flush of growth you may well need to keep up the full concentrate ration, perhaps all winter, particularly if he is a well-bred horse; in a mild winter cobs and native-type ponies often need nothing but nice hay to see them through in good condition. However, don't think to yourself that 'he ought to be alright'. Watch the horse or pony himself and you will clearly see whether he really is alright or not. It is surprising how individuals within a breed or type can differ as regards what they want and need.

THE GRASS-KEPT ANIMAL

It is a common misconception that grass-kept animals cannot be made fit enough for fairly hard work. This is not the case, as many endurance riders will confirm.

Pasture them on low-quality grass, which is generally best for horses and ponies anyway, and feed them more or less as if they were stabled. In fact, horses kept this way are often healthier and usually sounder and fitter than stabled horses. They are mentally calmer and more settled because they have freedom and space and, hopefully, congenial company, and so they are more co-operative and amenable to work. Physically, they are on the move most of the time as nature intended, and although this movement is not 'work' movement, it does constitute the gentle exercise which the horse's body has evolved to thrive on. The work under saddle or in harness can be reduced slightly as the basic walking part of it can safely be cut by half once they are half fit. In fact, they will only need to have schooling work, some walking, and the trotting and faster paces – and will come to hand quicker than stabled horses and stand up to their work better.

As regards grooming, some body brushing can safely be given, and wisping will be found particularly useful – it muscles and tones up, and gives a groomed appearance but without removing too much natural oil from the coat.

If the grass is more nutritious, problems can arise and either your ambitions must be tempered or the horse's grass reduced. If he has to stay out, try strip-grazing using electric fencing and moving it on a metre or so each day, or find a poorer field.

Yarded horses and ponies have similar advantages to the outdoor ones, except that they will not have so much space. Their diet will be exactly as for stabled animals, but nonetheless they are usually happier and sounder than fully stabled animals.

ROADWORK AND TRAFFIC

Few animals these days can get away with not using roads at all when they hack out, and it is only a small minority who can go straight from their yard onto a private road, public bridleway or open space without encountering traffic and hard roads.

Hard roads themselves are no detriment to a horse. It is the sort of work done on them which can cause trouble. Some riders think absolutely nothing of trotting fast, cantering and even jumping onto hard roads, particularly in the hunting field – obviously, keeping up with the field is more important to them than their horses' well-being. It would be interesting to know how many seasons these horses last without foot and leg problems; some will surely give years of service, but they will be the unusually hard and sound sort. In general, the concussion sustained by such treatment can ultimately result in damaged joints and arthritis in the leg, and navicular disease and laminitis in the feet.

Expert opinion varies, as ever, as to whether walking and a steady working trot really do 'harden up' the legs during a fitness programme.

Commonly seen in the hunting field, this horse is being jumped out of a field onto a hard road. The concussion on the legs resulting from this sort of treatment is tremendous and highly injurious over a relatively short period

of the foot

There seems to be no scientific evidence either way but however inconclusive, there is no doubt that such exercise does no harm whatsoever in the normal, healthy, sound animal. Some people even keep entirely to walk on roads. In fact, the problem is not so much the hardness of the road, but its camber and we tend to overlook the fact that the horse is working permanently on the side of a slight slope, as it were. Anyone who has ever worked on a good stage which slopes slightly to the footlights – particularly ladies, whose heels suddenly become two inches higher – will have experienced something similar and will appreciate why it can take young animals quite some time to adjust to going on roads; it is not merely the slippery surface which fazes them. Many horses, left to themselves, will wander naturally into the centre of the road onto the level crown – which, of course, is quite out of the question where traffic is concerned.

Unfortunately horses and ponies are not allowed on any footpath which would give them more level footing. Nor are roadside verges always the answer, since many are strewn with dangerous litter or intersected with over-grown little drainage channels. However, where conditions permit we could perhaps make more use of suitable verges, and on a clear stretch of quiet road allow the horse to use the crown and give him a break from the incline.

Many people exercise in knee pads, and it is important that these are fitted correctly: comfortably snug around the top just above the knee to prevent them slipping down, but not so tight that they cause discomfort, and the bottom strap probably on the last, loosest hole to keep the pad down but so as not to cause annoyance to the horse or interfere with his action and rub.

Roadwork can be made much safer by using tiny road studs in the shoes, or nails with roughened heads, or borium welded into part of the fullering. This is particularly useful with young horses to help them find their feet more readily on an unfamiliar surface. However, care should be taken that studs of any kind do not upset the balance of the foot – road studs should be put in both sides of the shoe, not just the outside heel, as they are often kept in all the time and would otherwise unbalance the foot and cause uneven stresses and strains.

· TRAFFIC TRAINING ·

Very few horses these days can avoid traffic completely and a horse who is not safe enough in traffic to be ridden out tends to have a very restricted use.

Normally, it is essential to traffic train all horses and ponies from a young age. Some, in fact, do not actually seem to need training; never having come across traffic nor had an unpleasant experience, they do not bother about it and treat it as just part of the scene. Others behave quite differently; perhaps in the past they have had a frightening experience – anyway, they consider it strange, noisy, big and smelly.

Every opportunity should be taken to let youngsters come into contact with traffic as a matter of course right from the beginning: have the horsebox, car or Land Rover running in the yard or alongside the paddock. Roadside paddocks do have disadvantages (litter, vandals, joyriders) but they are extremely useful for getting their occupants used to passing traffic.

It helps to ride youngsters (once they respond adequately to the aids) in the company of traffic-proof horses; ride up and down private roads or a driveway where a car is travelling slowly – if he shows no alarm at this, he can hack on quiet roads in the same company; and take things along very slowly in this vein till he is old and well-schooled enough to go out alone.

Police horses are trained in this way; they are gradually exposed to potentially more and more alarming situations, encouraged to go forward, but turned away just *before* the trainer feels the horse might start to react adversely. He is then praised and the hazard abandoned for that day. In this way, there is never a 'fight' and the horse never has a chance to discover he can resist or get the better of his rider. Of course, in traffic we cannot dictate the circumstances once we are on public roads, but the principle is a very sound one which obviously works.

In Britain, the British Horse Society actively encourages riders to take their Riding and Road Safety Test, for which the required reading is the BHS booklet, *Riding and Roadcraft*. The tests are carried out with the help of the police and the booklet itself is really excellent whether you are taking the test or not, especially as our Highway Code is somewhat out-of-date regarding horses on the road – its information is accurate and good, but at the time of writing is very incomplete.

There are arguments both ways between motorists and riders, and faults on both sides. They do agree, however, in that riders do not really want to use the roads and the motorists do not want them to either; but there are far too few bridleways and other safe routes available for horses, and riding round the same field time and time again is most unfulfilling. The roads take us to the bridleways and other riding areas, as well as often being the actual routes themselves. Just remember that horses have as much right to be on the roads as all other road users, motorised or otherwise; and riders have as much of a duty to behave correctly, courteously and responsibly.

Be polite and considerate to other road users, behave correctly and if in doubt or having trouble, keep well to the left (in Britain) and if possible stop or pull into a convenient gateway or layby. Some horses are worse when at halt than if kept walking on, however, but anyway try and get off the road – do not feel you *have* to win an argument with your horse on the public roads as this can certainly create a bad impression with the public and could cause a serious 'situation'. You may have to give in – but return as soon as possible to the same spot with a reliable companion or two so that the horse does not feel he can make trouble there every time.

Horses have lifelong memories, and learn quickly, too; if they once win an argument with their rider or have a frightening or painful experience in traffic, they will always remember it and may never be trustworthy in that respect again. It is therefore far better to traffic train a youngster correctly than try and retrain a horse who has become bad in traffic and who is often impossible to rehabilitate, even with the most confident, competent rider.

Remember that horses and ponies often take their cue from their handlers. If the rider is nervous of what the horse is going to do in traffic (or any other situation), the horse will sense it and it may persuade him to become difficult when in fact he was not intending to.

Appearance also creates a good or bad impression: if riders *look* as though they are responsible, concerned road users, others will treat them as such.

Road-safety tabards should become standard wear. Lettering cannot always be read by drivers, but the well-recognised red triangle containing an exclamation mark signifies 'Caution' to everybody. And there is nothing wrong with wearing a tabard with L-plates front and back – almost *every* road user respects learner drivers and usually gives them plenty of room, which is just what we want for horses.

The range of brightly coloured reflective clothing is now excellent and comfortable. Lightweight, reflective mesh tabards are readily available, and are more pleasant than the solid plastic ones yet just as effective. There are reflective boots and bandages for horses, and exercise sheets, plus reflective strips to stick on bridles and harness. But the most important item of equipment is lighting if you have to ride in dusk or dark conditions. Stirrup lights are essential, fixed as low as possible – under your right stirrup, rather than higher up round your leg – so that motorists see them at about eye level; so many people kit themselves and their horses out with reflective gear of all sorts, yet overlook the most important item of all – a light.

A light can be seen much further away than reflective gear which is only picked up by car headlights when the car may be too close to stop, even if travelling comparatively slowly. The light should show white to the front and red to the rear. Always check your battery before you go out and have at least one spare in your yard, and if the light is becoming at all dim, change the battery.

Cyclists' shops are an excellent source of lighting equipment. They often sell belts or simple harnesses with battery-operated lights along them, and wrist lights so that your signals can be clearly seen. So far, no one seem to have produced 'light boots' for horses which would be an excellent idea.

If you have reflective boots or bandages on your horse or pony, do not obscure them by having his tail too long; in winter anyway, it can be difficult to keep clean, so cut it so that it comes just below hock level when he is moving. If he needs a 'natural' tail, either knot it up or at least plait it down in a single plait so that the boots can still be seen.

The one occasion when you really should not go out at all is when it is misty or foggy. In such conditions exercise only at home, maybe on a manure track as if it is icy, because to take a horse out in fog is just sheer lunacy.

If two or more of you are riding out together, always try to have

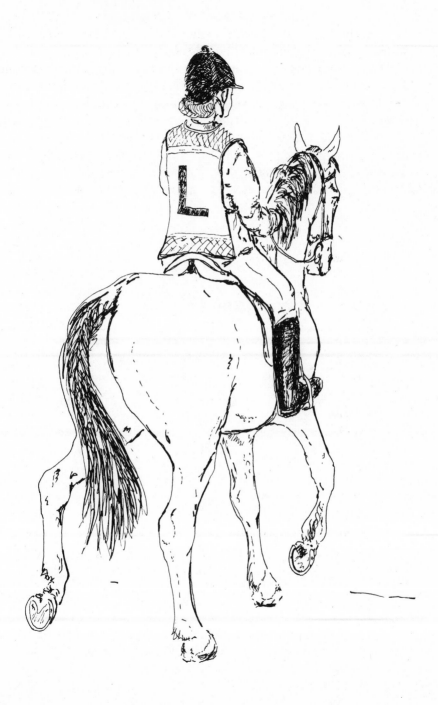

You may feel a little silly wearing an 'L' plate, but motorists certainly slow down

the palest horse at the rear and the next palest in front, providing their state of traffic training permits it. If leading horses on the road, always ride on the left (in Britain) with the led horse on your left. Lead from a bridle or lungeing cavesson, not an ordinary headcollar, wear gloves and have a long schooling whip in your right hand for extra control. Wear your hard hat, too. Try to have at least one assistant available who is *not* leading a horse, to help in emergencies.

If it is dark, for instance if you are leading horses and ponies to or from stables and field, the first and last leaders should wear or carry lights and preferably the assistant too. Do not have long convoys of animals – four in one group is plenty, and stay in single file well to the left.

Summary

●Most horses are kept too short of exercise, particularly those mainly stabled.

●Lack of exercise can result in temperament and behavioural problems, filled legs and lymphangitis, laminitis and colic, particularly when combined with over-feeding.

●Exercise improves the horse's body and mind: the body becomes stronger, the different physiological systems work better and the mind is more alert – yet the horse is calmer and more content.

●Too much exercise – which includes working the horse too hard for its state of fitness – causes excess stress and strain, can result in serious physical damage, and can sicken the horse of his job, maybe permanently.

●Sufficient rest is also important; after a moderately strenuous event a horse may need three or four days to recover energy stores and to clear himself of the metabolic waste products which have accumulated. About three weeks recovery may be needed after harder work.

Summary

●Youngstock deprived of exercise may never fully realise their potential physical development. However, overwork, particularly when too young, results in physical damage and mental disorders.

●The initial slow stage of a fitness programme is vital; it is the foundation upon which the faster work later on is based, and helps maintain sound, tough horses, whatever fittening methods are employed.

●Traditional training methods involve a fairly long, gradually increasing programme of work and feeding. At work, the horse is allowed to recover more or less fully before being worked again.

●Modern methods such as interval training rely on repeatedly stressing the horse by working him in regulated stints, each starting *before* his pulse rate has returned to pre-work levels; this encourages his body to adapt and strengthen up to the increasing work load without the stress and strain of longer, single stints of effort.

●If after work a horse's pulse rate has not recovered within ten minutes, to his pre-work rate, the horse should not be worked again that day and is not fit enough for the work being asked. The fitness programme should be modified otherwise more harm than good can result.

●At least two thirds of the horse's training should be done in the mode in which he will be working: if he is to be ridden, at least two thirds of his work should be under saddle; if driven, two thirds of it should be under harness. This ensures the adequate development of the appropriate muscles.

●Non-competitive horse and ponies must also be made fit for what can be an equally strenuous workload. Horses are not self-motivated and cannot be expected to get themselves fit; a programme is just as important for children's ponies, who are often overworked when in an over-fat condition.

●It takes six weeks to get a completely soft animal half fit, 12 weeks to get him fully fit for most normal work, and 16 weeks or more for strenuous activities like endurance riding or three-day eventing.

●Make yourself familiar with your horse's normal, at rest temperature, pulse and respiration rates, so that you can not only monitor his fitness but his state of general health.

●Beware of undertaking strenuous work in hot, humid conditions; speeds should always be reduced from what would normally be considered acceptable for the event.

●Bodyweight assists accurate feeding and can indicate when the horse is truly fit: most horses have an optimum weight at which they perform best, and by knowing what this is you can gauge when he is likely to do his best.

●Letting down a horse during his season greatly refreshes him mentally and physically without losing his physical fitness.

●Roughing off should receive more attention than at present, particularly in spring when the weather can still be chilly. It should be a gradual process and should depend on weather, grass growth and the individual horse not simply on the calendar. A New Zealand rug, supplementary feeding and a field shelter greatly help the process.

●Grass-kept animals can be kept just as fit as combined-system, or even stabled ones, *if* the grass on the field is of low nutritional quality – then they can be fed like stabled horses; but they stil have the advantage of being able to develop gradually and tone up their own bodies, since they can take a certain amount of exercise more naturally – this makes their fitness programme more easy.

●A working trot is fast enough on hard roads to avoid concussion injuries. The camber of the road can cause uneven stresses on a horse's feet and legs: work on verges or flatter surfaces; young animals in particular take time to adapt to working on the camber. Tiny road studs can be fitted against slipping (but in both sides of the shoe to avoid upsetting the foot balance); or borium can be used.

●Traffic training is very important; every horse should be exposed to it in increasing 'doses' to avoid a sudden fright, and every care taken to avoid a confrontation. Horses will never forget an unpleasant experience, which may well make them unsafe in traffic for life. It is often impossible to re-train a horse who has become bad in traffic.

●Horses and riders should behave correctly and wear road-safety equipment when on public roads. Use reflective tabards; at least one light – fixed under the right stirrup in Britain – is essential when riding in dusk or dark conditions

●*Never* take a horse or pony, ridden or driven, out in fog or mist.

●When leading horses on the roads use a cavesson or bridle; wear gloves and a reflective tabard. If it is dark, carry a light showing white to the front and red to the rear.
   Always stay well to the left (in Britain), behave correctly and ensure you can be seen.

Checklist

✓ **1** No horse or pony can work effectively or safely if he is not fit for the level of effort that work demands. A two-hour hack or drive may cause distress to the horse if we have not first made him fit through a gradually increasing programme of work and feeding.

2 It is hard to overwork a fit horse provided we balance his work sensibly. Remember: 'Slow work is always beneficial, fast work rarely is.' Most horses and ponies do not receive enough exercise, particularly stabled ones. Don't let yours be one of them.

3 There are times when exercising a horse ourselves *is* a chore. So give your horse better facilities for more freedom-type exercise (see Chapter 3) and make use of such time-saving techniques as ride-and-lead, horse walkers and limited lungeing and loose-schooling. However, turning out your horse or pony is probably one of the greatest favours you can do him, particularly if you ensure he is warm, well fed and has company.

4 Don't under-estimate the importance of the initial slow-work stage of a fitness programme: two weeks' walking for moderate fitness, four weeks if your horse is destined for strenuous work.

5 Learn your horse or pony's normal, at-rest temperature, pulse and respiration rates, and use them to gauge fitness and monitor general health.

6 When the weather is hot and humid – *slow down*.

7 When you let down, rough off, or bring up your horse or pony, do it *gradually* to avoid too sudden a change which will be a shock to his system and cause a lowering of health and condition.

8 You can get your grass-kept horse fit for hard work if you ensure the quality of grass in his feed is of low feed value – then feed and work him more or less like a stabled animal.

9 On the roads, behave correctly, wear road-safety equipment and *always* wear a light if it is dusk or dark. It is unlawful for a horse and vehicle to go on the public highway without lights.

10 As regards reflective colours, orange, yellow and pink are best for daylight, but reflective *white* is by far the most visible at night.

11 Don't always assume you can re-train a traffic-shy horse. It is often not possible.

11

GENERAL HEALTH

There are times when all our efforts at keeping the horse healthy are not enough and it succumbs to some injury or disease. Then we need the expert and highly qualified services of one of the most valuable people at our disposal – a veterinary surgeon. So often, owners and managers regard a vet as someone to be called upon as a last resort, not simply because he or she has to be paid, but often because it is not appreciated just how helpful a vet can be in general health care and management, and in disease prevention, not simply cure.

Your vet is the most logical person to ask about new developments in equine medicine and surgery, disease control and treatments for common ailments and disorders. He or she can also provide the latest information on exercise physiology, a vastly expanding field of knowledge, and the latest results from current research on general management methods for better health in the horse population.

Owners should keep as much up-to-date themselves as they can, too. Just about every equestrian magazine features regular veterinary articles and because most magazines are aimed at 'ordinary' owners, the technical articles are presented so that readers *can* understand them!

Everyone who is responsible for the daily care and management of a horse or pony should have at least one *up-to-date* veterinary book on their bookshelf. Unfortunately, some of the best known veterinary books are disgracefully *out* of date, at least in Britain, but continue to be widely used and bought – despite there now being several really good, modern books available (see p261–2).

When buying any veterinary or technical book which deals with an area in which research is currently going on apace – such as feeding or exercise physiology – always look in the front for its publication date and when it was last revised – *revised*, not reprinted which means that the same old information has simply been churned out again. It is *new* information you want in technical matters such as those affecting your horse's health and performance, and any technical book which has not been revised for five years or more is out of date. Although the basic information may in some areas still be accurate, more effective treatments will have been brought out since its publication; in other areas, scientific discoveries and modern thinking will have completely changed our understanding of physical processes, which in turn changes – sometimes drastically – the way we manage and treat our horses and ponies.

Magazines regularly review new books, so be sure you read the reviews as well as the veterinary and other technical articles; then you, too, can keep up to date.

SIGNS OF HEALTH AND DISEASE

Fundamental to the correct management of your horse or pony is the ability to recognise the difference between good health, slight 'off colour' and actual disease or injury. It is obvious that unless we know what is normal for a particular individual and for horses in general, we will not recognise what is *not* normal.

Even if your horse lives out and is, therefore, always greasy and muddy, he should still have a bright, glossy appearance to his coat, and his skin should feel alive and pliable, easily moved over the ribs with the flat of your hand. A dull, tight skin is a sign of disorder; so is a staring coat (one which stands rather stiffly away from the skin) or an unexplained loss of hair, and rubbed manes and tails can indicate skin parasite infestations.

The eyes should be bright and clear with no discharges other than the slight darkish discharge which is normal. The horse should have an alert, interested expression even when not excited (unless he is sleepy), with ears flicking back and forth towards whatever commands his attention.

The mucous membranes inside the eyes, nose and mouth should be salmon pink (not yellowish, pale, blueish or an angry red). After exercise, a horse may well have a watery discharge from his nostrils; however, such a discharge at any other time, or one which is thick and coloured (white, yellow, green or blood-stained) indicates disorder. There should be no swelling around the throat (or, indeed, anywhere) and the horse should not show undue sensitivity when being handled. For instance, if he suddenly becomes head-shy for no apparent reason, suspect soreness or pain. Head-shaking itself can be a sign of ear trouble, although this is a complex symptom which appears to have several, poorly-understood causes.

The horse should have a healthy appetite and eat normally for him. Some horses, particularly those on high concentrate diets, do go off their feed after a longish spell stabled or in hard work, and those consuming large amounts of concentrates often voluntarily reduce their hay/hayage consumption; but if this is normal for your horse it is not a sign of disorder. Generally going off feed, however, is.

Your horse's droppings are a good indication of his digestive state. Stabled horses' droppings will be a khaki colour and of such a consistency that they just crumble and break on hitting the ground. Grass-kept horses' droppings will be greener and probably looser, and a combined-system horse's obviously somewhere in between. If they are inordinately loose, hard and dry, pasty, thick, and doughy, if they have an unusual colour (say, yellowish or very dark, or are particularly blood-stained), or are coated with mucous, and any which smell unpleasant or downright nasty: all these are signs of disorder. He should do roughly eight piles in 24 hours.

Your horse or pony should normally appear nicely rounded and in good bodily condition. If he is quite fit, you should just be able to see the last two pairs of ribs – very fit, and he may actually appear scrawny; but you yourself will appreciate the lean, muscled-up physique of your equine athlete. Fatness is more dangerous than being slightly under-weight. Viewed from behind, a horse in good condition will generally have thighs the same width as the hips and the muscles between the thighs will meet. If he appears 'cut up behind' (where the thigh muscles do not meet between the legs) he is probably much too thin. His hips may well be slightly prominent if he is at peak fitness, but his muscling should indicate that he is in working condition and not thin.

Signs of thinness are: a dip in front of the withers, prominent vertebrae, lack of flesh generally but particularly on the neck, shoulders, back and quarters, and clearly visible ribs and hipbones. Some fit horses do 'run up light' during work and after a competition, which means they appear to lose weight and look 'tucked up', with marked hollows in front of the hip bones, but even if this is normal for them, they should put back the condition within a few days.

Any unusual heat or swelling anywhere is a sign of trouble. Legs should always be cool (as should feet) and the tendons should be clearly visible. You should be familiar with any 'leg jewellery' (lumps and bumps, hard or soft) your horse normally has.

The respiration should be barely detectable in the healthy, at-rest horse – the more obvious it is, the worse could be the trouble. Normal temperature, pulse and respiration rates have already been discussed; however, if the temperature varies more than a degree either way, call your vet. If the respiration changes rate or character, call your vet. And if the pulse also changes rate or character, becoming unusually slow or fast at rest, or seeming weaker or much stronger, call your vet.

Other signs of disorder are: a generally dull appearance, a lack of interest in surroundings, listlessness, staying apart from other horses, a lack of zest for food or work, and a generally dejected, hangdog look with floppy ears and low head. The horse may lie down more than usual, and if he does so for more than 30 minutes at a time, especially during the day, it is a bad sign. Take note of any unusual behaviour of any kind.

The horse's action should be even and level, free and confident. You do have to study your horse or pony carefully in this respect to get to know his normal way of going. If he has a gait abnormality, as long as it does not bother him, that does not matter so long as it is normal for him. It is when abnormalities arise that you should be alerted. How long has he been swinging that off hind out slightly? When did he start wearing his near fore shoe unevenly? He used to take a generally longer stride than he is now, didn't he? Questions such as this can all indicate something wrong, even if no actual lameness is apparent.

Lameness is a vast subject about which several highly complex and authoritative books have been written. To check for lameness, have the horse trotted up, first towards and then away from you – study his head when he is coming towards you, and his hocks when he is going away from you. A lame horse will nod his head *down* further when his *sound* foreleg hits the ground, and will seem to raise *higher* the hock of a *lame* leg. This is all because the horse is throwing his weight onto his sound legs, obviously to save himself pain.

Even slight lameness shows up at trot, whereas it might not at walk or canter. Have the horse lunged in trot on a hard surface such as a concrete yard – not fast, of course, just enough to show his action; trotting on a circle really does show up lameness. Lunge him both ways and study his way of going – he may be sound as a bell on one rein, but dead lame on the other, but you may have found this lameness harder to spot on a straight line. The horse's head must be completely unrestricted otherwise his action may be disguised. Trotting up and down a slight incline can also reveal lameness.

Coughing is a sound which most of those connected with horses dread. A cough is not a disorder in itself but a symptom of one, and can have many causes including disease, irritation or allergy. Because we so often keep our horses in such an artificial way by stabling them, their airspace is not as pure and clean as it should be and can cause coughing – ventilation is often insufficient and impure air results, mainly from the breaking down of organic waste, but also from the general dust and fungi contained in hay and straw. Infectious diseases such as influenza and strangles also cause coughing, obviously.

Normally, the character of a cough can tell us something about its origins. A sharp, hard cough is probably a throat irritation, a softer cough influenza and a deep, harsh cough may well be an allergy manifesting itself in the lungs.

Some horses cough for about the first ten minutes at exercise, apparently clearing their wind after being stabled in a less-than-perfect atmosphere, then stop. If such horses carry on for longer, or if a horse who does not normally cough like this starts to do so, stop work at once. With any cough, unless you are sure the horse is not just coughing to clear a bit of something stuck in his throat, it is always safest to call the vet. It is helpful if you can give the horse's temperature reading over the 'phone, and maybe the pulse and respiration too, with the details if they differ from normal.

Working a horse with a cough can be very detrimental to his wind and heart, so do not do so unless your veterinary surgeon has prescribed exercise.

VACCINATIONS

Vaccination is one of the most effective ways of protecting your horse or pony against any disease. In Britain we commonly vaccinate against influenza and tetanus (lockjaw), and often against the respiratory disease rhinopneumonitis (herpes virus); and another which we should certainly include is strangles. The reason we do not is because the very effective vaccine (available in some other countries) is not licensed for use here on the grounds that the disease is fairly rare, and confined to young horses; also that it can be cured and has no lasting deleterious effect on the horse and is therefore not of economic signficance.

In fact, strangles is quite common, and is not confined exclusively to young horses. It is a bacterial disease and so can be treated with anti-biotics, but in my experience, not *easily* so. It is also quite serious, and often has *permanently* damaging effects on the horse afflicted, reducing its performance capabilities for life and making it susceptible to other respiratory disorders, principally COPD (broken wind). Therefore, the economic significance within the industry (and *every* type of horse or pony can get strangles) is considerable.

I cannot understand why the 'young horses' argument is put forward as a reason for not bothering with a strangles vaccine in this country. Young horses are central to the buying and selling part of the market and are at the start of their competitive/working careers; it would be more understandable if the disease affected only *old* horses nearing the end of a useful life.

Perhaps the drug companies sincerely believe there is no demand for a strangles vaccine and feel there would not be enough in it for them, persuaded perhaps by those responsible for licensing the subsequent product. If so, it is up to all horse owners and managers to contact them direct, to assure them of the very real demand for a vaccine, and of the profitable advantage to them. And if they appear not to care about such a damaging disease as strangles, what about that caring image which they all promote? Fairly consistent pressure is required – the odd letter is not enough, it will only receive a diplomatic, dismissive reply – so that a vaccine is produced and licensed here in the UK, for the sake of our horses firstly and also because of the considerable economic significance of the disease.

Vaccines work by stimulating a horse or pony's immunity to a disease through the production of 'soldier cells' (antibodies) which are effective against it, and different diseases need different antibodies. In due course the antibodies themselves die off, which is why you need to repeat vaccinations to 'top up' the army, as it were. Horses and ponies in certain competitive disciplines are not allowed to compete unless their vaccination programmes are up to date. This is to reduce the spread of disease within the equine population.

Tetanus and 'flu are often administered in a joint vaccine but as 'flu vaccine needs to be given more often than tetanus (which is usually topped up once every two years), 'flu boosters are also given singly. The timing of any vaccination should be carefully worked out because horses are often a little under par after them; they should not be allowed to sweat up or work at all hard for about ten days afterwards, so two to three weeks should be allowed before the next competition, depending on the effort which is going to be required.

Your veterinary surgeon will help you work out a vaccination programme, and advise on the vaccines required (this depends on what strains of disease are prevailing at the time), and will inform you of the latest developments in the field.

ANNUAL CHECK-UP

You will probably find it most convenient to give your horse his booster vaccinations during his annual medical – something which all animals should have. The vet can, at this time, vaccinate the horse, check his general health, breathing, heart, teeth and perhaps take blood samples for profiling and testing.

Even if the horse seems in perfect health, the check-up is very well worthwhile. A professional can often spot something you have missed, and is more likely to be able to interpret new heart sounds. Providing the correct tests are asked for, blood samples are an excellent way of checking the horse for low-level (sub-clinical) disease (which would not yet be noticeable) and also assessing his general health and physical fitness for work. This is quite a complex subject which your vet should be happy to discuss with you. Some yards occasionally have x-rays taken of their animals' feet and legs so that any bone changes can be monitored and assessed in conjunction with the horse's way of going. In this way, diseases such as navicular can often be spotted.

Teeth, of course, are vital to a horse's digestion and therefore to his health and wellbeing, but checking them is often dismissed because 'he seems to be eating alright'. It is difficult for owners to check teeth themselves as a proper gag is needed; this opens the mouth sufficiently for the fingers to reach to the very back molars and check for sharp edges, and 'hooks' which may have formed on the teeth due to uneven wear. Few horses object to rasping of their teeth, when it is necessary. The vet may advise you to feed soft food for a few days afterwards in case there have been any cheek or tongue lacerations.

The annual check is also the time to formulate your horse's worming programme for the year. New drugs become available fairly regularly. Most popular today are drugs which kill the migrating larvae in the blood vessels as well as the mature, egg-laying adults in the gut; this should go a long way towards removing a not uncommon cause of death in horses, which is ruptured arteries due to parasite damage. This formula has the drug ivermectin and, like all new discoveries, had its opponents at first, with various side-effects wrongly attributed to it; now it is becoming more accepted. It is not necessary to give this drug as often as other drugs which are not effective against larvae. Much depends on your personal circumstances and facilities as to how often you should worm.

If you use an 'ordinary' drug, you should really worm *all* horses and ponies on the premises at the same time every six weeks all year round. The reason for doing them all at once is to ensure a proper rate of kill among the parasites. It only takes one infected animal to reinfect the others the very next day, so that your worming efforts would thus be a complete waste of time. By doing them all together, regularly, you effectively keep them all reasonably parasite free, particularly in the long term.

With ivermectin you need worm only every 8 or 12 weeks. Ivermectin circulates in the bloodstream and is therefore also capable of killing biting and blood–sucking parasites such as lice.

Two of the autumn and winter wormings should be with a drug effective against bots (the larval form of the gad fly) which will develop over winter in the horse's stomach and cause damage to the lining; this can cause colic and poor condition. Tapeworm, too, is apparently spreading among the equine population in Britain so periodic dosing against these (according to your vet's advice) should not be overlooked.

It is usually advised that you do not worm less than ten days before a competition or strenuous work, in case the horse feels a little 'off-colour' because of the drug.

Finally, ask your veterinary surgeon about fly repellents – the newer products now available are effective for several days after one application provided the horse does not get wet, and besides increasing his comfort, this is more economical; they can also significantly protect against sweet itch, a distressing and highly irritating skin allergy caused by the *culicoides* midge, by keeping the midge away.

These 'residual' repellents (so-called because they reside in the coat for some time) are available at most agricultural merchants; two are marketed specifically to the horse world at present – Absorbine Super-Shield from Constant Laboratories, and Coopers Fly Repellent Plus, both available from good saddlers and tack stores.

Do not think a fly repellent is not really necessary and that your horse can cope with his mane and tail: this is not the case. Nature is sadly inefficient at protecting her horses, presumably because she has to consider her flies as well! Some repellents are *not* good and even seem to attract flies, so do be sure to buy a really effective one.

SOME COMMON DISORDERS

This chapter does not aim to tell you how to be your own vet, nor does it even give much advice on first aid: it is to alert you as to how your horse should look and behave in general health and sickness, and to help you to decide when you *do* need the services of your vet. Signs of health and sickness have been discussed already, so here are a few common disorders which you should be able to identify. And whenever you are in doubt about how to proceed, it is far safer and more economical in the long run to call the vet anyway and be safe, rather than jeapordise your horse's welfare and be sorry after the event. With the aid of a good veterinary book, you should not go far wrong.

Laminitis is a painful and potentially fatal condition caused by an impaired blood supply to the feet, usually the front feet but not always. It is caused by over-feeding and too little exercise, blood poisoning, re-tained afterbirth, concussion, faulty trimming and shoeing which leaves long toes and lack of heel support, and inflammatory diseases themselves. Antibiotics and cortico-steroids can also result in laminitis.

In a mild case, the horse may not even show the typical, leaning-back stance, but may simply go a little short and pottery. There may or may not be heat present in the feet. Typical of laminitis is the excess horny tissue which forms between the sensitive and insensitive laminae, because these part company or 'loosen' in laminitis; so one way of checking an apparently sound horse for mild laminitis is to check the condition of the white line at trimming time – the line should be clearly defined. Any sign of softened horn or an expanded, blurred white line, indicates disease. Seedy toe is similar, where 'cheesy' horn is produced in that area.

In bad cases, the laminae separate completely and the pedal bones may well rotate downwards and press against the sensitive sole. The horse will obviously find moving very difficult or even impossible, he may sweat patchily, blow and have a raised temperature, and will lean back to get the weight off his toes.

The immediate things to do are remove all food except hay and water and ring the vet. Do not force the animal to walk around as you can cause great damage if the foot structure is coming apart. This can only really be confirmed by x-ray.

Influenza can permanently damage the lungs of affected horses and should be regarded as a serious disease. The horse will be listless and generally unhappy with a raised temperature and probably a watery discharge from the nostrils. He may or may not cough. Call the vet and keep the horse in a well-ventilated but not draughty loose box, rugged up if the weather is even slightly chilly.

Colic is simply a name given to a symptom, and means abdominal pain or discomfort; it is associated with digestive disorder. The horse will look anxiously at his flanks and may try to bite them; he will paw the ground, perhaps try to roll, groan, sweat patchily (a sign of pain generally), and may become restless and even violent. Remove all food and water and call the vet – ask him whether you should walk the horse around; some advocate this, some don't. Never give any kind of colic drink unless in the past your vet has given you one for your first-aid store and now advises you to administer it. The general practice these days is to leave well alone till the vet arrives. If the horse becomes violent, keep out of the way but try to reassure him verbally till help comes.

Lymphangitis is a hard swelling all up one leg – usually hind – and is caused by infection and over-feeding in relation to exercise. The horse will find movement difficult and may have a raised temperature; do *not* try home remedies but simply call the vet. Give the horse water but no food until you have advice. In bad cases the leg may ulcerate, so do not delay by thinking the condition will probably get better on its own.

Ordinary **filled legs** are common in many animals if they have to stand around for any length of time, even when adequately exercised; it is simply a general fluid congestion of the tissues in the limbs caused by inactivity. It is nothing to worry about unless the legs are hot and the horse feels uncomfortable. Stable bandages can help the condition.

Chronic Obstructive Pulmonary Disease/Small Airway Disease (COPD/SAD) is commonly known as broken wind or heaves. It is an allergy to fungi and mould spores in hay and straw and sometimes to pollen on summer pasture in dry weather; it is an over-reaction by the body's natural defence mechanism, and is depressingly familiar. Fortunately, much can be done to alleviate it: drugs to help relax and dilate the air-ways which have narrowed in response to the histamine produced against the irritants, drugs which 'damp down' the allergic response, and a general 'clean air' management regime, which involves shredded paper or *dust-extracted* shavings (rather than ordinary ones) for bedding, moist conserved forage such as hayage instead of hay, or hay which is *thoroughly* soaked for a good 12 hours – just to throw a bucket of water over the hay or a quick dunk in a bin of water, is not enough; the idea is to soak the hay so that the fungal spores swell to such a size that they cannot get down into the tiny airways where they cause such trouble. The water should be changed after each soaking session.

Ordinary dust can also act as an irritant in susceptible animals, so stables must be regularly swept or preferably vacuumed, including all ledges and rafters, and left fully open and ventilated for a few hours afterwards while the horse is out. It is useless to put a COPD horse on a clean-air regime if the horse next door is not on one, since the dust etc from his airspace will inevitably infiltrate the other horse's stable. Many experts believe that any challenge to a horse's system musters up the horse's resources in fighting it off and so uses up valuable energy which could be going elsewhere; and maintain that horses should all be on a clean-air regime anyway (a good idea!).

In days gone by, a broken-winded horse was usually written off or at least kept fully out at grass on restricted work; but nowadays, with more knowledgeable management principles plus veterinary assistance with drugs, COPD horses and ponies can continue to live long, useful lives once more.

Azoturia (equine rhabdomyolysis) or **tying-up syndrome** is a very painful condition for the horse and most distressing to horse and owner alike. Sometimes it comes on soon after starting exercise and sometimes after the horse has been working. It is being researched in Great Britain and the USA at present and whatever I write now may soon be out of date. We know that the main cause is too many concentrates and too little exercise, but the belief is now that it can also be caused by exhaustion, hereditary factors, hormone imbalance, electrolyte depletion, mineral deficiencies and infectious disease – quite a lot to choose from.

Basically, you must recognise the condition, however it is caused. It often comes on just after the horse has commenced exercise but can also develop after strenuous work (for the horse's stage of fitness). The back, loin and quarter muscles appear to cramp up painfully, the horse will stagger and find moving very difficult indeed, and may go down. He may show the usual signs of pain – patchy sweating, groaning and an anxious, distressed expression. Don't try to move him as exercise, however mild, may cause muscle damage; veterinary assistance must be summoned immediately. This is difficult if you are out or alone, but persuade a passer-by to ring your vet or leave the horse somewhere safe while you do so. If you *have* to move the horse, do so only at a very slow walk to the nearest 'phone. Cover his quarters with your jacket to avoid chilling and further cramp and muscle damage. At a show or similar venue, do not transport your horse home but call the show vet for immediate assistance. Obviously, you must dismount or unharness the horse to minimise stress.

Thrush is a fungal infection of the foot and is caused as much by wet conditions, as dirty, damp bedding. The frog will be sore on pressure, may have a dark discharge from the cleft of frog and down the side grooves (the lacunae) and will smell horrible. Some people attempt to treat with Stockholm Tar, but it is best to contact the veterinary surgeon or your farrier as the diseased horn will need to be pared away before treatment. The animal may or may not be lame.

Mud fever and **rain rash/rain scald** are caused by the same bacteria, but the former appears on the legs and the latter on the back, loins and quarters. The hair appears tufty and the skin scabby in the later stages, but one of the early signs is heat and puffiness, with the horse reluctant to have his legs handled. The bacteria lurks under the scabs, so for effective treatment these usually have to be removed (in extreme cases perhaps under a local anaesthetic) so that antibiotic medication can reach the raw, suppurating skin and kill the bacteria. Mud fever occurs mostly in winter, and rain rash mostly in warmer, wet weather. Obviously, tack and harness cannot be worn and since the horse's legs become so sensitive, shoeing can become difficult in long drawn out cases. Bedding should be soft and short – straw is often too prickly and uncomfortable. When the horse lies down, he can transfer the infection from his legs to his belly, and to his muzzle if he bites affected areas.

Do not delay proper treatment; many of the branded medications available from tack shops for mud fever and rain rash are simply not effective. Dermobion, however, is an *extremely* effective topical application and will soon clear up even bad cases – it will reduce inflammation and pain overnight in early stage fever. It can be obtained over the counter at your veterinary surgery. At the first signs, bring the horse in, get the affected areas as clean and dry as possible (certainly rinse off the mud which is the cause) and seek veterinary advice. The condition can be serious if the infection gets into the bloodstream.

Allergies to fertilisers and weedkillers on pasture will develop similar symptoms. All conditions like this are more common on pink skin under white hair than on stronger, coloured skin.

Strangles is a very virulent respiratory disease of mainly young horses. The horse has a very sore throat and shows difficulty and reluctance when eating and trying to swallow. He looks very ill and dejected and has a raised temperature; he may have swollen glands under his throat and may eventually refuse to eat or drink. Your vet may decide to treat with penicillin, but some believe that antibiotic treatment simply drives the infection to inaccessible places in the body where it can cause serious and long-term illness; so they do not, in fact, give any treatment but will advise you on careful nursing. If the disease is allowed to run its course and the abscesses burst spontaneously, it often clears up more quickly.

Tetanus is usually fatal, although today it can be treated more successfully than in the past. There should be no excuse for a horse catching tetanus as the vaccine against it is most effective. Initial symptoms include stiffness and difficulty in moving as the paralysis which characterises the disease sets in. If you push the horse's head up quickly, a membrane will shoot across the eye from the corner; this is a sure early sign. Later on the head and neck become extended and the legs stiffen. Ultimately, the muscles of the respiratory system become paralysed and the horse dies of asphyxiation.

At the very first suspicion of tetanus you must call the vet immediately. If your horse is *not* vaccinated, any wound he sustains is suspect and he should be given a precautionary quick-acting injection in case tetanus bacteria have gained access to it. Normally, airless wounds such as punctures are the main cause, but any wound can form an entry site.

Botulism has become more common in horses since the advent of big-bale silage as a feed; if air penetrates a bag after a puncture the silage can become contaminated and botulism results. Again, the horse is subject to gradual paralysis, early signs being listlessness and difficulty in eating and drinking, also saliva drooling out of the mouth. Most horses die from this disease which can run its course in only a few hours. Call your vet immediately.

Wounds of any kind must not be neglected; even a simple scratch may become infected, and deeper ones need stitching if they are to heal successfully without forming granulation tissue (proud flesh). Stitching is most effective when carried out on fresh wounds, so any wound which goes deeper than the very top layer of skin may need veterinary attention.

The safest way of bathing wounds is to trickle water from a syringe or bathe with gamgee tissue and slightly salted water. Be careful not to push dirt further into the wound. Most wounds heal best if they are clean and dry, but if the new skin formed continually cracks it may be advisable to use an antiseptic or antibiotic ointment, according to veterinary advice. Circumstances will dictate whether a dressing is needed or whether it is best to leave the wound exposed to the air. Obviously, it must be protected from dirt and it is normally best not to turn the horse out if he has a fresh wound, although some vets believe that the air in the field is cleaner than that in the stable! As ever, be guided by your veterinary surgeon.

Strains and sprains are usually characterised by heat, tenderness and swelling. When considering lameness, it is as well to remember that the foot is the most likely site, then the lower leg and on up the leg. Shoulder lameness is actually quite rare, as are hip problems, but back trouble is not uncommon, especially amongst jumpers.

The initial treatment for any sprain is usually cold hosing or cold packs applied for the first 48 hours or until the heat and swelling has subsided. Rest is always the best (and usually the least popular and convenient form of treatment) but healing can be enhanced if it is accompanied by physiotherapy, depending on the actual injury (physiotherapy is a complex subject, and for further reference see p260).

You should *not* allow, or even consider, either firing or blistering. These 'treatments' are barbaric and archaic, and are known to cause more damage than the injury they purport to treat, quite apart from the extreme pain and distress they cause to their unfortunate victims. And they do nothing to heal the injured tissues damaged by the sprain. Nobody would ever dream of firing or blistering a member of the family, yet horses are fired for no better reason than 'it's always been done'. In fact, veterinary schools stopped teaching how to fire and blister many years ago, and the veterinary authorities have themselves recommended that the practice be stopped.

Research is still continuing into the best ways to treat tendon sprains, but so far initial cold applications and anti-inflammatory drugs followed by rest and physiotherapy still seem to be the best course of action open to us.

When you read through your selected veterinary book, you may be horrified at the number and variety of disorders which could afflict your horse. Of course most horses, when well managed, go through their whole lives with surprisingly few ailments. Those they do get can be greatly lessened in effect if you can spot them early and call in expert help before the problem escalates – or before it becomes too late to save the horse.

YOUR FIRST AID KIT

You need on hand certain basic items by way of first aid. Your own veterinary surgeon can advise you on a full kit and may be able to supply most of your equipment, but here is a basic list for you to consider:-

●A mild antiseptic solution, or some salt, for adding to clear water for bathing wounds.
●Antiseptic or antibiotic cream to fight infection.
●Cleansing pads, pre-moistened, for situations where there is no water.
●Non-stick dressing pads for wounds.
●A poultice dressing, either a branded product or kaolin clay, which can be applied hot or cold for such situations as encouraging an abscess to burst or to cool down a sprain.
●Gamgee tissue, which is cotton wool lined with gauze to prevent fibres clinging to wounds. Used for both bathing and, when dry, protecting wounds under bandages.
●Clean elasticated bandages for keeping dressings in place, either exercise bandages or human surgical stretchy bandages.
●Blunt-ended scissors for cutting dressings.
●Solution for bathing eyes.
●Veterinary thermometer for taking temperature.
●Medicated, moist tulle dressings for use on discharging wounds. They do not stick to the wound.
●Dry gauze for use on dry wounds.
●Antibiotic spray or powder.
●Self-adhesive bandage, for security of dressing.
●Tweezers for removing splinters or thorns.
●Surgical spirit for drying up grazes and disinfecting superficial wounds.
●Plastic syringe with small hole for cleaning wounds.
●Liquid paraffin as mud fever preventative and skin protector.
●Menthol and eucalyptus mix for steam bath for horse's head in respiratory disease, to relieve congestion, if advised by vet.
●Fly repellent cream to protect uncovered wounds.

Your veterinary surgeon may suggest slightly different or additional items, but the above stock should see you through most first-aid situations.

You will also need a small, clean bucket (which you never use for anything else) and you can keep some of your equipment inside it, covered with a stable rubber. It is best, however, to have an easily cleaned, plastic-lined box or chest and/or to keep your equipment inside a clean, lockable cupboard – provided the key is always accessible! Make a list of your stock and replace items before you run out.

NURSING

This is one aspect of horse management which can be particularly difficult for working owners: just when their horse needs them most they have to go to work. If you cannot get some holiday time in an emergency, try your best to get someone reliable and responsible who will cover for you and do exactly as you say. If you keep your horse at a good livery stable, the staff should nurse your horse appropriately. Otherwise you may be faced not only with the morning and evening trips to the yard, but also lunch-hour and late night ones, too, because this is one time when your attention really is vital – and it comes to most horse and pony owners at some time.

Precise nursing will obviously depend on the particular illness or injury. Generally speaking, however, sick or injured animals are not partial to being unnecessarily messed about, particularly in the early and middle stages of sickness. The stable should be mucked out as quickly as possible; alternatively, consider deep litter for a while, depending on the circumstances. Thorough grooming should be stopped, but the horse should be quickly brushed over daily, damp-sponged about the head and 'back end' to freshen him up, and have his feet picked out. Pay particular attention to his clothing – it *must* be comfortable and well-fitting otherwise it will simply add to his misery.

Needless to say, veterinary instructions must be carried out to the letter. It is far safer to write everything down as the vet tells you what to do, and if you do not understand something, do ask. For the sake of your horse, it is better to double check than be afraid of looking silly because you do not know what the vet is talking about. Fresh instructions should be obtained at each visit.

The horse may well appreciate your quiet company in his box, may like his ears being gently pulled and may, or may not, wish to see other horses; if he has had to be isolated due to some infectious disease, it is important that he does not feel abandoned.

After any illness, be very careful about returning the horse to work. Many owners are far too precipitate and their horses suffer a relapse or even permanent damage because they start working them again too quickly. Respiratory disorders in particular need many weeks and sometimes months of complete rest and recuperation before the horse can undergo any significant stress at all; so do leg injuries, and serious tendon sprains can mean the horse completely off work for six months or a year.

EUTHANASIA

This is one topic which many people find distressing, but we all have to face up to it at some point. A number of people send their horses away either to hunt kennels or to a local abattoir; I still firmly believe that the only right way to put a horse down is at home with someone he knows and trusts holding his leadrope. To send an animal away alive and never actually *know* what happened to it is something no truly caring owner could live with. Even if the horse *is* put down on arrival, strange surroundings and people will not add to his peace of mind, especially at an abattoir where there may be the smell of blood, perhaps the sight of other dead animals, and an atmosphere of fear which sometimes pervades these places.

The veterinary surgeon can put the horse down either by injection or with a humane killer, and some vets use both, injecting the horse first and then using the humane killer. A horse killed by drugs has no meat value, but this should not even enter into your considerations. The vet can arrange for disposal of the body, and you do not have to witness the sad affair if, understandably, you cannot face it. The horse will presumably know your vet and perhaps a friend known to him will hold the leadrope.

Whatever precise arrangements are made, the two main considerations are that the horse is put down by your vet – if not personally, then under his/her direction – and that he is put down at home.

Summary

●Veterinary surgeons can be called not only in times of sickness and injury, but also to provide up-to-date management information and advice on preventive medicine.

●Have at least one good, up-to-date veterinary book and read the veterinary articles regularly published in equestrian magazines.

●The signs of health and disease given in this chapter should be familiar to all owners/managers, so that disorders are spotted early and appropriate treatment given quickly.

●Vaccinations should be kept up to date and protect the horse against influenza, tetanus and rhinopneumonitis. Regular boosters should be given to maintain immunity.

●An annual medical check should be a regular part of the horse's programme and should involve: normal bodily functions; blood samples being taken for monitoring fitness and the possibility of sub-clinical disease; teeth, which should be checked again in six–months time; and the latest information on worming programmes and products.

●Owners should recognise the symptoms of common disorders, in addition to the general signs of health and disease; then they will immediately spot if something is wrong, and can call in expert help if necessary. If you call in the vet too late, treatment may be more difficult or even impossible.

●Every yard should have a well stocked first-aid kit (See p.000); replace stock *before* it runs out.

●When nursing a sick or injured horse, steer a middle course between leaving him in peace and letting him know he has not been abandoned. Keep him comfortable and administer whatever the vet has prescribed.

●Euthanasia should be carried out by your veterinary surgeon, at home. Fair treatment at the very end is the least we can offer for a lifetime of service and companionship.

Checklist

✓ **1** Familiarise yourself will all the signs of good/bad health relating to horses and ponies in general. Get to know your own horse: in time, you will develop a 'sixth sense' for sickness and can then watch the horse more closely, check his temperature, pulse and respiration or request a blood test to be done – your suspicions could well be scientifically confirmed.

2 Buy a good, up-to-date veterinary book; read it carefully and keep it available for immediate reference. Read management and veterinary articles in good magazines, and check with your vet the latest developments in management and preventative medicine techniques.

3 Keep your horse's vaccinations up to date.

4 Worm your horse regularly. Remember a worming programme must include *all* animals on the premises to be dosed at the same time otherwise one still-infected horse could reinfect all the others the very next time it is turned out with them.

5 Make sure your first-aid kit is fully stocked with in-date products all the time.

6 Should euthanasia be necessary, have your horse put down by your vet in his home yard.

12

What and When?

With so much to consider, and so many significant responsibilities always involved when caring for horses and ponies, it is not always easy to decide which jobs are the most important and should be done first, and which can, if necessary, be delayed.

Owners who work all day are in the worst position, and may read with envy the detailed routines sometimes set out in the older stable management books:

8am	Check horse over, feed and go to breakfast.
9.30am	Quarter, tack up and exercise.
11.30am	On return from exercise, untack and rug up. Muck out and bed down.
12.15pm	Second feed. Go to lunch.
2.15pm	Thorough grooming. Skip out droppings. Clean tack.
4.00pm	Third feed. Adjust rugs.
8.00pm	Fourth feed. Put on night rugs. Skip out and set fair bed.
11.00pm	Late night check. Adjust rugs, replenish hay.

Such a basic routine is still fine for an owner who has nothing else to do but enjoy himself with his horse. These days, however although the number of pleasure horses and ponies seems to be increasing, more and more of their owners have to work to support them and are simply not free to adopt such a routine. Children and teenagers are often at school or college or working themselves, and the horse or pony has to be fitted round not only school hours but homework as well. However, it is quite possible to look after a horse adequately with a little rearrangement of duties and a bit of imagination.

Divide all your tasks into those which *directly* affect the horse's wellbeing, and those which are related to horse management but do not concern the horse himself. So the most important are feeding, watering, mucking out, exercising, grooming, laundering clothing and numnahs and cleaning at least the underside of tack. Secondary tasks are things like sweeping the yard, tidying the tack room, keeping the muck heap under some sort of control, reorganising the feed room and painting fencing.

As you can see, the jobs in the first category are all things which directly affect the comfort and wellbeing of the horse. Those in the second do need doing – at some point; but are not jobs which the horse himself would care about, as it were. He would, however, care very much if he were not fed, had nothing to drink, was living constantly in his own filth and was never exercised. And although wanting to keep one's premises tidy and reasonably smart-looking is understandable, it should not be at the expense of the horse or pony.

I do feel many owners have their priorities quite wrong in this respect. I have often visited a yard for some reason where the owner, apologising for the state of it, is in the process of tidying up – yet he seems quite unconcerned that the horses are standing in filthy rugs, their feet clogged with muck and with water buckets which obviously have not been scrubbed out for days.

Perhaps some of the fault lies in the fact that so much of our equine education has come to us through 'The System', from the days when military establishments set the standards, with their over-emphasis on 'bull' – immaculate order and super-cleanliness for its own sake, beyond all practical requirements. They had – and often still have – the manpower to maintain such standards whereas most civilian establishments do not. In fact, I have visited several military and police establishments, and although there is still 'bull', it is never at the expense of the horses. I have never seen dirty horses, grotty rugs and smelly beds in any of them.

Unfortunately it seems that in many cases The Word has been mis-interpreted or misunderstood: many people now seem to put superficial appearances before the wellbeing of those very horses and ponies who are the reason for the existence of the yard in the first place.

If you do have time to get everything done every day, that is very nice, but most people do not when they have a family, a job, a business or other responsibilities making calls on their time. In this case you can make life easier for yourself and still get your horse or pony properly cared for if you simply put first those jobs which directly affect him. The other jobs can be done occasionally or when you have more time such as on a day off, at the weekend or on a day when you have help.

Remember that creating facilities for turning the horse out, even in a smallish, surfaced 'play pen', can make more time for you. There is no need for you to ride or drive him seven days a week *provided* he can be turned out. On that subject, I do realise it is common practice to give a horse 'a day off', which, put that way, sounds like a nice relaxing rest day. In fact if the horse is stabled, it is nothing of the sort. Horses are movement-orientated animals; it is most unnatural for them to be vir-tually stationary for more than a few minutes at a time. Stabled horses suffer from over-confinement as it is, and 'a day off' can actually result in considerable frustration and mental distress for them, in addition to the adverse physical effects of being deprived of the exercise they need so badly. A quick lead in hand does practically nothing to alleviate the situation. By all means give your horse or pony a day off, but *not* if it means he is going to be stabled practically all of that time.

If he is ridden on, say, Sunday afternoon, and you wish to give him Monday off without turning him out for a few hours, consider that by the time he is exercised again (probably Tuesday morning, before you go to work) he will have been without proper exercise for about 38 hours, which is roughly the length of the average human's working week. So, our conventional idea of 'a day off' for the horse is far from doing him a favour! If he is not due to be exercised again till Tuesday evening, his time without exercise will stretch to about 48 hours, two whole days. This sort of treatment can hardly be described as good horse management!

Feel free to give a horse or pony as many days off as you wish – but *only* if he can be turned out for several hours on those days so he can at least walk and trot about and stretch his legs. If this cannot be arranged, then in the interest of your horse's mental and physical health he will have to be exercised by you or someone else, and not just led about in hand to nibble some grass (although he would appreciate this, too). This, of course, all takes time, and if you are very busy it may be time you do not have, which simply emphasises the need to create turning–out facilities.

If you have to cut your horse tasks to the bare minimum, the four jobs which absolutely must be done each day are these: watering, feeding, and if the horse is stabled, skipping out droppings and exercising. If the horse is rugged up, his clothing will have to be adjusted too, to maintain his comfort. And if you can possibly spare another five or ten minutes, do pick out his feet and sponge the front and back ends.

Next in importance come the other 'direct contact' jobs such as quartering, full grooming, and so on; the yard, tack room, muck heap and so on should be put firmly aside so that his wellbeing is seen to first.

If you work in this order, your horse jobs should all fall neatly into place and you will no longer be trying desperately to do everything 'the books' say you must. Put the horse first, adjust your standards for the sake of your sanity and energy resources, and I am sure you will be happier and more relaxed.

Just when you actually do your jobs depends entirely on your personal routine. Horses will soon adapt to whatever routine you offer, provided you do try to keep it that, a reasonable routine – do not mess them about with erratic feed and exercise times as this can unsettle them. However, they do seem to adapt on special days such as at a show, hunting and so on, and horses who are frequently away from home become quite blasé about it all and just accept it after a while.

Erratic hours, such as shifts, need not worry you so long as some semblance of routine is adhered to. If you ride in the mornings one week but have to change to afternoons the next, have your horse turned out every morning and every afternoon, as appropriate. This will occupy him and he will not be standing in his stable wondering what to expect.

If you have to fit your horse round your work, be sure never to let him become really hungry; if you are delayed he will not then be fretting for a feed and you will not be gnashing your teeth worrying about him. Make sure he always has enough hay or other roughage to keep him busy – leave two crammed full haynets in his box (if you cannot get anyone else to top up his hay supply in your absence) for him to pick at as he wishes. He will not eat more than he needs and become gross, but will spin out his ration to suit himself as nature intended, and will therefore always have a little food passing through his digestive system – again, as nature intended – so will not become unduly hungry waiting for you. An ample water supply must also be arranged, of course.

This is especially important for horses which are used to being exercised early mornings and evenings Monday to Friday. When the weekend comes, the owner might understandably feel like at least a short lie-in, and will be later at the stables than usual; but if the horse has had a generous hay ration the night before, he will be fine. The fact that his exercise or work on those two days will be at different times from normal will, likewise, not bother him too much as such horses do get to know when it is weekend! They simply seem to switch to weekend mode and take things in their stride, sensing the different atmosphere. However, when things are changed about from day to day, some horses and ponies, particularly the more highly strung ones, become a little disorientated.

Giving a horse a large ration of roughage overnight helps, too, with early morning exercising on work-days. You can take him out for exercise before feeding him, knowing he is not hungry, and this saves you having to wait for him to digest his breakfast before riding him. Then you can feed him when you leave and he can enjoy his breakfast and morning hay in peace.

All in all, there is no set routine you have to follow because it is 'correct'. Make your own routine according to your circumstances. Just bear in mind the most important tasks, those directly relating to the horse himself, and ensure that the horse always has enough roughage and water available so that if you *are* a bit late sometimes it is not the end of the world, and the horse will be alright.

Summary

●It is possible to cope with a job or family etc, and look after a horse or pony if you categorise your horse-tasks into those which directly affect the horse's wellbeing and those which can be postponed until you are less busy.

●Extra exercise facilities so that the horse can be turned free can be a great time-saver for busy owners. A conventional 'day-off' for the horse without alternative exercise (such as being turned loose somewhere) is very poor horsemastership and adversely affects the horse both mentally and physically.

●The four most important jobs which must always be done are: watering, feeding, skipping out droppings and exercising (probably by turning out). Clothing, if worn, must be made comfortable too; feet should be picked out; and if time, sponging done to freshen up the horse.

●Horses are very adaptable, but as a general rule try to keep to a reasonable routine to avoid unsettling them, particularly the highly strung types. Never let him become thirsty or too hungry – always leave him a large supply of water and his normal roughage food so that he can eat and drink when he pleases, as nature intended.

Checklist

✓ 1 Categorise your horse-tasks: give priority to those which directly affect the horse's comfort and wellbeing.

2 Remember the Big Four (jobs which must be done, come what may): watering, feeding, skipping out, exercising. Also, adjust clothing. *Remember* that even an un-rugged horse or pony at grass must still be checked over.

3 Make sure you leave enough hay or other roughage so that your horse never becomes very hungry (plus water, of course); then delays in your normal routine will not matter too much.

13

A Big Day

'Just hacking' can constitute as strenuous a day's work to your horse or pony as a day's competition – the only difference is that in a non-competitive situation you should be feeling no tension or nerves so will not transmit these to your mount. And a short, sharp morning's work can be as wearying as a long day hanging about waiting to compete.

Most animals guess that 'something's in the air' because of your preparations – shampooing, trimming extra carefully, busy in the yard preparing equipment, getting the horsebox or trailer ready. Some horses refuse to eat their evening feed if they know there is A Big Day tomorrow, and it helps if you can stay calm and not rush about on such occasions.

About a week before the event, check your transport arrangements or vehicle carefully; check your horse's shoes thoroughly, too, and call the farrier if there is the least little thing wrong – a broken-down box or shoeless horse, all for want of a little advance planning, can mean you don't go at all. Tack and other equipment should be similarly checked in time to get any suddenly-needed repairs done, and preferably put aside (provided you have other equipment you can use meantime).

The amount you feed and exercise your horse should remain according to the work and fitness programme you have scheduled for him. So often the temptation is to step things up too much and overdo the horse. He certainly does not want a heavy week before an important event; if anything, slacken things off a little so that he arrives fresh and on his toes, *not* going wild from lack of work and too much food. It is *not* advisable to give extra food the evening before the day to 'stoke up' the horse's energy reserves; this can often result in all the problems caused by over-feeding – colic, azoturia, etc. Just give a normal feed.

It is a good idea to make logically arranged lists of your equipment for a competition (all tack listed together, all veterinary supplies and so on) and to tick off each item as it is laid ready for loading next morning. This way you are sure you have everything and that nothing is left behind.

The horse should be given his normal work, including a pipe-opener if required, and then groomed or shampooed, as you wish. If your horse or pony is kept at grass, it will help if he can be stabled the night before, especially in wet weather; otherwise you will have an almost impossible task on the morning of the event cleaning him up.

ON THE DAY

The horse should have his normal feed, hay and water. The old idea of witholding these for several hours before work is now known to be counter-productive, causing discomfort and depriving the horse of essential nutrients at the very time he needs them most. Removing them an hour before work is quite adequate unless the work is going to be hard and fast, in which case two hours is enough.

Human athletes have in recent times practised 'carbohydrate overloading' immediately prior to an event. This involves eating large amounts of energy-rich foods such as pasta and other starchy foods, to build up energy stores. This is not normally recommended for horses on the day before an event; however, coming onto the market at the time of writing are dietary supplements called carbohydrate boosters, which aim to provide a readily available source of extra energy before hard work. Some trainers used to feed glucose with this intent, but this was actually found to result in greater fatigue later on, caused by lowered blood sugar because of the way the body processes glucose; it also resulted in fatigue-related injuries and poor performance.

Instead of giving an extra-large ordinary feed the night before, carbohydrate boosters fed on the morning of an event do so far appear to give an energy boost to working horses. Equine Products (UK) Ltd market Equine Carbohydrate Booster in this country, and claim that in trials where their product has been fed to endurance horses before, during and after competition, the response from competitors has been enthusiastic; they noted prolonged stamina and also good recovery from exertion. Obviously *all* working horses need energy, whether they are sprinters, jumpers, endurance horses or whatever. It seems that carbohydrate boosters are making a place for themselves in the diets of working horses today, and it is well worth discussing them with a vet, equine nutritionist or management consultant.

That working horses need electrolytes is quite well-known, but there are still owners and trainers who believe that giving electrolytes *before* work will help delay depletion afterwards. However, the body does not store up electrolytes like this – it simply excretes what it does not need. Furthermore, during long-drawn-out work and after any work, particularly in hot and/or humid weather, electrolytes are almost sure to require supplementing to aid recovery and restore the body chemistry, in which case both carbohydrate boosters and electrolyte supplements can be used – and indeed, are recommended to be so used.

Horses should be accustomed to these additives because of their unusual taste (particularly electrolytes), otherwise they may not be persuaded to take them when they are needed in competition. Many management consultants recommend that an electrolyte supplement be kept on hand after training stints alongside the horse's normal water supply – then if he feels the need for electrolytes, he can help himself. According to Gillian McCarthy of the Equine Management Consultancy Service, human athletes report that electrolyte supplements taste like nectar when you need them but absolutely revolting when you don't, and perhaps this is the case with horses, too.

Electrolytes are, of course, mineral salts lost in sweat. They are essential for efficient metabolism, energy utilisation and recovery, and their importance to 'ordinary' riders for their 'ordinary' horses should not be under-estimated. Unfortunately expert opinion does vary as to when exactly the supplements should be used – and some even maintain that they should not be used at all, as providing them 'teaches' the horse's body not to make up its own supplies! This is not much help to the less knowledgeable among us, and the best we can do is to read as much as we can, and check the facts with the experts available to us, before making a decision. However, different opinions always seem to abound among experts in any field, and research may well throw up new ideas and more knowledge at any time, so we simply have to do what seems best at the time.

Certainly it seems that nowadays a carbohydrate booster and an electrolyte supplement should form part of every working horse's management regime, and should always be taken to an event which is expected to be unusually demanding; then our horses and ponies will be able to do their best and also recover quickly, since they will benefit from all the legitimate aids we can give them.

Giving the horse hay to eat en route helps keep his digestion working properly; if the journey is quite long, regular stops should be made to rest the horses, maybe unload them for a leg-stretch, and, of course, give a normal feed at the appropriate time. Because travelling itself can be so distressing to many animals, you might consider travelling the day before if your venue is a long way away, to allow time to recover from the journey; otherwise the horse will surely be in no condition to do his best for you on arrival. This may be inconvenient, expensive and unpopular, but the journey, the strange surroundings and the competition/work itself may all be too much for the horse and could easily result in serious colic due to metabolic disturbances brought on by the over-stress. This has happened to many horses but the cause has only generally been recognised in fairly recent times.

If your venue is fairly near home and you are hacking, with maybe your family or friends taking ancillary equipment along for you in a car, do set off in plenty of time so you can make your own way at a relaxed walk and trot, with maybe a quiet canter if conditions are right. Your horse or pony should be sufficiently warmed up on arrival and there will be no need for long riding in when you get there.

If going by transport, when you arrive unload and walk the horse round – if it is raining a waterproof sheet would be most useful now and for riding in. Obviously, it is basic horsemastership not to use your horse as a private grandstand – he should only be ridden or driven when required. And if the weather is hot, do not stand him in the sun or leave him in a stuffy, stifling horsebox or trailer – horses *can* suffer from heat-stroke, so stand with him in the shade if cool stabling is not available. If it is cold and wet, try to shelter him properly; otherwise put on a rug or blanket under a waterproof sheet and periodically walk him gently around so he does not become too cold and stiffen up.

If the horse is hot and sweaty after his work, you should help him to cool down without risking sudden chills. Check his pulse and respiration rates (at some competitions a veterinary ground jury will be doing this anyway) and sponge him down with lukewarm water. Lukewarm water is advised because it is completely safe – it will help him cool off as it evaporates but will not cause seizing up of muscles or chills, as cool water can. In cases of heat stroke, however, some vets *do* actually recommend dousing the horse with cold water to cool him off quicker. In this case you can only be guided by the on-the-spot experts since your own usual consultants are not likely to be present.

Whatever the weather, your aim should be to keep your horse or pony at a normal, equable temperature, neither too hot nor too cold, using water, clothing, shelter (box or stabling) and leading in hand, as appropriate. Commonsense tells us to warm a horse up if he is cold and cool him down if he is hot!

Give your horse or pony a chance to stale – you could lead him to some quiet area and shake some straw under his belly to encourage him. It is useful if a horse will stale on command – accustom him to a low whistle every time he does stale, then whistle like this whenever you want him to stale and praise him when he does so. Holding back urine is just as uncomfortable for a horse as it is for us; it is also rather embarrassing if a horse or pony stales in front of the judges when receiving his rosette or during a halt at X!

If you are entered for several classes at a show, or if there is a longer check out hunting or a break in the general procedure, it is perfectly alright to let your horse graze for a few minutes. Many hunters, for example, are out of their stables all day with no chance of hay or a lunchtime feed unless the owner is changing horses. A few mouthfuls of grass every now and then does certainly help keep the horse's digestive system ticking over and keeps him more comfortable, even if it *is* winter grass. Some owners prefer their horses not to eat when they are working, and may be concerned that when hunting, for example, and galloping soon after a check, their horses might choke if grass gets stuck around the bit.

It also pays dividends to be prepared to give up when the horse has had enough, even if you haven't. This prevents not only physical injury but also the mental sickening of the horse in relation to his work. Do keep a careful check on his condition. Any reasonably sensitive horseman can tell when a horse is feeling over-tired and thoroughly fed up, and any horse or pony which persistently heaves, blows and sweats despite opportunities to recover, is obviously not fit enough for the work being asked of him. This particularly applies to long-coated animals in winter, and animals living out from spring onwards if the grass is, perhaps, of better feeding value than you had thought.

THAT NIGHT

After the day's work, try and get the horse cool and dry, and home as quickly as possible, unless he is a long way from home. If he faces a long, tiring and probably stressful journey immediately after working all day, it is much better in the long run to stay over that night and give him a chance to recover; then make the journey next day.

After hard work or a whole day without proper food, do *not* let the horse have as much water and food as he wants. Water should be offered in small amounts, say up to half a bucket at a time, and offered every 20 minutes or so, along with an electrolyte solution if the work has been at all stressful so that the horse can choose between that and plain water. If only small amounts of water are offered, the temperature does not matter and once the horse has quenched his thirst, it can, of course, be left with him all the time.

As regards food, offer the horse a haynet to eat rather than giving him a corn feed straightaway. This is easier to digest and gets his digestion going again before his normal feed later on – and use, perhaps, a carbo-hydrate booster as well, although these can also be given in the water.

After hard work, the horse should initially be *trotted* slowly in hand rather than walked: this keeps the blood circulating and results in a more effective removal from the tissues of waste products which have built up during work. After about ten minutes or so, bring him to walk and walk him briskly round, more or less continuously except when he is having a short drink, gradually slowing down till his pulse and respiration are more normal. Respiration is more difficult to judge – if the horse is very hot he may well pant like a dog to help cool himself down. The pulse is a better guide; once it has reached about 60 to 80 beats per minute, depending on his normal at-rest rate, it should be safe to put him away in his stable and attend to him normally in the way of washing down, cleaning up and so on. Incidentally, it is quite alright, indeed desirable, for a hot, sweating horse to drink *provided* the amounts are small, about four swallows at a time being enough till he is cooler and more composed.

If you are hacking home, let the horse or pony have short drinks, if convenient, from troughs along the way, but beware of other sources such as streams which may well be polluted depending on the locality. Keep him walking and trotting on gently, especially if it is raining and chilly; if he is slightly warm he will dry off quicker once home.

If going home in transport, an anti-sweat rug should be worn under a summer sheet or winter rug, or one of the modern permeable rugs; this will help him keep warm and avoid chilling too quickly, and will also allow moisture to evaporate from his body without his becoming clammy. Such clothing should be worn when cooling down after work in all but the most equable weather.

Once home, his stable should be ready bedded down so he can have a good roll after you remove his travelling gear; he will probably stale, too. Then clean him up quickly – put a haynet for him to nibble at, and when you have finished and tended any wounds etc, re-rug him in his normal stable rugs and give him half his normal feed; then let him eat in peace. He should also have his water available now.

Horses who break out again in a sweat later on are believed to have been cooled down insufficiently. It is a sign that the animal was very tired, and that there are still too many waste products circulating in the bloodstream; hence the importance of cooling down thoroughly after physical effort, a process which is often not given the attention it deserves. If he does break out, more walking around and rubbing down are necessary, more small feeds and whatever hay and water he wants.

With a horse or pony who is to spend the night in the field, do not make the common mistake of believing that the field is the best place for him even if he is still steaming hot. This is absolutely wrong. The animal *must* be cool before going out again. If he is going to wear a New Zealand rug he will have to be dry before it is put on, unless it is of a permeable material which will allow any remaining moisture to evaporate off. Basically, however, such an animal should be treated like a stabled one, and only put out again once he has recovered to more or less normal temperature, pulse and respiration rates and is cool and dry.

THE DAY AFTER

The next morning you should check the horse over as usual; it is a good idea to take his TPR (temperature, pulse and respiration) rates to check as closely as you can whether he has recovered normally. Obviously, injuries will need further attention. If possible, the horse should be led around and trotted up to check on his soundness; study him to see whether he looks normal, or particularly tired, or simply not his usual bright self, which could indicate that he has been overstressed.

He should be carefully groomed according to whatever system you normally use and whether he lives in or out; as well as freshening him up this gives you a chance to really go over him for any lumps, bumps or little wounds you missed the night before. It is assumed that if there was anything you could not cope with or which appeared serious, you called the vet last night.

With a healthy, fit horse or pony, it should take three or four days for the horse's energy levels to be restored and for him to fully recover from a day's hard work. However, particularly stressful work often involves a three-week recovery period or longer. One of the practical signs is whether or not the horse has fully recovered his appetite. A hard-worked horse often goes off his feed if he has been extremely tired or had a hard day, and the return to normal of his appetite is a good sign, ie that he is back to normal, too. The three week rule, however, is a good one with horses in stressful, high-performance work. Many a time a good horse wins a prestigious race only to be back on the racecourse within two weeks or even less because the trainer decides 'he's recovered fine, so we thought we'd give him this opportunity'. In the second race, however, the horse is very often seen to trail in, way down the filed. Perhaps what he really needed was an opportunity to recover a bit longer, not to go through it all again.

Feeds should initially be normal but of smaller size, with possibly a carbohydrate booster or other additive if your consultant (vet, nutritionist) advises it. Do not give the horse mashes, despite what the old books advise for tired horses. Feeds of normal energy content will aid recovery much more than an indigestible, unpalatable mash. If, for any reason, the horse is confined due to some injury, it is better to feed roughage and water, with possibly small feeds of dried grass and soaked sugar beet pulp, plus whatever else the horse likes such as carrots. Molassed chaff plus sliced or grated roots, or soaked sugar beet pulp, are also useful in such circumstances.

Assuming all is well and the horse or pony is neither exhausted nor injured, there is no reason why he cannot work again next day – he does not *have* to have a day off. He should be quite able to take you for an hour or two's relaxing hack or drive if that is what you want, and it will certainly help him ward off any stiffness from the previous day's exertions. If you do wish to give him a day off, do not leave him stabled all day. Make sure he is turned out somewhere to stretch his legs for a couple of hours at least.

Particular checks should be given to long-coated ponies – they can lose a lot of condition under all that hair without showing it on the surface. Feel down through their coats to see how much weight they are carrying and feed accordingly. Do not work them hard again till their weight has been restored – a repeated, gradual weight loss can take place which, in winter, will be hard to make up. Of course, ponies with a lot of long coat should not be worked *hard* anyway, but even moderate work can make them sweat too much, so do keep an eye on them.

On subsequent days, if you check your horse regularly and perhaps more carefully than usual, you should spot anything not right with him. Pay particular attention to his appetite and general demeanour and if you feel he is not right, do call your vet.

Summary

•Careful preparation helps ensure a successful, enjoyable day with a horse fit and ready for work. Keep your horse calm by making your preparations surreptitiously and not rushing about.

•A week before the event, check: transport arrangements, the horse's shoes, all tack and equipment. Do not: give the horse a heavy week's work (if anything slacken off slightly to freshen him up); do not overfeed, particularly the night before – it does not 'stoke up' the horse's energy reserves, but can result in serious consequences (colic, azoturia, etc).

•Make logically organised lists of your equipment and tick things off as they are laid ready, also when you leave. Give the horse his normal work; groom or shampoo the day before. If kept out, try to bring him in the night before to help in this respect.

Summary

●Feed normally. Do not withhold hay, feed and water for several hours before the event as this can result in hunger, discomfort and loss of performance. Feed as normal up to an hour before moderate work (showing), or up to two hours before more strenuous work.

●Carbohydrate boosters and electrolyte supplements may be advisable particularly if the work is strenuous and/or the weather hot or humid (glucose is less favoured now: it can result in lowered blood sugar and considerable fatigue, plus fatigue–related injuries). It is necessary to accustom the horse or pony to additives, particularly in the case of electrolyte supplements.

●If travelling by horsebox or trailer on a long journey, give the horse hay to eat to keep his digestion and metabolism working properly. Stop at intervals and allow the horse to stretch his legs and stale. Consider travelling the day before; travel is much more stressful than generally realised – combined with work on arrival, it can result in actual illness caused by the combined over-stress.

●If hacking, set off in plenty of time to hack there in a relaxed way; the horse will be ridden in by the time you arrive.

●On arrival, only ride or drive the horse when needed. Use commonsense about weather conditions: if it is hot, stand with him in the shade; if it is cold and raining, either stable or shelter him, or keep him comfortable with clothing and/or a waterproof sheet – walk him gently about.

●After work, aim to make the horse cool and dry as soon as possible. Keep checking his pulse and respiration, particularly the former, so you can see how well, or otherwise, he is returning to normal. Lukewarm water is advised for washing down a sweaty horse.

●Give the horse or pony the opportunity to stale.

●Do let him graze a little now and then. A long day without food, is bad for his digestion, whereas a few nibbles of grass increases his comfort and ability to work well.

●Be prepared to stop when the horse has had enough, for safety's sake: a tired horse may trip and fall more easily, or become overstrained. Long-coated and outdoor animals may become tired more easily than expected.

●If the horse faces a long drive home, it might be better to let him recover overnight; travel the next day, to avoid over-stressing him.

●Aim to get the horse back to his stable (at home or away) cool and dry. Trot the horse in hand first – this facilitates better removal of waste products from the muscles – then walk. Allow only short drinks; offer an electrolyte solution as well, plus mouthfuls of hay once the horse has started to cool down. Once the horse is cool and dry and appears to have quenched his thirst he can have water available all the time, as normal. The horse can then have a small feed containing his normal ingredients, plus, maybe, a carbohydrate booster after hard work.

●If hacking home, walk and trot gently on, allowing the horse to take short drinks from any convenient troughs; be careful of streams which may be polluted.

●If travelling home, an anti-sweat rug under a top layer will assist cooling and drying off without chills. Once home, get him clean, dry and warm as soon as possible and give hay, water and a small feed of normal ingredients. If the horse is to be off work, give false feeds of dried grass meal plus sugar beet pulp or molassed chop with sliced roots or beet pulp, plus an *ad lib* roughage supply.

●If the horse breaks out it may be because he was extremely tired or has not been cooled down properly. Walk round and rub down till dry again.

●Never turn a hot animal out into the field unless it is a very warm summer night. Otherwise he could be chilled. He must be cool, if not quite dry.

●The following day, check the horse as normal and take the TPR rates – this will tell you how he really is. If he is alright, he can hack out to alleviate any stiffness, or be turned out. If he seems dull and off his feed, he needs good, tempting food and rest and relaxation. Appetite is a good guide.

●Normally, it takes three or four days for energy reserves to be restored, three weeks after hard work, but it can be much longer if the horse has been over–worked for his state of fitness.

●Keep an especial eye on long-coated animals working in winter as they can lose condition without our noticing it. Feel through the coat to check body condition.

●Keep an eye on the horse's appetite and general demeanour; if they are not normal, call the vet.

Checklist

✓ 1 Advance preparation is half the battle. Make certain all your equipment is in good order and that your horse or pony is sufficiently fit.

2 Adequate warming up prepares the horse's muscles for strenuous effort: if they are 'cold' it is more difficult and risky for both of you.

3 Witholding feed and water for several hours before an event will make your horse uncomfortable and may deplete some energy stores before you even start. Remove supplies one hour before moderate work and two hours or so before hard work.

4 A hard day, particularly with travelling, greatly decreases the horse's energy reserves. Investigate carbohydrate boosters, electrolyte supplements and other legitimate dietary aids, which may help your horse do his best for you and be less likely to succumb to fatigue-related injuries.

5 Before and after work, try to maintain your horse at an equable, comfortable temperature and to get, and keep, him dry. Use shelter facilities, clothing and walking in hand to do this. Lukewarm water is safest for washing down a sweaty horse and will help him cool down by assisting heat loss through evaporation.

6 You should be alert for signs of fatigue and *stop* when the horse has had enough.

7 Recovery can take three days, three weeks or longer depending on how hard the horse worked and how fit he was beforehand. The horse should not be stressed again till he has properly recovered. Practical signs of recovery are the horse's appetite and general demeanour.

14

GOING PLACES

If you own a horse or pony who is a bad traveller you may feel that there was something to be said for the old days when there were no horseboxes or trailers, and when all a horse's appointments could be met locally. Travel was by train for long journeys, even only a very few decades ago, and the animals then made the journey from the station to their destination under their own steam. People always hacked to hunt meets, sometimes many miles, did a day's hunting, and hacked home again. These days, people only do that if the meet is very close, and sometimes not even then.

There is often only a limited market for an animal who is a bad traveller, especially if the new owner wants to compete at more than very local level; so every horse or pony will almost certainly have to get used to travelling at some point in its life. Unfortunately, very many horses and ponies *are* bad travellers, or at least are borderline cases. In every yard with more than two or three animals there is almost certainly at least one, and often several in large yards, who is frightened of or dislikes travelling.

The reasons are varied. Obviously, travelling is completely unnatural – the animals are expected to go boldly into what amounts to a gaping cavern, and can certainly be forgiven for regarding it with suspicion or even dread. As horses have such interminable memories it only takes one unpleasant or even mildly frightening experience to put them on their guard for the rest of their lives, and to make them very difficult or even impossible to travel. Their very effective self-preservation instinct ensures this, and they will always be expecting it to happen again. They cannot, like us, think of it as just an isolated incident, with the chance of its happening again as so many thousands to one; they believe that it *is* going to happen again, probably every time they set foot in the vehicle. Therefore it is not surprising that getting a horse over an unpleasant experience in a box or trailer is not always possible.

What is not generally realised, or accepted, is that the way in which most animals are transported, facing the direction in which they are going, is probably the most stressful. Dr Sharon E. Cregier has fully researched the subject of transporting horses (see *Behaviour Problems in Horses*, David & Charles, in which Dr Cregier is a guest contributor); briefly, she concludes that, particularly during braking and accelerating, and also travelling in any way off a straight line such as cornering, pulling out to go round a parked vehicle or to overtake a slower one, roundabouts etc, the movement felt by the horse goes completely against his natural balance.

A horse carries about two thirds of his weight on his forehand. The hindquarters are not structured particularly well for carrying weight but for forward propulsion. The forehand is actually intended to carry weight, which is pushed forward by the hind end, travels along the spine and drops onto the forehand and forelegs during action. The horse also stands naturally with two thirds of his weight on his forehand/forelegs.

However, during acceleration in a horsebox or trailer, the horse's weight is thrown back onto his hind quarters, causing sudden contraction of the back, loin, quarter and hind leg muscles to prevent the horse

Sadly, another common sight. This sort of treatment shows loss of temper and lack of understanding and patience in the handlers. The horse will be thoroughly frightened and will be even harder to load next time. It will be extremely difficult to overcome the bad memories this horse will carry with him for the rest of his life, and he will probably become a permanently bad, or impossible, traveller

falling onto his tail. The sensation is as if someone suddenly pulled a rug forward from under our feet.

During braking, the weight is thrown forward and the horse again tries to compensate for the forward thrust to protect his all-important and sensitive head.

A vehicle never travels along on a dead straight line at a constant speed; any journey consists of constant changes of speed and direction, even on a motorway, and the horse is bracing his muscles all the time to save himself from falling and to combat the artificial directional thrust of his weight. He is forced to brace and splay his legs, a stance which is highly stressful if adopted for more than a few seconds (as during staling) in order to prop himself up against the motion of travel. The horse's hip joint is not structured to move sideways like this, and this type of movement can cause the horse considerable discomfort and pain.

Because the horse is expending considerable and constant physical effort just to stay upright during the journey, he is often physically very tired when he arrives at his destination. The unpleasant sensations are, obviously, remembered and the horse may act upon them in future by resisting travelling. On a long journey, muscular cramp is quite common, if not entirely recognised, and cramp causes muscle damage, all of which results in pain.

Horses who are travelled with their tails to the engine, facing away from the direction of travel, are able to adopt a completely natural, more relaxed stance; they do not need to brace their legs and only minimal muscular effort is needed during motion – they will often even rest a hind leg. During braking, the horse is not in fear of his head being knocked and simply uses his well-padded rear end to absorb the thrust. During acceleration the horse's weight is pushed onto the forehand which is the best able to take it.

In practice, any observant horseman can soon see for himself which way horses and ponies travel best by simply staying in the back of a horsebox in which horses can travel tail-to-the-engine. Their relaxed stance and air are plainly evident as compared with horses facing the other way, who will almost without exception be bracing themselves against the motion.

Remember that it is against the law in the UK for a human to travel in a trailer because of the greater possibility of accident. This does not apply to a horsebox.

As a final test, if you travel a horse loose in the back of a horsebox, with all the space to himself and no partitions, you will notice when you come to unload him that he has, himself, adopted a tail-to-the-engine stance as being the most comfortable, least stressful and least risky, from his point of view.

The Fédération Equestre International is, at the time of writing, undertaking a detailed clinical study of transit stress in horses, with the International League for the Protection of Horses providing the money. It is hoped that the results will soon be available and that they will result in legislation which will ensure that horses and ponies, and animals in general, are travelled in such a way that they undergo minimal stress in transit.

As well as the unnatural motion in the vehicle, the inside temperature and humidity can rise to unacceptable levels and this alone will over–stress the occupants. It is known that bacteria and other 'germ' levels can rise significantly, placing the horse at increased risk of disease; and significant stress-related changes in the blood can also take place after a trip of only three hours. Respiratory disorders can result, and animals show abnormally high pulse rates. Improved ventilation will therefore greatly increase the horses' health and comfort.

In the UK it is not easy to allow horses to travel 'back to front', since we are confined to trailers which at the time of writing are all made to transport the horse the other way round. Some trailer manufacturers *will* make to order trailers correctly designed and balanced to take horses travelling about-face. It is not simply a case of making minor adjustments to the interior fittings so that the horses can be 'turned round'. Because of the horse's natural weight carriage, turning him round in an ordinary trailer can result in the trailer being over-weighted to the rear with a corresponding lift at the hitch end – and it does not take much imagination to visualise what can happen then! The axles need re–siting to account for the change of weight distribution inside the trailer.

In other countries, particularly in the USA and Australia, rear–face trailers are more easily available. For more information on rear-face trailer construction, write to Dr Cregier in Canada (see p266 for her address); it would be appreciated if international reply coupons (available from all main post offices) were enclosed, to cover the cost of sending relevant literature by air mail.

When purchasing any vehicle, new or second-hand, box or trailer, really effective ventilation fittings should be demanded. If they are not present, get them put in. Mechanical extractor vents, louvres, roof flaps and the like should be open in boxes, and in trailers leave the top rear doors open; but perhaps fit perspex shields along the sides to prevent undue draughts from the slipstream coming in. If the horse soils the bedding in the vehicle every effort should be made to clean it out before the return journey to avoid the horse having to travel home in a putrid atmosphere which, along with possibly less-than-ideal ventilation, is an ideal environment for the development of disease.

It is also important to ensure that your horse is neither too hot nor too cold when travelling. Over-rugging can be a source of significant over-heating, sweating and dehydration in horses, all of which combine to make the horse feel most uncomfortable, worried and even unwell. Conversely, if he is cold he will not only be uncomfortable and using up energy resources in keeping warm but could also develop cramp which will seriously affect his performance and wellbeing. Regularly check during your journey, particularly if it is more than an hour or so long, that your horse is comfortable under his clothing, and adjust it accordingly. Whether or not you favour anti-sweat rugs, traditional fabrics or synthetics, take plenty of clothing with you but only use what the horse needs.

DIFFERENT VEHICLES

Most of us, given the choice, would choose a horsebox for transporting our horses and ponies. They are purpose built and give a much more comfortable, stable ride than anything else. Cattle waggons should be avoided – they should even be avoided for cattle, in my opinion! They have no proper partitions, simply bars, so if animals do fall they can be trodden on by others, resulting in fatal injuries. Such vehicles frequently oblige the horses to travel sideways cramped up from nose to tail, which is very stressful and unpleasant. In addition, their ventilation gaps are usually half-way down the sides, creating draughts on the horses' bodies which is not only unpleasant but can cause cramp and muscular stiffness – hardly what we should be aiming for in an animal intended to perform.

Trailers are extremely common and are custom built for horses (despite usually forcing them to face forward). In my experience, they are much of a muchness; the significant design features are modern aero-dynamic shaping which reduces air turbulence and buffeting, and the axles. Twin-axle trailers are far more stable than single-axle types, even if the latter have four wheels. They are less inclined to rock and sway and are recommended above single-axle ones.

Whatever vehicle is chosen, the horse or pony will be much more comfortable if he has enough room around him. He should have not less than a foot (30cm) on each side and in front of his breast at the breast bar, and also behind his thighs where there will be a solid partition or a breeching strap or chain. He should have twice that distance in front of his nose and any solid structure. Headroom is never satisfactory: really, at least 3ft 3in (1m) or more should be allowed above the poll, although this is rarely the case in any trailer design.

The flooring is often special non-slip matting (usually dimpled or ridged rubber) but it also helps to have bedding material down. The perfect footing is 6in (15cm) of damp-ish sawdust, which really gives a firm, padded, secure feel. Tough polyurethane sponge matting is now available, and excellent. No floor will stay in good condition if it is constantly wet. After each use, the vehicle should be cleared out, rinsed down and allowed to air and dry thoroughly before next time – it is not really the wet which can cause floors to rot, but the caustic nature of decomposing organic matter such as urine and droppings.

ELEMENTS OF GOOD DRIVING

Probably the single most important factor in transporting horses and ponies is the competence and caring attitude of the driver. All too often, people are in a hurry or have become blasé about travelling. All they care about is getting there and to blazes with the horses in the back. 'They're used to travelling. They take it in their stride', we so often hear, yet it is just such people who fail to observe the very noticeable signs of travel stress in their animals, particularly sweating and raised pulse levels. Pulse rates up to twice the normal at-rest rates are common in forward-facing transport, which is indicative of significant apprehension or even fear in the horse; this is also the level to be expected of a horse who has been warmed up before fast work or competition – so it is hardly a restful or stress–free journey.

However, even in conventional transport, the driver can do a great deal to improve matters: quite simply, aim for the impractical ideal of taking the vehicle along at a constant speed on a smooth road and on an unwavering straight line, and the horses should arrive almost as fresh as they set off. The driver should speed up and slow down *very* gradually indeed so that the forward/backward thrust felt by the horses is very slight. Cornering should also be done very slowly and gradually to minimise as much as possible the swinging effect of centrifugal force, which is typical of high-sided or articulated vehicles. Roundabouts are real terrors for this. The horses are swung first to one side, then to the other, then back again – so negotiate all turns, but especially roundabouts, with extreme caution and at a slow speed.

Jerky gear changes are also upsetting to the horse's mental and physical equilibrium as they lurch the horse back and forth, so make them all as smooth as possible, and look for the smoothest part of any road – not easy on the narrow country lanes and tracks leading to and from some competition venues. Obviously, bouncing up and down in potholes is exactly what the horses or ponies in the back do *not* need.

Keep much more distance between yourself and the vehicle in front than you would in an empty lorry or a car, so that you can slow down very gradually when its brake lights show. When pulling out to overtake or get round an obstruction such as roadworks or a parked vehicle, do so again slowly and gradually.

In conclusion, imagine you have a glass of fine, vintage wine balanced on your dashboard or bonnet, filled to within $^1/_4$in (6mm) of the rim. If you spill any during your journey, you have given the horses a rough ride; if, however, you arrive with as much wine as when you set off, your horses have been reasonably comfortable – and you can reward yourself by drinking it!

Summary

●Animals who are bad travellers have a limited use and market value. One traumatic incident is sufficient for a horse to associate travelling with pain and discomfort; this can also result from the horse being habitually badly driven.

●Horses travel most satisfactory if they can face away from the direction of travel (tail-to-the-engine); this way, their natural balance and weight (carried on the forehand) can counteract the forces of acceleration and braking better, which results in less stressed passengers.

●Adverse physical effects of conventional travel include: constant muscular effort perhaps resulting in cramp and muscle damage; biochemical changes in the blood; heat and humidity stress; respiratory disorders and high pulse rates.

Good ventilation plus frequent cleaning and drying of the box floor all help alleviate environmental stress; it also helps maintain a sound floor.

●Horseboxes are the vehicle of choice, next trailers and finally, if they really must be used at all, cattle waggons. Horses and ponies need ample room around them when travelling if they are to feel comfortable and unharrassed. A thick layer of flooring/bedding material gives a greater sense of security and does help horses keep their feet.

Summary

- The competence and caring attitude of the driver is vital. Aim for impractical ideal of taking the vehicle along at a constant speed on an unwavering straight line, and this will greatly lessen the stress on the passengers.

- Accelerating, braking, cornering and lane deviation should be done *very* slowly and gradually. A generous distance should always be left between the horses' vehicle and the one in front so that sudden braking should not be necessary.

- Imagine a glass of fine wine balanced on the dash board and filled to within $1/4$in (6mm) of the rim: if you spill any you have given your horses a rough ride. If you don't, reward yourself by drinking it!

Checklist

✓ 1 Next time you take your horse or pony anywhere check his pulse on arrival and see just how far about his at-rest rate it is. Note whether he has sweated up, even slightly.

2 When towing or driving horses, remember the constant speed/straight line ideal and aim for it at all times.

3 Let your horse or pony travel tail-to-the-engine whenever possible. This will be difficult in the UK because most trailers are not designed for it (although see Appendix D for some manufacturers who will produce rear-face trailers to order); however, many horseboxes do have rear-face partitions.

4 When ordering a new horsebox or having one re–fitted, stipulate rear-face stalls.

5 Keep the floor of your vehicle clean and dry to prevent rot. Provide thick, padding bedding, ideally 6in (15cm) of damp–ish sawdust.

6 Ensure adequate ventilation without creating draughts. Neither over nor under-clothe your horse during his journey. Being too hot or too cold are equally stressful and debilitating.

7 Consider fixing to the underside of your rear ramp a red and white, or red and yellow, notice saying: LIVE CARGO. PLEASE KEEP CLEAR AND PASS QUIETLY AND SLOWLY. 'Caution – horses' conveys absolutely nothing to the average road–user, who has no idea what he or she is expected to do about it.

8 Finally, enjoy your drink!

APPENDIX A
FURTHER READING

Ainslie, Tom and Ledbetter, Bonnie. *The Body Language of Horses* (Morrow, 1980) ISBN 0 688 03620 1

Brock, Ann. *Riding and Stable Safety* (David & Charles, 1980) ISBN 0 7153 7951 8

Bromiley, Mary. *Equine Injury and Therapy* (Blackwell Scientific, 1987) ISBN 0 00 383285 6

Emery, Leslie, Miller, Jim and Van Hoosen, Nyles. *Horseshoeing Theory and Hoof Care* (Lea and Febiger), revised edition

German National Equestrian Federation. *Horse Management* (Threshold Books, 1987) ISBN 0 901366 73 0

Hartley Edwards, Elwyn. *Buying Horses and Ponies* (Pelham, 1985) ISBN 0 7207 1537 7

Hayes, Captain M. Horace, FRCVS. *Veterinary Notes for Horse Owners* (Stanley Paul, 1987, revised by Peter D. Rossdale, PhD, FRCVS)

Hughes, Christine and Oliver, Robert. *Practical Stable Management* (Pelham, 1987) ISBN 0 7207 1759 0

Hyland, Ann. *Foal to Five Years* (Ward Lock, 1980) ISBN 0 7063 5899 6

Kiley-Worthington, Dr Marthe. *The Behaviour of Horses in Relation to Management and Training* (J.A. Allen, 1987) ISBN 0 85131 397 3

Larter, Chris and Jackson, Tony. *Transporting Your Horse or Pony* (David & Charles, 1987) ISBN 07153 8938 X

Leighton Hardman, A.C. *Young Horse Management* (Pelham 1976 and 1987) ISBN 0 7207 1574 1

McCarthy, Gillian. *Pasture Management for Horses and Ponies* (Blackwell Scientific, 1987) ISBN 0 00 383330 5

Macdonald, Janet W. *The Right Horse* (Methuen, 1982) ISBN 0 413 51080 8 (hardback) 0 413 51090 5 (paperback)

Mortimer, Monty. *The Horse Owner's Handbook* (David & Charles, 1987) ISBN 0 7153 8910 6

Naviaux, James L., DVM. *Horses in Health and Disease* (Lea and Febiger, 1985) ISBN 0 8121 0935 X

Pavord, Tony and Fisher, Rod. *The Equine Veterinary Manual* (Crowood Press, 1987) ISBN 0 9466284 29 6

Pilliner, Sarah. *Getting Horses Fit* (Blackwells Scientific, 1986) ISBN 0 00 383197 3

Rees, Lucy. *The Horse's Mind* (Stanley Paul, 1984) ISBN 0 09 153660 X

Richardson, Julie (editor) *Horse Tack: The Complete Equipment Guide for Riding and Driving* (Pelham, 1981) ISBN 0 7207 1377 3

Rossdale, Peter D., MA, FRCVS. *Inside The Horse* (California Thoroughbred Breeders' Association, 1976) Library of Congress Catalogue Card Number 76-50424

Rossdale, Peter D., MA, FRCVS. *The Horse from Conception to Maturity* (J.A. Allen) ISBN 85131 198 9

Rossdale, Peter. *Horse Breeding* (David & Charles, 1981) ISBN 0 7153 7987 9

Rossdale, Peter D. and Wreford, Susan M. *The Horse's Health from A to Z* (David & Charles, 1989) revised edition

Schäfer, Michael. *An Eye for A Horse* (J.A. Allen, 1980) ISBN 0 85131 320 5

Schäfer, Michael. *The Language of The Horse* (Kaye Ward, 1975) ISBN 0 7182 1120 0 (UK) ISBN 0 668 03762 8 (USA)

Sevelius, Fritz, Pettersson, Harry and Olsson, Lennart. *Keeping Your Horse Healthy* (David & Charles, 1978) ISBN 0 7153 7638 1

Smythe, R.H. MRCVS. *The Horse, Structure and Movement* (J.A. Allen, 1967, second edition revised by Goody, PC BSc, PhD 1972)

Snow Dr D.H. and Vogel, C.J. *Equine Fitness: The Care and Training of the Athletic Horse* (David & Charles, 1987) ISBN 0 7153 8732 2

Williams, Moyra. *Horse Psychology* (J.A. Allen 1976) ISBN 0 85131 238 1

APPENDIX B
USEFUL ORGANISATIONS

Readers are strongly recommended to purchase a copy of *The British Equestrian Directory*, which is published yearly by Equestrian Management Consultants Limited, Wothersome Grange, Bramham, Wetherby, West Yorkshire, LS23 6LY. This is a comprehensive listing of organisations, companies and individuals in just about every imaginable sector of the horse world. Meanwhile, here is a selection of just some of the more commonly needed organisations, correct at the time of writing.

Association of British Riding Schools, Old Brewery Yard, Penzance, Cornwall, TR18 2SL.

British Driving Society, 27 Dugard Place, Barford, Warwick, CV35 8DX.

British Equestrian Federation, British Equestrian Centre, Kenilworth, CV8 2LR.

British Equestrian Trade Association, Wothersome Grange, Bramham, Wetherby, LS23 6LY.

British Equine Veterinary Association, Hartham Park, Corsham, SN13 0QB.

British Hay and Straw Merchants Association, Hoval House, Orchard Parade, Mutton Lane, Potters Bar, EN6 3AR.

British Horse Society, British Equestrian Centre, Kenilworth, CV8 2LR.

British Seeds Council, 25 Knightsbridge, London, SW1X 7NJ.

British Show Hack, Cob and Riding Horse Association, Rookwood, Packington Park, Meriden, Warwickshire.

British Show Jumping Association, British Equestrian Centre, Kenilworth, CV8 2LR.

The Coaching Club, c/o D.H. Clarke Esq, 33 Lombard Street, London, EC3V 9BE.

Commons, Open Spaces and Footpaths Preservation Society, 25a Bell Street, Henley-on-Thames, RG9 2BA.

Equine Behaviour Study Circle, Leyland Farm, Gawcott, Buckingham, MK18 4HS.

Farriers' Registration Council, 4 Royal College Street, London, NW1 0TU.

Fellows and Instructors of the British Horse Society, Clavering, Wooler, NE71 6EU.

Horses and Ponies Protection Association, PO Box 83, Burnley, Lancashire, BB12 9QP.

Hurlingham Polo Association, Ambersham Farm, Midhurst, GU29 0BX.

National Master Farriers' Association, Avenue R, 7th Street, National Agricultural Centre, Stoneleigh, Kenilworth, CV8 2LG.

Point-to-Point Secretaries Association, 97 Hurlingham Road, London SW6.

Ponies of Britain, Chesham House, 56 Green End Road, Sawtry, Huntingdon, PE17 5UY.

The Pony Club, British Equestrian Centre, Stoneleigh, Kenilworth, CV8 2LR.

Riding for The Disabled Association, Avenue R, National Agricultural Centre, Stoneleigh, Kenilworth, CV8 2LY.

Royal College of Veterinary Surgeons, 32 Belgrave Square, London SW1X 8QP.

Side Saddle Association, Highbury House, Welford, Northampton, NN6 7HT.

Society of Master Saddlers, 2 Orchard End, Longhope, Gloucester, GL17 0LG.

Worshipful Company of Saddlers, Gutter Lane, London, EC2V 6BR.

APPENDIX C
SOURCES OF
EDUCATIONAL COURSES

There are many outlets for employment in the horse world. The best known qualifications are those for instructors which are organised by the British Horse Society. The Association of British Riding Schools also organises courses and examinations and is particularly well-known for its excellent grooms' qualifications. Some agricultural colleges run what can best be described as horse business courses, aimed particularly at those who wish to make a high-level career in the horse world, possibly in management, marketing or in their own businesses; write to the organisations concerned to find out just what courses are currently available. Local education authorities and riding centres often run part-time courses of varying lengths; these do not lead to qualifications but simply help participants further their own knowledge for interest's sake.

British Horse Society, National Equestrian Centre, Stoneleigh, Kenilworth, CV8 2LR.

Association of British Riding Schools, Old Brewery Yard, Penzance, TR18 2SL.

National Pony Society, Brook House, 25 High Street, Alton, GU34 1AW.

Equi-Study Limited (correspondence courses), 44 Fleet Street, London, EC4Y 1B5.

Bicton College of Agriculture, East Budleigh, Budleigh Salterton, EX9 7BY.

Cambridgeshire College of Agriculture, Milton, Cambridgeshire.

Carmarthenshire College of Technology and Art, Pibwrlwyd Campus, Carmarthen, SA31 2NH.

North Tyneside College of Further Education, Embleton Avenue, Wallsend, NE29 9NJ.

Joint National Horse Education and Training Centre c/o BHS at Stoneleigh.

Lackham College of Agriculture, Lacock, Chippenham, Wiltshire, SN15 2NY.

Warwickshire College of Agriculture, Moreton Hall, Moreton Morrell, Warwick, CV35 9BL.

West Oxfordshire Technical College, Holloway Road, Witney, Oxfordshire.

Worcestershire College of Agriculture, Hindlip, Worcester, WR3 8SS.

Youth Training Scheme, Horse Management (enquire at your local Job Centre).

APPENDIX D
USEFUL PRODUCTS OR SERVICES

Cottage Craft, Cottage Industries (Equestrian) Ltd, Crown Lane, Wychbold, Droitwich, Worcestershire, WR9 0BX. Wintec synthetic saddles, plus wide range of equestrian equipment.

J.A. Allen (The Horseman's Bookshop) Ltd, 1 Lower Grosvenor Place, off Buckingham Palace Road, London, SW1 0EL. Specialist publisher and retailer, including mail order, of equestrian books. They 'aim to stock all publications currently in print relating to equine and equestrian matters whether published in the UK or overseas.' They also have an extensive stock of second-hand and antiquarian books and offer a search service for customers.

Messrs R.E. and G.B. Way, Brettons, Burrough Green, Newmarket, Suffolk, CB8 9NA. Specialist suppliers of second-hand and antiquarian equestrian books. Search service.

The Equestrian Book Club, Readers' Union, Newton Abbot, Devon. Book club offering selected books at reduced prices. Members must purchase four books a year as a minimum.

Equestrian Care, 4 Salem Grove, Leesbrook, Oldham, OL4 5HR. Freeze marking and lip tattooing with national security registration.

Premier Farmkey Ltd, PO Box 42, Southam Road, Banbury, Oxon, OX16 7EU. Freeze marking of horses, also tack security scheme.

George Perks Brothers, 47 Gatwick Road, Crawley, Sussex, RH10 2FF. Studrail flexible rail fencing.

Horse Requisites Newmarket Ltd, Black Bear Lane, Newmarket, Suffolk. Excellent range of saddlery and other equestrian requirements.

Diceabed International Limited, Haven House, Haven Bank, Haven Road, Exeter, EX2 8BP. Shredabed and Diceabed shredded paper bedding, virtually sterile and excellent for maintaining a healthy, clean-air environment.

Natural Animal Feeds Ltd, High House, Penrhos, Raglan, Gwent, NP5 2DJ. Good range of reliable nutritional products, including Hygrass, a vacuum-packed hayage-type product, and Thrive, a feed supplement especially intended to calm nervous horses by assisting digestion and the neutralising of metabolic toxins.

Stable Boy, Baystrait House, Station Road, Biggleswade, SG18 8AL. Stable floor hygiene product and stable deodoriser.

A.C.A. Forage Ltd, Rooksgrove, Warnford, Southampton, SO3 1LJ. Mollichaff molassed chop.

Landsaver MCP Ltd, 74 Earlstree Road, Corby, Northants, NN17 2AZ. Hydroponic grass-growing equipment and units.

Equine Products (UK) Ltd, 22/23 Riversdale Court, Newburn Haugh Industrial Estate, Newcastle-upon-Tyne, NE15 8SG. Nutritional products, including Transvite pro-biotic.

Glentona Equestrian, 44 Ferry Road, London, SW13 9PW. Wide range of just about everything equestrian, from tack and harness (including synthetic items) to veterinary and feed products.

Gillian McCarthy, BSc (Hons) Equine Management Consultancy Service, 20 Victoria Road, Bulwark, Chepstow, Gwent, NP6 5QN. As the name suggests, professional, up-to-date advice on equestrian management in general but specialising in nutrition and exercise physiology. Advice presented in an easily-understood way!

Sedgemoor Developments plc, Mannaman House, Sealand Road, Chester, CH1 6BW. Dust Cure hay and straw cleaning machine, instrumental in maintaining clean-air regime and healthy stable environment.

Nimrod International Ltd, 124 Mount Street, Berkeley Square, London W1Y 5HA. Ribot shoe, shoe-replacement boot.

Dr Sharon Cregier, University of Prince Edward Island, Charlottetown, Prince Edward Island, Canada, C1A 4P3. Dr Cregier is an acknowledged expert on transportation of horses. Although not commercially involved in the horse world, she is willing to assist and further the interests of horse owners and managers interested in balanced, less stressful travel. Please send international reply coupons if writing from outside Canada.

The author, Susan McBane, contacted thirty British trailer manufacturers to ask if they could, or would, be able to supply or be willing to make to order a rear-face trailer. Very few replied but the following four companies expressed a willingness to co-operate.

Equiluxe, Cherry Tree Farm, Barton Bendish, King's Lynn, Norfolk, PE33 9DJ, tel. Fincham (03664) 229.

J & B Towing Trailer Centre, Cottismore Farm, Kingsclere, Newbury, Berkshire, RG15 8SY, tel. Kingsclere (0635) 298928.

Sinclair Trailers, Wargate Bridge, Gosberton, Spalding, Lincolnshire, PE11 4HH, tel. Spalding (0775) $840442/_{840640}$.

Trail West, 3 Mill Lane, Lochavullin Industrial Estate, Oban, Argyll, PA34 4EX, tel. Oban (0631) 63638.

Dr Cregier has provided the names and address of these manufacturers in other countries.

About Face, 1975 Bee Canyon Road, Arroyo Grande, California 93420, USA, tel. 805-489-5454.

Taylor Industries, Box 997, Melfort, Saskatchewan, Canada, SOE 1AO. tel. 306-752-9212.

Stratford Motor Body Builders, Stratford, New Zealand.

ACKNOWLEDGEMENT

I should like to acknowledge the technical help given during the preparation of this book by Gillian McCarthy, BSc (Hons) of The Equine Management Consultancy Service, 20 Victoria Road, Bulwark, Chepstow, Gwent NP6 5QN. Her advice is always accurate, scientifically-based, easy to understand and practical to put into effect. Her patience is amazing, her promptness reassuring and her distinct lack of a patronising attitude unusual in a scientist.

I also wish to thank Jan Eley, BVSc, MRCVS, for general help and advice readily given, and for checking Chapter 11. Her advice is always up-to-the-minute, her attitude down to earth and her first priority the well-being of the horse, while always bearing in mind the practical problems of the owner.

I should also like to thank Joy Claxton for illustrating yet another of my books very efficiently and attractively and for getting over the points I couldn't describe adequately in words.

INDEX